Reinhold Organic Chemistry and Biochemistry Textbook Series

Consulting Editor:
Professor Calvin A. VanderWerf, Department of Chemistry,
University of Kansas, Lawrence, Kansas

Biochemistry of Steroids

Reinhold Organic Chemistry and Biochemistry Textbook Series

"of making many books there is no end . . ."

Certainly in the college chemistry textbook field that is the case. For as long as chemists heed the challenge of the unknown and teachers of chemistry are aware of widening chemical horizons and endeavor to improve their approaches and methods, new textbooks of chemistry are needed.

The aim of the *Reinhold Organic Chemistry and Biochemistry Textbook Series* is to provide what chemists are waiting for—not more books, but better books—books that illuminate new areas, pioneer superior methods of organization, develop broad new conceptual patterns, and revolutionize outmoded teaching methods.

Through the constant encouragement of new approaches to the study of organic chemistry and biochemistry and through the closest kind of cooperation among individual author, editor, and publisher, we, at Reinhold, pledge to present a well-balanced series of select modern texts, each of which will make a noteworthy contribution to teaching. In so doing, we are confident that each text in the Reinhold series will become a trusted friend and ally of teachers and students alike.

Thus at a time when the full significance of the biochemistry of the steroids is just beginning to be appreciated, and when interest in the field is mounting daily, Reinhold is proud to present "Biochemistry of Steroids" —the first complete book on the subject.

Written by two recognized leaders in steroid biochemistry, this timely new text fills a pressing need and is destined to take its place as a worthy supplement to the classical chemical treatise "Steroids" by Fieser and Fieser. Students and research workers in biochemistry, endocrinology, pharmacology, physiology, and medicine, as well as teachers of organic chemistry, will welcome the "Biochemistry of Steroids" and will applaud the noteworthy service it renders—that of providing a clear and concise orientation in this intriguing and all important field. They will, in addition, find the list of 774 references a constant and invaluable aid in study, teaching, and research.

Calvin A. VanderWerf
Consulting Editor

BIOCHEMISTRY

OF STEROIDS

Erich Heftmann and Erich Mosettig

Steroid Section, Laboratory of Chemistry
National Institute of Arthritis and Metabolic Diseases
National Institutes of Health
Bethesda, Maryland

Reinhold Publishing Corporation, New York

Chapman & Hall, Ltd., London

Printed in the United States of America
THE GUINN CO., INC.
New York 1, N. Y.

Preface

The discovery of the therapeutic effects of cortisone on rheumatoid arthritis in 1949 marks the beginning of an era of intensified research activity in the steroid field. Although progress in the organic chemistry of steroids has been covered in several excellent monographs, including the Reinhold publication "Steroids" by Louis and Mary Fieser, recent information on the biochemical aspects of this important class of compounds has remained more or less scattered in the scientific literature. It has been our experience as teachers and consultants that many students and research workers in biochemistry, plant and animal physiology, endocrinology, pharmacology, and medicine need for one reason or another a brief introductory book on the biochemistry of steroids in which organic chemistry is treated in simplified fashion. Many organic chemists in the pharmaceutical industry are undoubtedly also in need of a concise source of information on the biochemical aspects of steroid hormones. In writing this book we have attempted to fill these needs.

The classes of steroids are arranged in the text as much as possible in the sequence required for an understanding of their biogenetic relations and not necessarily in the order of increasing complexity as organic compounds. After a brief introduction to structure and nomenclature, each class is discussed with regard to distribution, biosynthesis, metabolism, physiological significance, structural specificity, and analytical determination.

The subject is presented in an expository style, without footnotes, tables, and other distracting ancillary material. The juxtaposition within the text of numerous structural formulae should also, it is hoped, increase comprehension and readability. Arrows are used to indicate metabolic conversions that have been observed, dotted arrows reactions presumed but not observed, and

v

double lines through arrows reactions that do not occur. Nomenclature and conventions in the representation of structural formulae correspond to those used in "Steroids" in order to facilitate supplementary reading.

At the end of the text is a classified reading list, organized, for the most part, along the same lines as the text. References to 774 of the pertinent books and review articles that have appeared in the last ten years are arranged in the order of recency of publication. This should provide an adequate introduction for readers who become interested in more detailed information and more extensive bibliographies of the voluminous literature in this field. If gaps in existing information become apparent and stimulate further investigation, our highest ambition in presenting this book will have been fulfilled.

We feel very fortunate that "Biochemistry of Steroids" has been a cooperative undertaking and are grateful to the many persons who have given us valuable suggestions and criticisms. We particularly wish to express our gratitude and deep appreciation to Louis Fieser and Calvin A. VanderWerf for their careful review of the entire manuscript and their constructive suggestions. As a result, we feel sure that the usefulness, validity, and accuracy of the book have been greatly enhanced.

Bethesda, Maryland
February, 1960

Erich Heftmann
Erich Mosettig

Acknowledgments

The authors are indebted to the following colleagues, who have reviewed parts or all of the manuscript and have contributed many valuable suggestions:

C. A. Baumann, University of Wisconsin
W. Bergmann (deceased), Yale University
J. J. Bunim, National Institutes of Health
M. E. Davis, University of Chicago
N. B. Eddy, National Institutes of Health
L. L. Engel, Massachusetts General Hospital
L. F. Fieser, Harvard University
S. Hajdu, National Institutes of Health
D. F. Johnson, National Institutes of Health
A. Katz, University of Basel
C. D. Kochakian, University of Alabama
D. Kritchevsky, Wistar Institute
S. Lieberman, Columbia University
S. Lindstedt, University of Lund
M. B. Lipsett, National Institutes of Health
H. L. Mason, Mayo Foundation
J. T. Matschiner, St. Louis University
W. R. Nes, Clark University
E. J. Plotz, University of Chicago
Y. Sato, National Institutes of Health
S. Solomon, Columbia University
D. Steinberg, National Institutes of Health
M. J. Thompson, National Institutes of Health
C. R. Treadwell, George Washington University
W. W. Tullner, National Institutes of Health
C. A. VanderWerf, University of Kansas
M. E. Wall, Eastern Regional Laboratory, U. S. Department of Agriculture
E. Weiss, University of Basel

We also gratefully acknowledge the cooperation of Mrs. M. S. Hicks and Mrs. E. C. Piazza in the compilation of the bibliography.

Contents

Biochemistry of Steroids

Cholesterol

1. Structure

ABOUT 200 YEARS AGO it was discovered that human gallstones consist largely of a white, crystalline substance. This substance was named *cholestérine* (Greek *chole*, bile and *stereos*, solid) in 1816 by Chevreul, who showed that it was unsaponifiable, in contrast to other animal waxes. After 1859, when Berthelot demonstrated the presence of an alcohol group in the molecule, the more descriptive name cholesterol became generally accepted, although *Cholesterin* is still used in the German and Russian literature. Later, a dibromide of the substance was prepared, indicating the presence of a double bond, and in 1888 the empirical formula of cholesterol was established as $C_{27}H_{46}O$. In the years that followed, Windaus, Wieland, and many other brilliant chemists devoted their efforts to the elucidation of the structure of this intriguing substance. The correct structure was finally established in 1932 by Windaus and Dane, partly on the basis of Diels' discovery that cholesterol is converted to the hydrocarbon shown in Figure 1.1 by selenium dehydrogenation and partly on the basis of X-ray studies by Bernal. The total synthesis of

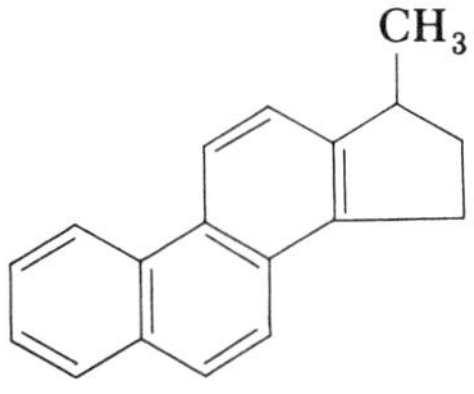

FIGURE 1.1. DIELS' HYDROCARBON.

cholesterol was an outstanding achievement, accomplished in 1952 by Woodward's group in the United States and in 1953 by Robinson's group in England.

In the cholesterol molecule three six-membered rings are joined as in phenanthrene (Figure 1.2) and fused to a five-membered ring. The completely saturated tetracyclic hydrocarbon is called

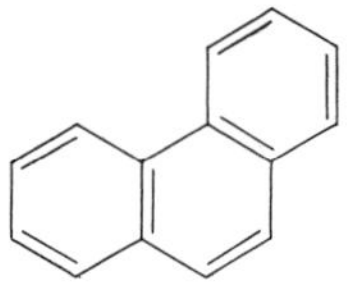

FIGURE 1.2. PHENANTHRENE.

1,2-cyclopentenoperhydrophenanthrene. This ring system is common to a large group of compounds, collectively known as steroids. This class of compounds includes such natural products as sterols, bile acids, sex hormones, corticosteroids, and various plant steroids. Cholesterol is the most important representative of the sterols, which are characterized by an alcohol group and a long aliphatic chain.

The complete structure of cholesterol is shown in Figure 1.3. The carbon atoms marked with asterisks are asymmetric, and the steric configuration is represented by full lines for bonds of hydrogen atoms and hydroxyl and methyl groups above the plane of the paper and dotted lines for bonds extending below that plane. In a more convenient version of the foregoing formula (Figure

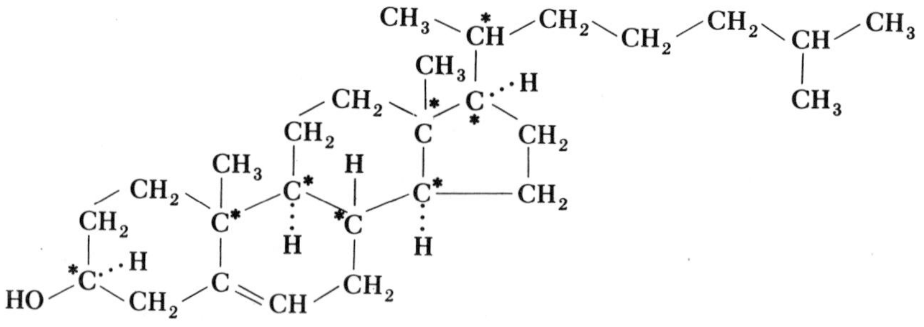

FIGURE 1.3. CHOLESTEROL.

1.4) carbon atoms are represented by corners of straight lines. Many authors indicate the methyl groups as ends of straight lines and show hydrogen atoms only where necessary; i.e., at the ends of straight lines not occupied by methyl groups. The four rings are designated by letters, and the carbon atoms are numbered as shown. The hydroxyl group at C-3, the "angular" methyl groups at C-10 and C-13, and the attachment of the side chain at C-17 are shown to be above the plane of the paper or β-oriented. The hydrogen atoms at C-3, C-9, C-14, and C-17 are α-oriented or below the plane of the paper. The methyl group at C-20 is drawn

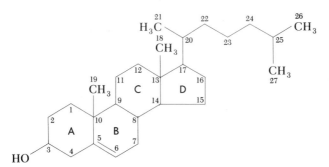

FIGURE 1.4. CHOLESTEROL.

to the left in the projection formula and defined as β-substituted. It should be pointed out that α and β orientation in the side chain have a different meaning from the α and β orientation in the ring system.

2. Biosynthesis

Practically all mammalian tissues are capable of synthesizing cholesterol to a greater or lesser extent. Liver, skin and intestine are most active in this respect; kidneys, lungs, adrenals, and gonads show moderate activity; muscle and adipose tissue, very low activity. While fetal brains and brain tumors can synthesize cholesterol, the normal adult brain has lost this ability.

The mechanism whereby cholesterol is synthesized in the animal body has been investigated for the past two decades and the principal reactions are now known, largely as a result of the efforts of the research teams led by Bloch in the United States, by Cornforth and Popják in Great Britain, and by Lynen in Germany. Early experiments in which deuterium-labeled compounds were administered to rats indicated the high efficiency of acetate as a precursor of cholesterol. However, much of the labeled material was diverted into other metabolic pathways, diluted, or rapidly excreted. Subsequent experiments were therefore carried out *in vitro*. Rat liver slices were incubated with acetate labeled with C^{14} in the carboxyl group, then carrier cholesterol was added, and the cholesterol was isolated and degraded carbon by carbon to determine which atoms were radioactive. In another experiment it was found that after incubation with methyl-labeled acetate those carbon atoms which had not been radioactive in the previous experiment were now radioactive and *vice versa*. Each carbon atom of cholesterol originated from acetate, 12 from the carboxyl carbon and 15 from the methyl carbon. Their location in the molecule, as determined by degradation experiments, is shown in Figure 1.5, where the carbon atoms of cholesterol are labeled C and M to indicate their origin from the carboxyl and methyl group, respectively, of acetic acid.

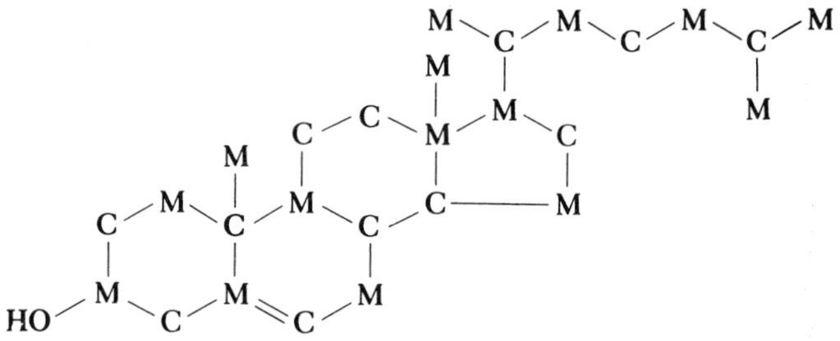

FIGURE 1.5. DISTRIBUTION OF C AND M CARBONS IN CHOLESTEROL.

Many natural products, including steroids, carotenoids, fat-soluble vitamins, rubber, etc. may be regarded as isoprene polymers. Head-to-tail addition of isoprene (Figure 1.6), C_5H_8, produces terpenes. Squalene, $C_{30}H_{50}$, is an acyclic dihydrotriterpene. It consists of two chains of 3 isoprene units formed by head-to-tail addition, which are joined tail-to-tail (Figure 1.7). With four central double bonds 8 geometric isomers of squalene are possible.

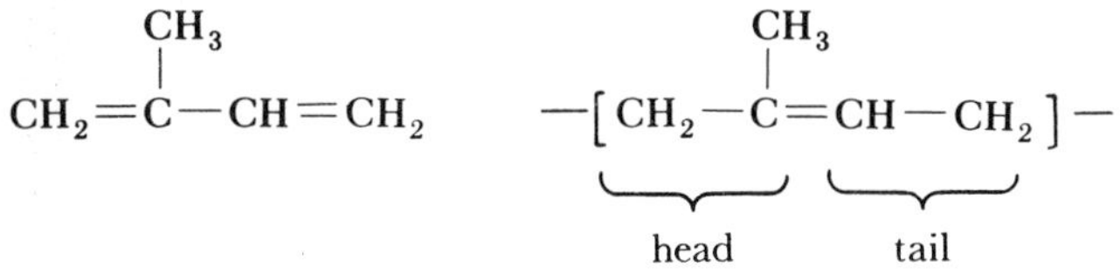

$$CH_2{=}C{-}CH{=}CH_2 \qquad\qquad -[\,CH_2{-}\underset{|}{\overset{|}{C}}{=}CH{-}CH_2\,]-$$

with CH_3 substituents on the carbon atoms as shown, labelled head and tail.

Isoprene   Isoprene Monomer

FIGURE 1.6. ISOPRENE AND ISOPRENE MONOMER.

Natural squalene, found principally in fish (e.g. *Squalus*) liver oils and also in certain vegetable oils, has an all-*trans* configuration.

In 1926, several years before the structure of cholesterol was firmly established, Heilbron, and later Karrer, suggested that squalene might be a precursor of cholesterol. The actual demon-

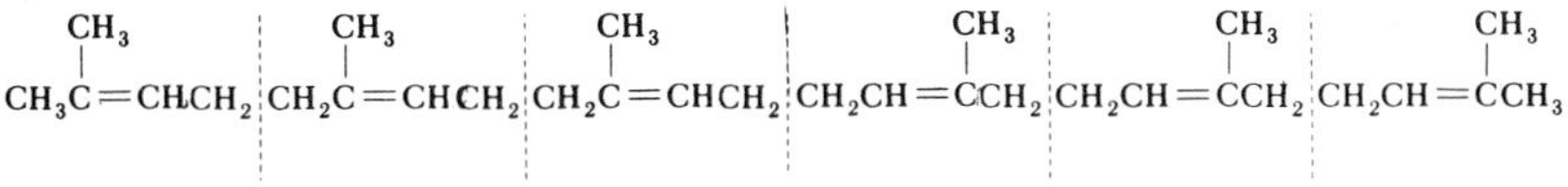

$$CH_3C{=}CHCH_2 \mid CH_2C{=}CHCH_2 \mid CH_2C{=}CHCH_2 \mid CH_2CH{=}CCH_2 \mid CH_2CH{=}CCH_2 \mid CH_2CH{=}CCH_3$$

FIGURE 1.7. SQUALENE.

stration that squalene is an intermediate in the biosynthesis of cholesterol required the isolation of radioactive squalene from liver tissue incubated with radioactive acetate and the subsequent demonstration of the conversion of squalene to cholesterol. Since the amount of squalene in rat liver is very low, the isolation of labeled squalene was accomplished by trapping it with unlabeled squalene. The radioactive squalene was then incubated with rat liver and, indeed, yielded radioactive cholesterol. One question which now had to be answered was how the aliphatic hydrocarbon chain of squalene had been cyclized. By the use of squalene, biosynthesized from either methyl- or carboxyl-labeled acetate, and of degradative methods similar to those applied to cholesterol, it was again possible to determine which carbon atoms in the squalene molecule originated from the methyl and carboxyl carbons of acetic acid. Figure 1.8 shows the distribution of methyl (M) and carboxyl (C) carbons in squalene, drawn to the extended all-*trans* form.

In any scheme of folding the hydrocarbon chain in such a way that cyclization may be visualized the distribution of C and M

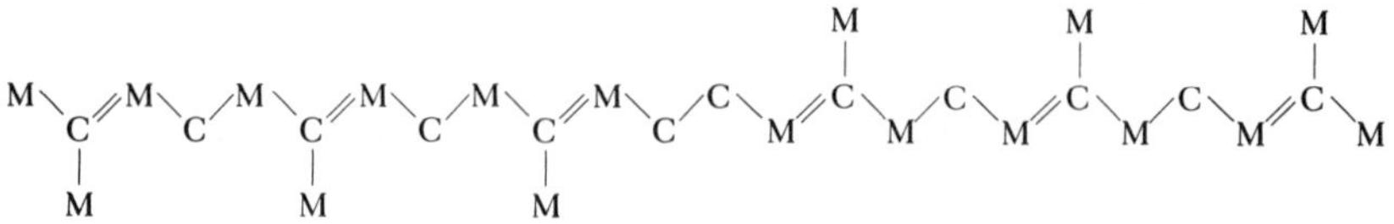

FIGURE 1.8. DISTRIBUTION OF C AND M CARBONS IN SQUALENE.

carbons in squalene and in the cyclization product had to agree. Moreover, it was necessary to postulate a plausible cyclization mechanism. Such a scheme was proposed by Woodward and Bloch in 1953. If squalene is drawn as in Figure 1.9, it can be seen that

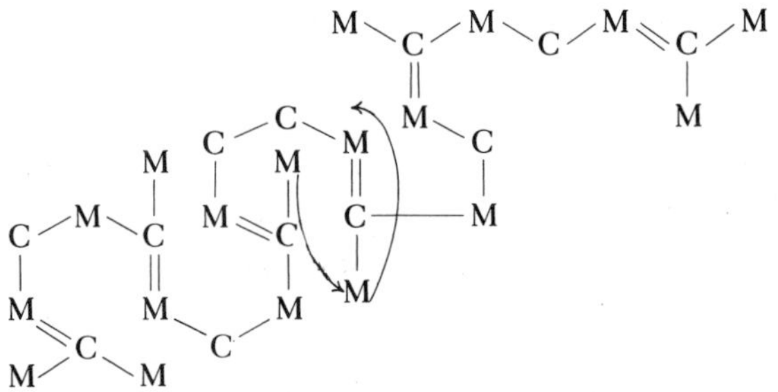

FIGURE 1.9. FOLDING OF THE SQUALENE CHAIN.

the cyclization involves the migration of two methyl groups and the formation of a C_{30} intermediate. The chemical mechanism, first proposed by Ruzicka, is presented in Figure 1.10, where **R** stands for the C_6 hydrocarbon chain. In the presence of the liver

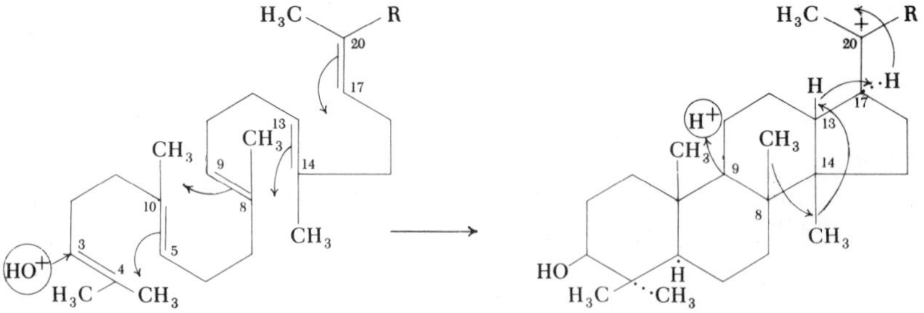

FIGURE 1.10. CYCLIZATION OF SQUALENE.

enzyme "squalene-oxidocyclase I" cyclization is initiated by the attack of a hypothetical OH^+ at C-3, which polarizes the 3,4-double bond and forms a carbonium ion at C-4. This causes the migration of one electron pair from the 5,10-double bond to form a bond between C-4 and C-5, leaving a carbonium ion at C-10, etc. Finally, a positive charge is left at C-20, requiring the migration of a hydride ion from C-17. Another hydride shift from C-13 to C-17 and two 1,2-methyl shifts (8→14, 14→13) then produce the 8,9-double bond and a proton is eliminated at C-9. The double 1,2-methyl shift was experimentally demonstrated by the ingenious use of isotope methods.

No sooner had the cyclization scheme been proposed than evidence from other laboratories converged to support the hypothesis of Woodward and Bloch. It had been observed that cholesterol biosynthesized from radioacetate was always contaminated by some sterols of high specific activity, which obviously seemed to be precursors of cholesterol. At the same time, the structural elucidation of lanosterol, a constituent of wool fat, was completed. Lanosterol is a tetracyclic triterpene and its structure (Figure 1.11) differs from that of cholesterol in two respects: There are 3 extra methyl groups (two at C-4 and one at C-14) and there are two double bonds (one at C-8 and one at C-24). Radioactive lanosterol was finally isolated from rat liver incubated with radioacetate. The conversion of lanosterol to cholesterol in-

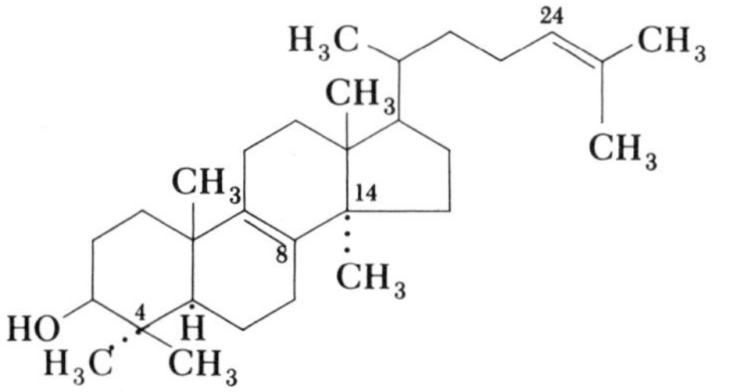

FIGURE 1.11. LANOSTEROL.

volves the loss of three methyl groups, and it has been established that the methyl group at C-14 is the first one to be removed.

After much speculation about the steps intervening between acetate and squalene, a clue of great importance was received from unexpected quarters. It was discovered that 3,5-dihydroxy-3-

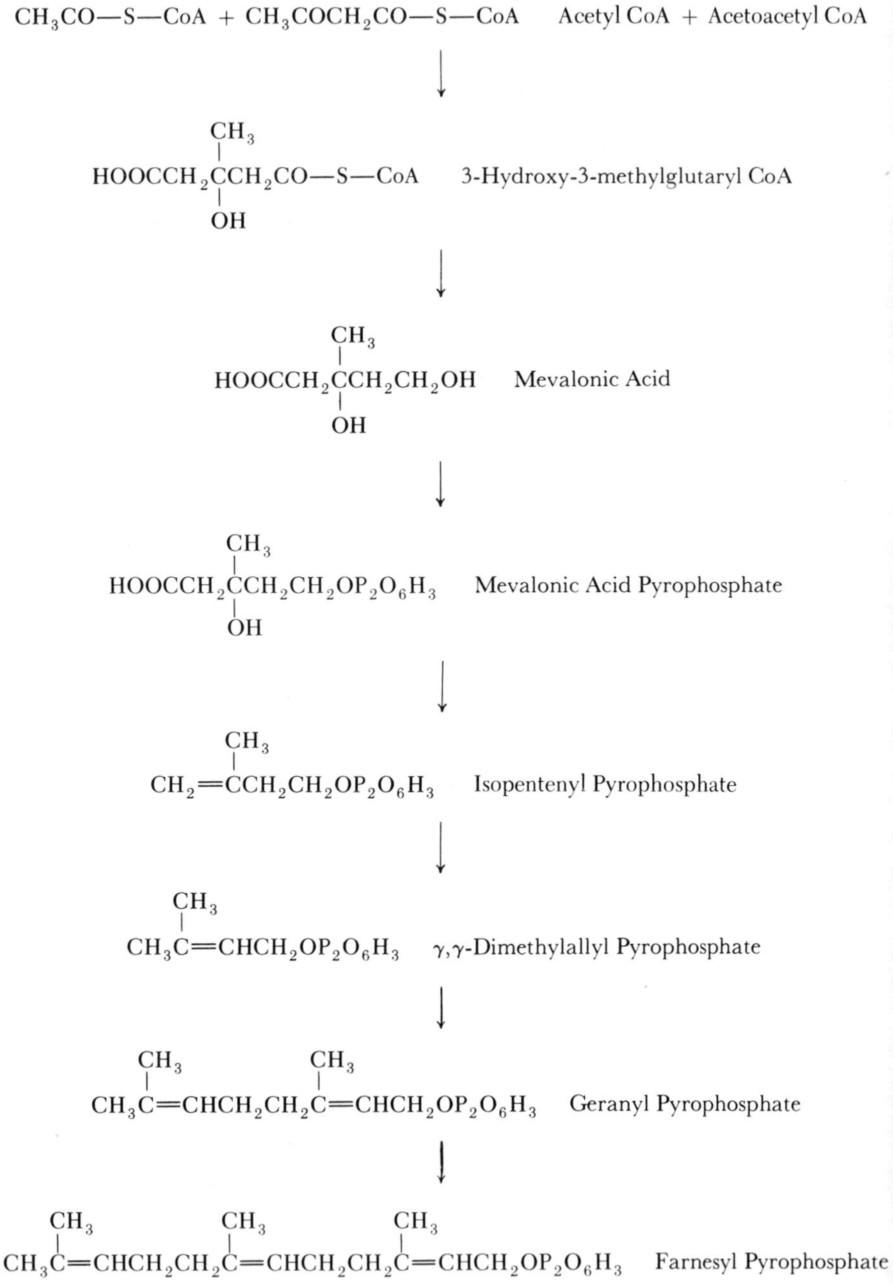

$$CH_3CO-S-CoA + CH_3COCH_2CO-S-CoA \qquad Acetyl\ CoA + Acetoacetyl\ CoA$$

$$\downarrow$$

$$\underset{\underset{OH}{|}}{HOOCCH_2\overset{\overset{CH_3}{|}}{C}CH_2CO-S-CoA} \qquad 3\text{-Hydroxy-3-methylglutaryl CoA}$$

$$\downarrow$$

$$\underset{\underset{OH}{|}}{HOOCCH_2\overset{\overset{CH_3}{|}}{C}CH_2CH_2OH} \qquad Mevalonic\ Acid$$

$$\downarrow$$

$$\underset{\underset{OH}{|}}{HOOCCH_2\overset{\overset{CH_3}{|}}{C}CH_2CH_2OP_2O_6H_3} \qquad Mevalonic\ Acid\ Pyrophosphate$$

$$\downarrow$$

$$CH_2{=}\overset{\overset{CH_3}{|}}{C}CH_2CH_2OP_2O_6H_3 \qquad Isopentenyl\ Pyrophosphate$$

$$\downarrow$$

$$CH_3\overset{\overset{CH_3}{|}}{C}{=}CHCH_2OP_2O_6H_3 \qquad \gamma,\gamma\text{-Dimethylallyl Pyrophosphate}$$

$$\downarrow$$

$$CH_3\overset{\overset{CH_3}{|}}{C}{=}CHCH_2CH_2\overset{\overset{CH_3}{|}}{C}{=}CHCH_2OP_2O_6H_3 \qquad Geranyl\ Pyrophosphate$$

$$\downarrow$$

$$CH_3\overset{\overset{CH_3}{|}}{C}{=}CHCH_2CH_2\overset{\overset{CH_3}{|}}{C}{=}CHCH_2CH_2\overset{\overset{CH_3}{|}}{C}{=}CHCH_2OP_2O_6H_3 \qquad Farnesyl\ Pyrophosphate$$

FIGURE 1.12. FORMATION OF FARNESYL PYROPHOSPHATE.

methylvaleric acid (mevalonic acid), which had been used as an acetate-replacing factor for *L. acidophilus*, is converted to cholesterol by rat liver slices in almost quantitative yield. The formation of mevalonic acid in the body is catalyzed by an enzyme system in the microsomes. It apparently involves the steps outlined in Figure 1.12. Condensation of acetyl CoA with acetoacetyl CoA yields 3-hydroxy-3-methylglutaryl CoA. This is followed by reduction of the thioester group to mevalonic acid in the presence of TPNH. This intermediate is then phosphorylated by ATP to mevalonic acid pyrophosphate. Decarboxylation and dehydration of the latter leads to isopentenyl pyrophosphate, which is isomerized to γ,γ-dimethylallyl pyrophosphate. Condensation of these two C_5 units produces geranyl pyrophosphate (C_{10}), and addition of another C_5 unit forms farnesyl pyrophosphate (C_{15}). The tail-to-tail condensation of two C_{15} units then yields squalene (C_{30}).

In summary, the chief intermediates in the biosynthesis of cholesterol from acetate are mevalonic acid, squalene, and lanosterol. Details of the reaction sequence are still under active investigation and subject to modification as more evidence accumulates. The first step in the activation of acetate undoubtedly involves combination with coenzyme A. This explains the impaired ability of the liver of pantothenic acid-deficient animals to incorporate acetate into cholesterol. Another factor seems to be responsible for the decrease in hepatic cholesterogenesis in fasting animals. It has been found that in such animals the enzymatic reduction of hydroxymethylglutaryl coenzyme A to mevalonate is inhibited.

2-Phenylbutyric acid and related compounds interfere with cholesterol biosynthesis by inhibiting the acetylation of coenzyme A. The mechanism whereby Δ^4-cholestenone and certain stenols inhibit cholesterol synthesis is not yet clear. The inhibition is believed to occur in the synthesis of mevalonic acid.

3. Disposition

Cholesterol is always found in vertebrates, often in invertebrates, but rarely in plants. Until it was recently discovered in algae, cholesterol was considered to be a characteristic animal sterol. Human gallstones may contain as much as 99 per cent cholesterol, and wool fat or animal skins are also rich sources of this substance. The spinal cord and brain of cattle constitute the most important raw material for the industrial production of cholesterol.

On a wet weight basis human adult brain contains about 1.0 per cent cholesterol in the gray matter, 4.2 per cent in the white matter, and 1.3 per cent in the cerebellum. The cholesterol content of infant brain is lower than that of adult brain. Human nerve tissues contain about 1.5 per cent cholesterol; the spinal cord, even 3.9 per cent. The adrenals are particularly rich in cholesterol, containing 2.6 to 6.7 per cent cholesterol in the case of fresh tissue from human adults, but fetal adrenals show lower concentrations. The lipides of spermatozoa contain considerable amounts of cholesterol, e.g. 2.4 per cent in man, 8 per cent in the ram.

Only the diet of strict vegetarians is cholesterol-free. Ovo-lacto-vegetarians may ingest considerable quantities of cholesterol. Cow's milk contains only between 9 and 14 mg per 100 ml, but butter 280 mg per 100 g, and eggs are the richest dietary source of this sterol. A hen's egg contains an average of a quarter of a gram of cholesterol.

The dietary cholesterol, together with that in the intestinal juices and bile, is absorbed in the small bowel with the aid of the bile salts, particularly of cholic acid. The efficiency of the intestinal absorption decreases with the amount of cholesterol and increases with the amount of fatty acids in the diet. Soybean sterols in the diet interfere with the absorption of cholesterol. Cholesterol is esterified in the gut wall with the aid of an enzyme, cholesterol esterase. The thoracic duct lymph transports cholesterol, partly in esterified form, to the systemic circulation in the chylomicra. On entering the blood stream it is still in colloidal form, but it is soon solublized or "cleared" and circulates in combination with the α- and β- lipoproteins.

In nerve tissues cholesterol is associated with structural components, notably the myelin sheath, and may well act as an insulator. While there is very little esterified cholesterol in brain tissues, 70 to 75 per cent of the plasma cholesterol is in the ester form. The assumption has been made that esterified cholesterol is metabolically more mobile than free cholesterol. The fatty acids involved are to a large extent unsaturated, and cholesterol may serve as a vehicle for the transport of these fatty acids. While human plasma contains an average of 50 mg of free and 170 mg of esterified cholesterol per 100 ml, the cholesterol of human erythrocytes and leucocytes is largely in the free form. In the red blood corpuscles cholesterol is concentrated in the cell wall. Hemolytic substances, such as saponins, are detoxified by combination with erythrocyte cholesterol.

The plasma cholesterol level is regulated chiefly by the liver, which is the most important site of cholesterol biosynthesis and metabolism. The biosynthetic activity of the liver is, in turn, under homeostatic control. Feeding of cholesterol or its precursors to animals decreases their hepatic cholesterogenesis. Chronic administration of cholesterol produces fatty infiltrations, so-called cholesterol fatty liver. Bile acids and other surface-active agents have the ability to increase serum lipides, including cholesterol, by mobilizing the liver lipides in some manner. Endocrine glands also exert some control over lipide metabolism and influence the cholesterol concentration in the blood. Thyroid hormones increase the rate of both cholesterol biosynthesis and catabolism and produce, especially in the human organism, a decrease in the plasma cholesterol level. Conversely, in thyroid deficiency, either produced experimentally in animals or due to hypothyroidism in patients, the rate of cholesterol biosynthesis is low and the blood level is high. In men there is more cholesterol in the β-lipoprotein fraction than in the α-lipoprotein fraction, whereas the reverse is true in women. The administration of estrogens to men lowers the cholesterol concentration in the β-lipoproteins, but raises the cholesterol level in the α-lipoproteins. Lack of androgens, as in the castrate, raises the serum cholesterol level in all species so far examined. The adrenal cortex responds to various types of stress with a rapid fall in its cholesterol ester content, presumably owing to an increased rate of conversion to adrenocortical hormones. At the same time the plasma cholesterol, particularly the ester fraction, decreases perceptibly.

Endogenous and dietary cholesterol form the metabolic pool from which the organism manufactures steroid hormones and bile acids. Bile acids and unesterified cholesterol are secreted into the intestine via the bile and reabsorbed to be reutilized, but the enterohepatic circulation of cholesterol is less efficient and slower than that of the bile acids. The main excretory route of cholesterol is via the feces, but some cholesterol is also lost by secretion into the sebum. The metabolic fate of cholesterol will be discussed in subsequent chapters.

Larvae of carnivorous insects require cholesterol for growth and metamorphosis, but herbivorous species of insects can also utilize C-24 homologs of cholesterol. Insect larvae lack the ability to synthesize cholesterol from acetate. Analogs of cholesterol in which the 3-hydroxyl group is replaced by a sulfhydryl (thiocholesterol), chloro (cholesteryl chloride) or methoxy (cholesterol methyl ether) group inhibit cholesterol utilization. Some but not all protozoa also require cholesterol or related sterols. Very little is known about the steroid hormones in insects or the metabolic functions of sterols in protozoa.

4. Clinical Significance

The determination of cholesterol in blood is a relatively simple procedure and consequently much information has been accumulated concerning the behavior of the serum cholesterol in various diseases. A range of 180 to 230 mg per cent total cholesterol is generally accepted as normal for the American adult. The average serum cholesterol level in men rises with age until the sixth decade of life and declines thereafter. In women the average cholesterol concentration is lower, but continues to rise with age. Fat persons generally have higher serum cholesterol.levels than lean ones. Statistical analyses indicate that populations with a high percentage of animal fats in the diet have a higher serum cholesterol level than populations subsisting largely on a vegetarian diet. The degree of unsaturation of the dietary fatty acids seems to be important, since Eskimos, who use unsaturated fish oils, have relatively low serum cholesterol concentrations.

In biliary obstruction the serum cholesterol level, especially the concentration of free cholesterol, shows an increase. This is apparently due to increased hepatic synthesis and concomitant decrease in liver esterase activity. Hypocholesterolemia, and particularly a decrease in the percentage of esterified cholesterol accompanies parenchymatous liver damage. The increase in α- and β-globulin concentrations in nephrotic patients may account for the hypercholesterolemia observed under these conditions. Increases in serum cholesterol are also encountered in uncontrolled diabetes. The effect of thyroid hormones has already been mentioned. Hyperthyroidism is associated with hypocholesterolemia, whereas hypothyroidism leads to hypercholesterolemia. In hyperfunction of the adrenal cortex high serum cholesterol levels are frequently observed, whereas Addison's disease tends to lower the cholesterol concentration in the blood.

The role of cholesterol in atherosclerosis has been studied intensively, but is still not very clear. In view of the presence of cholesterol in the atherosclerotic plaques of the aorta it seems reasonable to assume a causal relationship between the disease and an excess of the substance. It is indeed possible to produce atherosclerosis in susceptible animals by cholesterol feeding, and in man the disease is frequently associated with conditions in which the blood cholesterol is elevated, such as diabetes and nephrosis. Although much has been written about the relation between dietary lipides (especially cholesterol) and atherosclerosis, the evidence for a causal connection between diet and atherosclerosis in man is still indirect and circumstantial. Arterial tissue is undoubtedly capable of synthesizing cholesterol *in situ*, and the cholesterol deposits may originate from either endogeneous or dietary cholesterol. In the absence of more conclusive evidence it must be assumed that atherosclerosis is probably due to some abnormality in lipide metabolism, perhaps in the handling of cholesterol. It is generally agreed that hypercholesterolemia favors the appearance of atherosclerotic lesions, and factors which decrease the serum cholesterol level, such as estrogens, or interfere with cholesterol absorption, such as soybean sterols, have attracted considerable attention.

The abnormal deposition of cholesterol, called xanthomatosis, is sometimes observed in man and can be produced experimentally in rabbits by cholesterol feeding. In essential hypercholesterolemia in man, a familial disorder of lipide metabolism, yellowish tophi, consisting mainly of cholesterol and its esters, together with carotene may be deposited in the eyelids (xanthelasmas) or in the tendons. Secondary hypercholesterolemic xanthomatosis may be due to chronic biliary obstruction, and manifests itself in skin xanthomata. In the rare condition known as Hand-Schüller-Christian disease deposits of cholesterol and carotenoids are found in various locations, especially in the skull. Gallstones are formed when the bile for one reason or another loses its ability to keep cholesterol in solution. In addition to cholesterol, human gall-stones may contain varying amounts of calcium bilirubinate.

Cholesterol has been shown to be carcinogenic in certain strains of mice. Considering the difficulties inherent in the preparation of absolutely pure cholesterol and also its relative instability towards light and air, the possibility cannot be dismissed that cholesterol preparations owe their carcinogenicity to the presence of oxidation products. The structural relationship to steroids of such potent carcinogens as 20-methylcholanthrene and steranthrene (Figure 1.13) make hypotheses of endogenous carcinogenesis appear plausible, although they are not supported by experimental evidence.

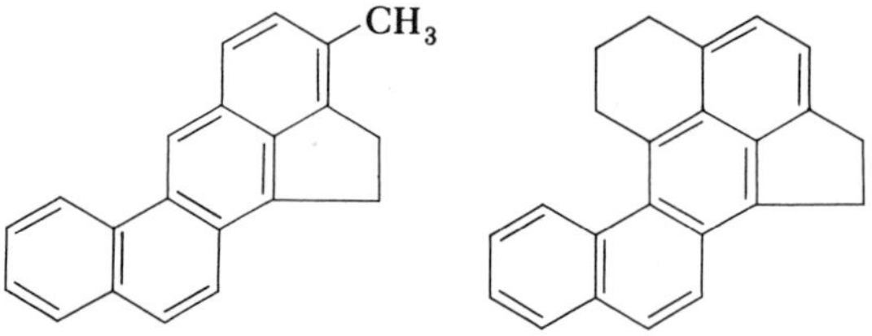

20-Methylcholanthrene   Steranthrene

FIGURE 1.13. CARCINOGENIC HYDROCARBONS RELATED TO STEROIDS.

Efforts have been made to trace skin cancer to irradiation products of skin sterols and to produce carcinogenic diets by heating of cholesterol. The possibility that cholesterol acts as a co-carcinogen has also been explored. It has been shown that malignant tumors contain more cholesterol than benign ones, especially in the central, necrotic portion. The exact role of cholesterol in the biochemistry of cancer remains to be established.

5. Analysis

The isolation of the cholesterol-containing lipoprotein fractions involves the various tools of protein fractionation: solvent fractionation according to Cohn, ultracentrifugation by the Gofman technique, electrophoretic methods according to Tiselius, or the more convenient electrochromatographic methods, especially paper electrophoresis.

Basically, all methods for the analysis of cholesterol in body fluids and tissues involve an isolation procedure, followed by a more or less efficient purification step and some quantitative assay procedure.

Homogenized tissues, feces, etc. may be dried by warming under vacuum, by lyophilization, or by alcohol extraction. The dry material is then extracted in a Soxhlet extractor or percolator. Wet extraction methods are less laborious and may be even more efficient. For the wet extraction of blood, tissue homogenates, etc., Bloor first proposed a 3:1 mixture of ethanol and ether, but other solvent mixtures, e.g. chloroform-methanol (2:1), are also suitable.

The lipide mixture may be worked up by saponification with alcoholic alkali. On dilution with water the soaps, glycerol, etc., dissolve in the aqueous phase, while the nonsaponifiable material, including cholesterol, can be extracted with ether or other organic solvents. Digitonin, a steroid saponin, forms an insoluble molecular complex with cholesterol as with many, but by no means all 3β-hydroxysteroids. It can therefore be used either for the isolation of cholesterol from the nonsaponifiable fraction, or for the separation of cholesterol from its esters prior to saponification in the determination of free and ester cholesterol. For the recovery of both the cholesterol and the digitonin, which is relatively expensive, the digitonide may be treated with pyridine, acetic anhydride, acetic acid, or boiling benzene or xylene. Further purification of cholesterol may be obtained by preparing the insoluble dibromide, by countercurrent distribution, or by chromatography. Adsorption chromatography, especially on alumina, is a very simple, yet efficient separation method, which has been used extensively in the sterol field. The separation of cholesterol esters on a microscale can be effected by paper chromatography, particularly the reversed-phase method of partition chromatography.

The determination of cholesterol in extracts that have gone through more or less extensive purification can be carried out by weighing the cholesterol digitonide. Crude extracts are conveniently assayed by colorimetric procedures. The color changes

produced by the addition of sulfuric acid to a solution of cholesterol in acetic anhydride were first observed by Liebermann in
1885. Burchard later obtained a green color by adding acetic anhydride and sulfuric acid to cholesterol in chloroform solution.
The Liebermann-Burchard reaction forms the basis of the colorimetric procedure of Schoenheimer and Sperry, which is the most
widely used method for the routine determination of cholesterol in
blood. In the Salkowski reaction a chloroform solution of cholesterol is treated with concentrated sulfuric acid. The chloroform
solution turns red, while the sulfuric acid shows a green fluorescence. The Tschugaeff method is based on the red color produced by heating cholesterol in chloroform or in glacial acetic
acid with zinc chloride and acetyl chloride. Cholesterol in acetic
acid gives a purple color on addition of ferric chloride in glacial
acetic acid and concentrated sulfuric acid.

II

Sterols

1. Structure

CONFIGURATION (cf. Chap. I, p. 3) describes the spatial arrangement of the substituents at a single asymmetric center, e.g. of the four substituents of a carbon atom. The arrangement of atoms in a molecule which can arise as a result of rotation around a single bond (e.g. the carbon-carbon bond of ethane) is defined as conformation. The usual presentation of the cyclohexane rings of steroids (cf. Figure 1.4) fails to show the actual conformational relationships in the molecule. By inspection of a three-dimensional model or of a conformational formula it can be appreciated that the rings are not planar. Cyclohexane can exist in two steric forms: the so-called chair form, which is thermodynamically more stable, and the boat form (Figure 2.1). Seen from above, the substituents connected by dotted lines are farther away from the observer than those connected by full lines. The lines lie more or less in a plane passing through the center of the molecule (equatorial, e) or they are more or less perpendicular to it (axial, a).

By saturation of the 4,5-double bond of cholesterol a new asymmetric center is created at C-5, where the hydrogen atom may lie either on the same side of the molecule as the methyl group at C-10 (*cis*-fusion of rings A and B) or on the opposite side (A/B *trans*-fusion). In the former case the steroid is derived from the hydrocarbon coprostane (5β-series), in the latter from cholestane (5α-series) (Figure 2.2).

In the 5α-series the spatial arrangement of the hydrogen atom at C-5 is axial with regard to both rings A and B, but in the 5β-series the arrangement of the hydrogen at C-5 is axial with regard

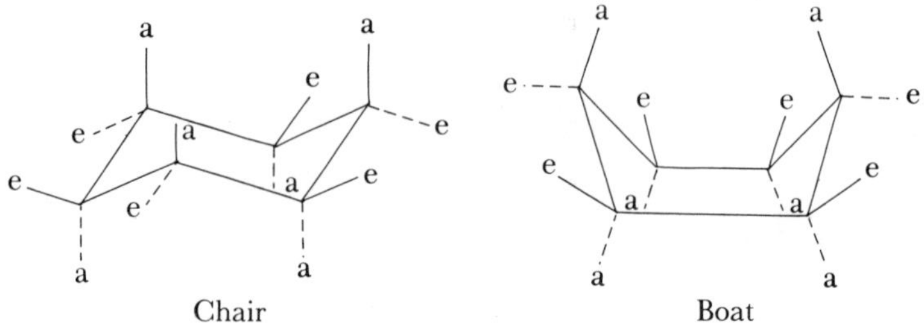

FIGURE 2.1. CYCLOHEXANE.

to ring A and equatorial with regard to ring B. Concerning the arrangement of substituents at C-3 (e.g. a hydroxyl group), it should be noted that the equatorial substituent in the A/B *trans* series is β-oriented; whereas the equatorial substituent in the A/B *cis* series is α-oriented. The equatorial substituents are formed preferentially and they are more stable (e.g. cholestan-3β-ol and coprostan-3α-ol) than the corresponding epimers (cholestan-3α-ol and coprostan-3β-ol). In the 5,6-unsaturated compounds the

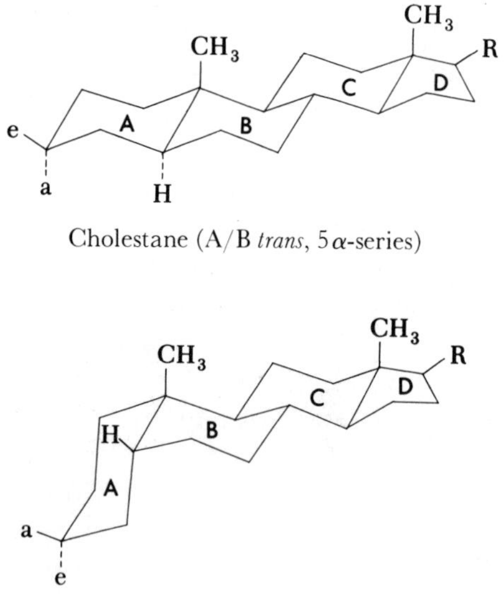

Cholestane (A/B *trans*, 5 α-series)

Coprostane (A/B *cis*, 5 β-series)

FIGURE 2.2. CONFORMATIONAL FORMULAE.

3β-isomer (cholesterol) is more stable than the 3α-epimer ("epicholesterol").

In order to show how the numbering system and convention in stereochemical presentation are extended to C_{29} sterols, the structural formula of stigmasterol is given in Figure 2.3. Since in natural steroids rings B and C are *trans*-fused (hydrogen atom at C-8 β-oriented, at C-9 α-oriented) and in practically all of them rings C and D are also *trans*-fused (methyl group at C-13 β-oriented, H at C-14 α-oriented), the hydrogen atoms at 8, 9, and 14 may be omitted. The ethyl group (C-28 and C-29) creates a new asymmetric center at C-24. Since it lies on the same side of the hydrocarbon chain as the methyl group (C-21) at C-20, it is drawn upward and also designated as β-oriented. Stigmasterol and other natural steroids are *trans* isomers with respect to the 22,23-double bond.

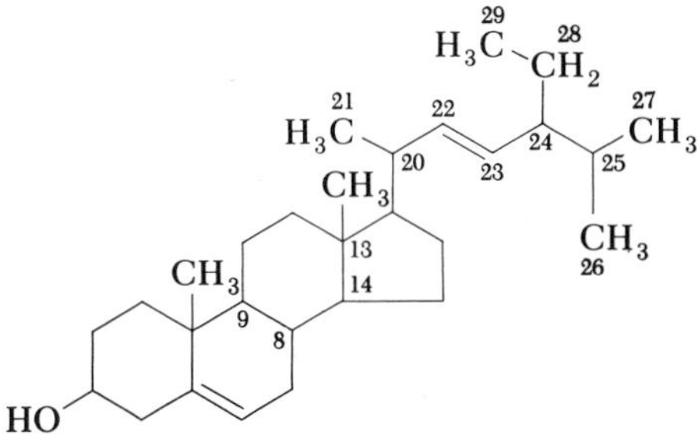

FIGURE 2.3. STIGMASTEROL.

A number of conventions are used in the nomenclature of steroids. For the sake of simplicity we shall use the names of the parent hydrocarbons with suffixes for the functional groups. Cholesterol, being derived from the unsaturated hydrocarbon cholestene is named Δ^5-cholesten-3β-ol. In indicating the location of the double bond (5,6) the higher number is omitted when it is the next one in the system or whenever the lower number describes the location unequivocally. Some authors omit the Greek Δ (e.g. 5-cholesten-3β-ol), but for the sake of clarity Δ will be used in this book. The position and orientation (3β) of the functional group is inserted between root and suffix by hyphens and the last vowel

(e) in the root is elided before a vowel (o) in the suffix. Stigmasterol is the trivial name of the 24β-ethyl-$\Delta^{5,22}$-cholestadien-3β-ol, or, using the name of the C_{29} parent hydrocarbon stigmastane as the root, it may be called $\Delta^{5,22}$-stigmastadien-3β-ol. Where the orientation of the substituent is unknown a wavy line is drawn in the structure and a ξ (xi) is written in the name.

2. Tetracyclic Triterpenes

Sterols of some kind occur in all living organisms, with the possible exception of certain species of bacteria and certain primitive algae. Some authors feel that sterols must therefore be of vital importance, whereas others regard them as complex waste products. Be that as it may, it is becoming increasingly evident that the same sterol may occur in plants and animals and that the older classification into phyto- and zoosterols is losing its meaning. In general, lower animal species contain a greater variety of sterols than higher ones. As the evolutionary scale is ascended, variations are eliminated and cholesterol becomes more and more prominent. It thus seems, in the words of Bergmann, "that in cholesterol we witness the survival of the 'fittest' sterol." In the plant kingdom the situation is somewhat different. The higher plants have elaborated more complicated sterols and such specialized steroids as sapogenins and alkaloids.

It is generally assumed that all steroids are formed by similar biogenetic processes. This has been demonstrated experimentally in but a few cases. However, reasoning from analogy to other biochemical processes, this appears to be a valid assumption. The arrangement of sterols in this chapter is based on this assumption and begins with the triterpenes containing a cyclopentenoperhydrophenanthrene nucleus.

Wool fat or lanolin contains, in addition to squalene, a mixture of C_{30} sterols involved in the biogenesis of cholesterol. The mixture, which was earlier thought to be a single compound, "isocholesterol", contains the sterols (or tetracyclic triterpenes) shown in Figure 2.4. These sterols may be named systematically as derivatives of cholestane (e.g. lanosterol is $4,4,14\alpha$-trimethyl-$\Delta^{8,24}$-cholestadien-3β-ol) or as derivatives of the saturated C_{30} hydro-

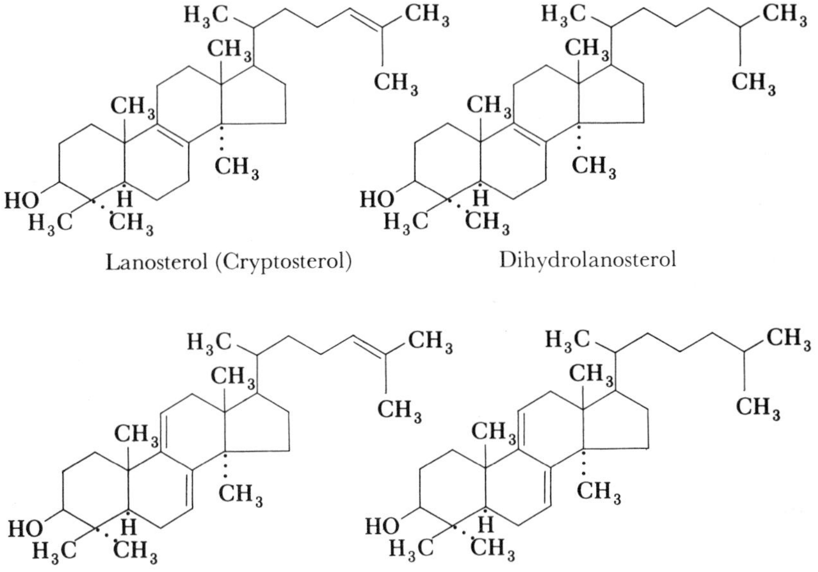

Lanosterol (Cryptosterol)   Dihydrolanosterol

Agnosterol   Dihydroagnosterol (γ-Lanosterol)

FIGURE 2.4. TETRACYCLIC TRITERPENES IN WOOL FAT.

carbon lanostane (e.g. agnosterol is $\Delta^{7,9(11),24}$-lanostatrien-3β-ol. Lanosterol occurs not only in animals, but it has also been isolated from the latex of spurge (euphorbia) and from yeast.

A group of acids related to lanosterol is found in various wood-rotting fungi. Eburicoic acid (Figure 2.5) has a methylene group in C-28. It has been shown by Dauben that the C-28 carbon atom is derived from formate and not from acetate. Polyporenic acid A

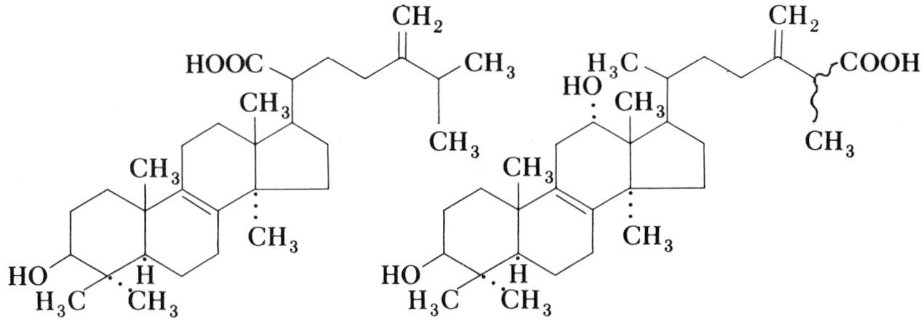

Eburicoic Acid   Polyporenic Acid A

FIGURE 2.5. TETRACYCLIC TRITERPENES IN FUNGI.

(Figure 2.5) differs from eburicoic acid in having a 12α-hydroxyl group and a carboxyl group attached to C-25 instead of C-20. It appears likely that the antibiotics elaborated by fungi of the genus *Cephalosporium* are steroids of a similar nature.

Various resins contain acids related to euphol (Figure 2.6), the 13, 14, 17-antipode of lanosterol. Euphol was first isolated from euphorbia resin, and elemolic acid (Figure 2.6), a 20-iso compound, occurs in elemi resin. It is quite possible that euphol and lanosterol have a common precursor and that their derivatives are therefore biochemically related. No C_{27} sterols with a euphol skeleton have been found in nature so far.

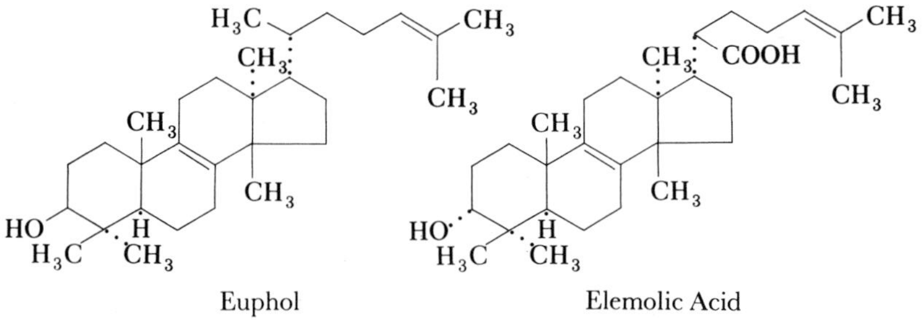

Euphol   Elemolic Acid

FIGURE 2.6. TETRACYCLIC TRITERPENES IN RESINS.

Djerassi has isolated a sterol from the cactus *Lophocereus schottii* which may be an intermediate between tetracyclic triterpenes and C_{27} sterols. It is identical with a sterol almost simultaneously isolated from rat feces by a different group of researchers and named methostenol. Lophenol (4α-methyl-$Δ^7$-cholesten-3β-ol) (Figure 2.7) lacks not only the methyl group at C-14, but also one of the geminal methyl groups at C-14. 4α-Methyl-$Δ^8$-cholesten-3β-ol (not shown) has recently been identified in a preputial gland tumor of mice. Another 4α-methylsterol, citrostadienol (Figure 2.7), has been found in citrus peel oil. Its structure suggests a biogenetic relationship not only to tetracyclic triterpene precursors, but also to the C_{29} sterols. Reduction of the 24,28-double bond could give rise to either a 24α- or a 24β-ethyl group. β-Sitosterol, (24β-ethylcholesterol) (Sec. 5, p. 29), has actually been isolated from the same source.

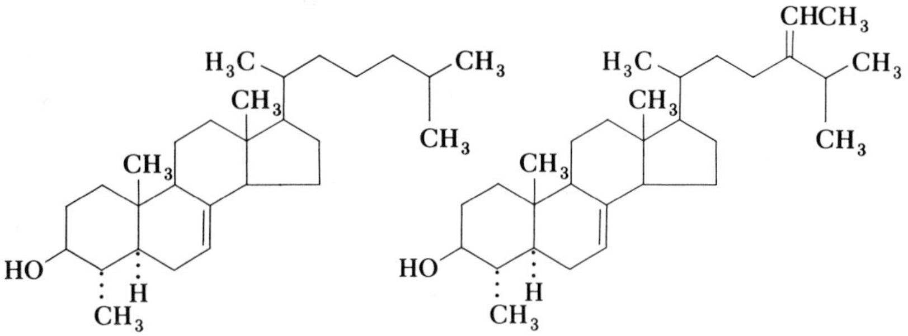

Lophenol   Citrostadienol

FIGURE 2.7. 4α-METHYLSTEROLS.

3. C_{27} Sterols

Two sterols, which may well be the penultimate and ultimate precursors, respectively, in the biosynthesis of cholesterol, have been found in nature. Zymosterol (Greek *zyme*, yeast) (Figure 2.8) was isolated from yeast, and desmosterol (Greek *desmos*, link) (Figure 2.8) from chick embryos and also from barnacles. Both sterols are efficiently converted to cholesterol by the rat liver.

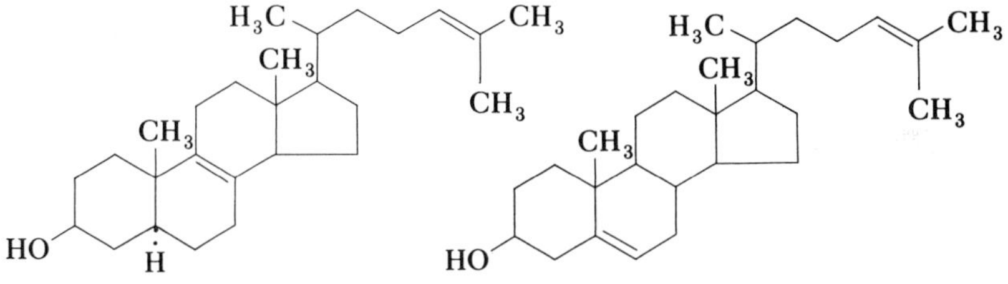

Zymosterol   Desmosterol

FIGURE 2.8. PRECURSORS OF CHOLESTEROL.

In the skin and intestines cholesterol is converted to 7-dehydrocholesterol ($\Delta^{5,7}$-cholestadien-3β-ol) (Figure 2.9), and pig skin is a rich source of this sterol. The secretions of the preputial gland of mice and of the anal gland of guinea pigs, the epididymis of the testes and the bulbi vestibuli of female rats are also rich in 7-dehydrocholesterol. Microorganisms (*Azotobacter* sp.) are capable of dehydrogenating cholesterol to 7-dehydrocholesterol. It also occurs in certain snails and in duck eggs. It is not known whether the 7-dehydrocholesterol in the egg yolk comes from a fish diet or is synthesized in the egg from cholesterol. Irradiation of the skin converts this diene to vitamin D_3 (Chap. III, p. 37). Another companion of cholesterol was isolated by Fieser in the course of an intensive investigation of the carcinogenic properties of commercial cholesterol preparations and named lathosterol (Greek *lathos*, hidden). It is Δ^7-cholestenol (Figure 2.9), which was isolated from rat skin. The sterols in the sebum and also in the intestines act as lubricants and protective coating.

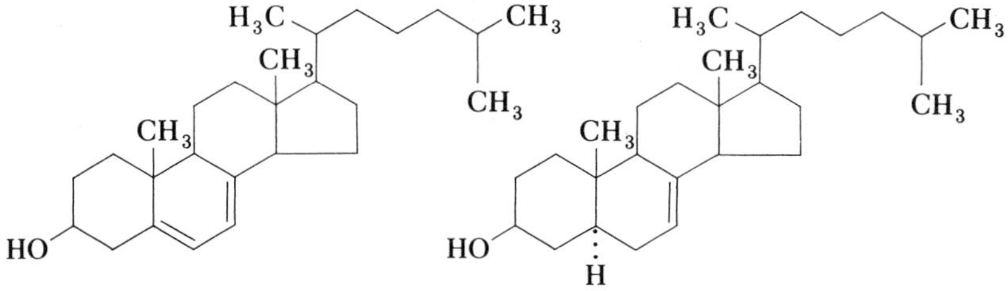

7-Dehydrocholesterol Δ^7-Cholestenol (Lathosterol)

FIGURE 2.9. STEROLS IN SKIN.

In the large intestine cholesterol is exposed to the action of the intestinal flora. While some cholesterol is excreted in the feces in unchanged form, the major fecal steroid in man is coprostan-3β-ol (Figure 2.10). Coprostanol was first isolated from this source in 1857 and later named *Koprosterin* (Greek *copros*, dung) by Bondzyński. The name coprosterol is still in use, but it is somewhat misleading since cholesterol refers to the Δ^5-compound. Figure 2.10 shows the partial structure (rings A and B) of four fecal steroids. Coprostan-3α-ol is present in dog feces and in ambergris. Small amounts of cholestan-3β-ol (dihydrocholesterol) and coprostan-3-one have been found in human feces.

It has long been believed that coprostanone is an obligatory intermediate in the bacterial conversion of cholesterol to coprostanol, but direct conversion without production of a 3-ketone has recently been demonstrated. The origin of cholestanol, a constant companion of cholesterol, is more complicated than previously be-

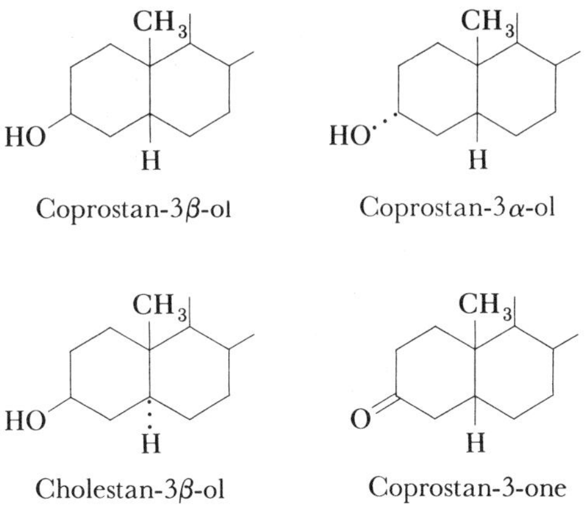

Coprostan-3β-ol   Coprostan-3α-ol

Cholestan-3β-ol   Coprostan-3-one

FIGURE 2.10. STEROLS IN FECES.

lieved. It does not seem to be a simple reduction product of cholesterol, but it is known to be formed from Δ⁴-cholesten-3-one.

The intestinal absorption of steroids depends both on their structure and on the species of experimental animals used. Neither cholestanol nor coprostanol are appreciably absorbed in man, but
rabbits and rats can absorb cholestanol. The addition of cholestanol to the diet of these animals inhibits cholesterol absorption.
Epicholesterol (Δ⁵-cholesten-3α-ol) is poorly absorbed in rats,
but lathosterol and 7-dehydrocholesterol are readily absorbed.

Cholesterol derivatives with an additional hydroxyl group in
the side chain occur in nature. *Narthecium ossifraga*, a lily species,
contains a 22α-hydroxycholesterol, and cerebrosterol (Figure 2.11)
(24β-hydroxycholesterol) occurs in the lipide fraction of human
brain. Incubation of mouse liver mitochondria with cholesterol

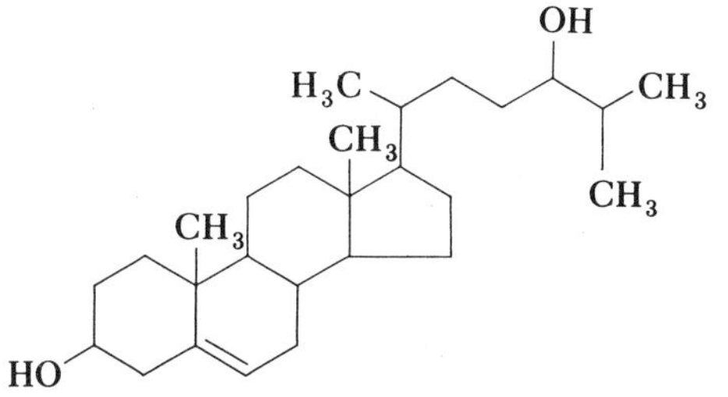

FIGURE 2.11. CEREBROSTEROL.

produces both 25- and 27-hydroxycholesterol, which are further oxidized to steroid acids.

4. C$_{28}$ Sterols

It seems reasonable to discuss the C$_{28}$ sterols after the C$_{27}$ sterols, since they appear to be biogenetically derived from the latter. All carbon atoms in ergosterol (Figure 2.13), biosynthesized in yeast from radioacetate, have been shown to be derived from either the carboxyl or methyl carbon of acetate, save C-28. As in the case of eburicoic acid, mentioned in Section 2, this carbon atom is derived from formate or from a methyl group by transmethylation. Reduction of the methylene group in eburicoic acid and in 24-methyl-enecholesterol (Figure 2.12) could give rise to either a 24α- or a 24β-methyl group. Representatives of both series of sterols are known.

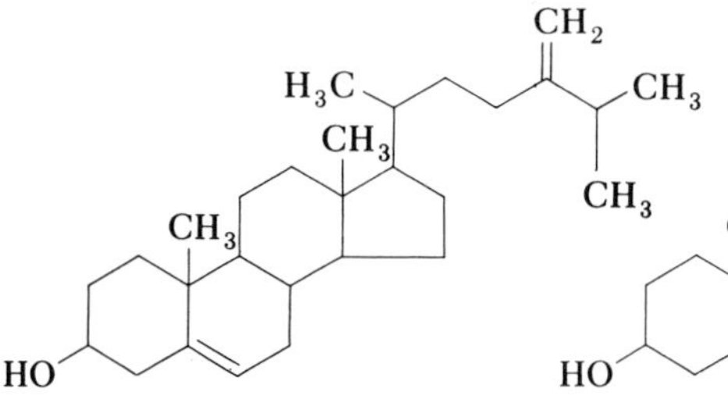

24-Methylenecholesterol
(Chalinasterol, Ostreasterol)

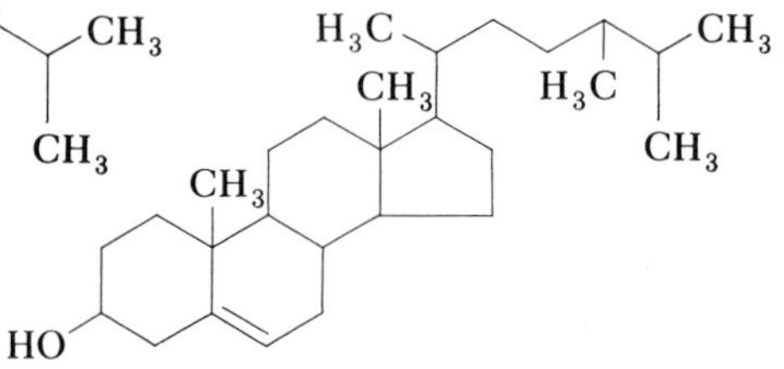

Campesterol

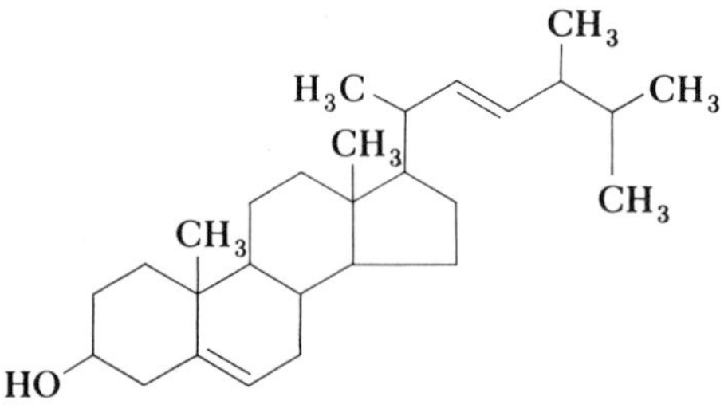

Brassicasterol

FIGURE 2.12. C$_{28}$ STEROLS RELATED TO CHOLESTEROL.

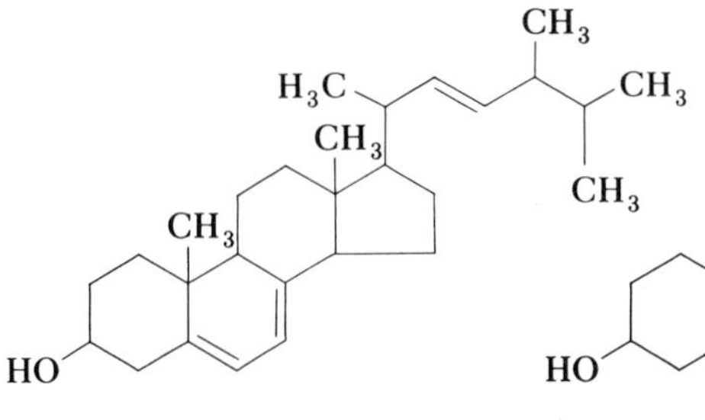

Ergosterol

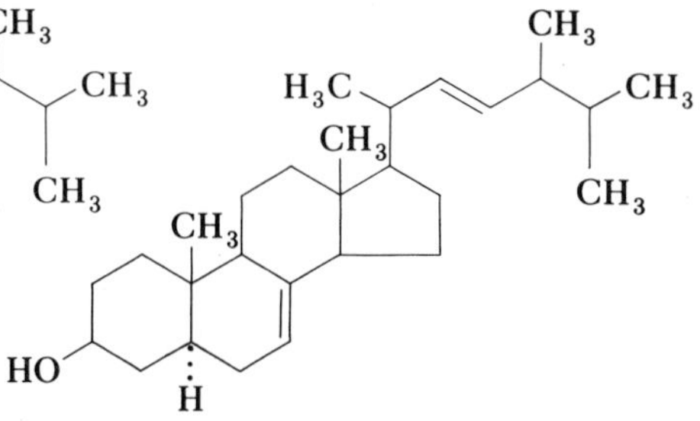

5-Dihydroergosterol

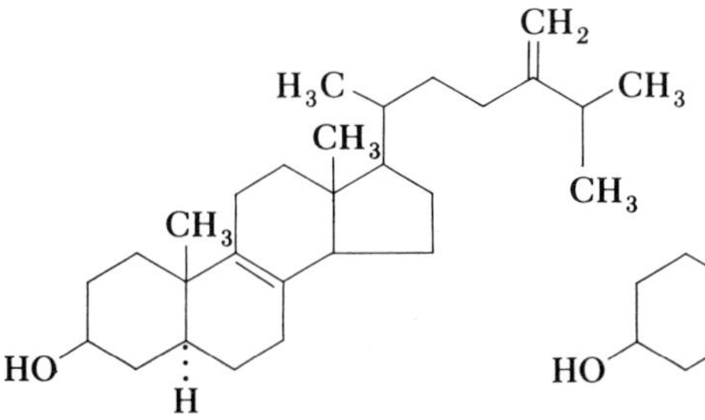

Fecosterol

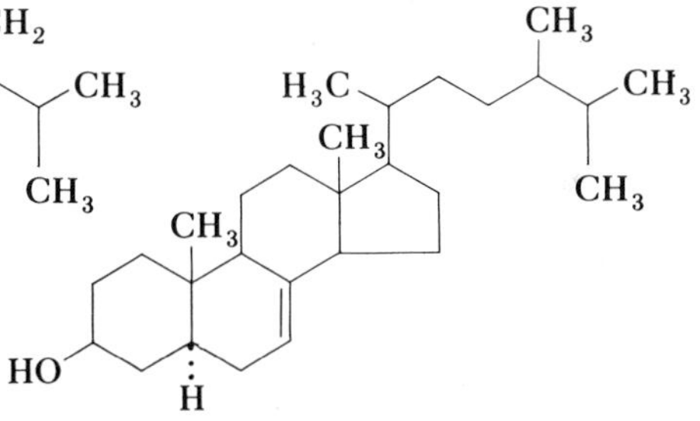

Fungisterol

FIGURE 2.13. C_{28} STEROLS IN FUNGI.

24-Methylenecholesterol (Figure 2.12) was first isolated from the sponge *Chalina arbuscula* and named chalinasterol. It was later shown to be identical with a sterol isolated from oysters and named ostreasterol. The 24-methylcholesterols occur in higher plants as well as in marine invertebrates, but they are not so widely distributed as the 24-ethylcholesterols. The 24α-methylcholesterol, campesterol (Figure 2.12), has been found in rapeseed oil from *Brassica campestris*, in soybean and wheat germ oil, and in sponges, while the 24β-methylsterol with two double bonds, brassicasterol (Figure 2.12), occurs in rapeseed oil from the closely related *Brassica rapa*.

By far the most important C_{28} sterol is ergosterol (Figure 2.13), which was first isolated from ergot, but also occurs in yeast and other fungi, in vegetable oils, as well as in lichens, algae, in the common earthworm, snails, and egg yolk. The presence of ergosterol in eggs is due to the fact that chickens, unlike most other animals can absorb small amounts of dietary ergosterol. Ergosterol owes its commercial importance to its availability as a by-product of the fermentation industry and to the opportune location of its double bonds. Ultraviolet irradiation readily converts it to vitamin D_2 (cf. Chap. III, p. 35). The 22-double bond is readily broken by oxidation. This provides access to the C_{21} steroids, including progesterone and the adrenocortical hormones. The 5,7-diene system confers reactivity to the steroid nucleus and was, prior to the advent of microbiological conversion, a very desirable feature for the introduction of oxygen functions. Ergot also contains a 22-dihydroergosterol. The other sterols shown in Figure 2.13 are biogenetically related to ergosterol and also occur in yeast (Latin *faex*, yeast) and other fungi. The structure of fungisterol is still in doubt. A 14-dehydroergosterol (not shown) has been found in *Aspergillus niger*.

5. C_{29} Sterols

The most widely distributed sterols in higher plants are stigmasterol (Figure 2.14) and the sitosterols (Figure 2.14). Sterols occur in plant tissues to some extent in the form of glycosides (the so-called sterolins), but largely in the free state and in the form of esters. Stigmasterol was first isolated from the calabar bean (*Physostigma venenosum*). The commercial source is the soybean, but sugar cane wax also contains substantial amounts of this sterol. Its abundance and the double bonds at C-22 and C-5 make stigmasterol an important starting material for the synthesis of progesterone and other steroid hormones. The 24-epimer of stigmasterol, poriferasterol (Figure 2.14), occurs in various marine invertebrates. Recently 5-dihydrostigmasterol (Figure 2.15) has been isolated from a slime mold, *Dictyostelium discoideum*. This substance has acrasin activity; i.e., it causes the amoeboid cells of the mold to aggregate in a multicellular unit, which undergoes further differentiation.

The trivial names of the sitosterols (Greek *sitos*, grain) antedate precise knowledge of their structure and the Greek letters are, of course, not related to stereochemistry. α-Sitosterol was shown to be a mixture. β-Sitosterol (Figure 2.14) happens to be 24β-ethyl-

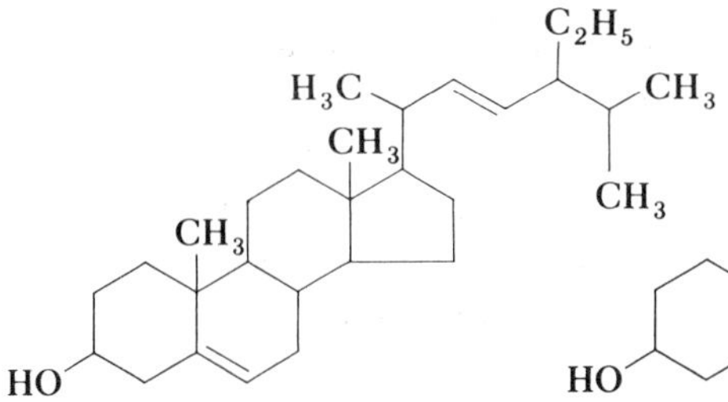

Stigmasterol

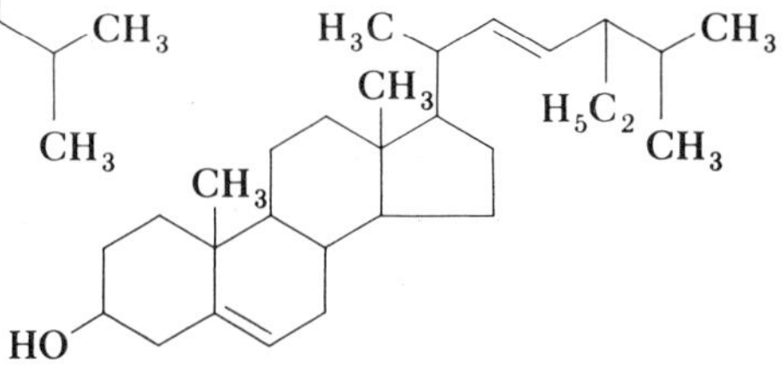

Poriferasterol

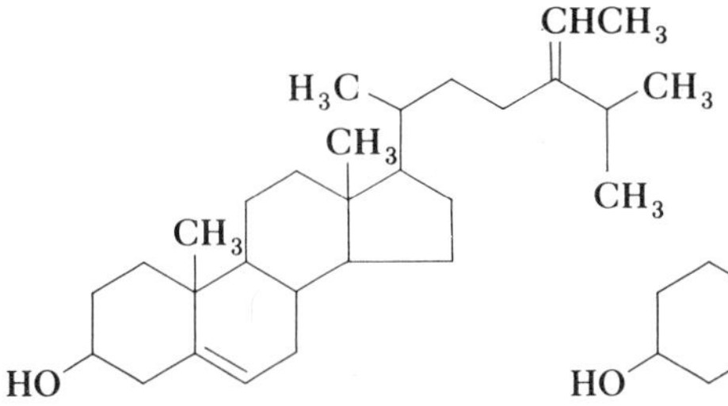

Fucosterol

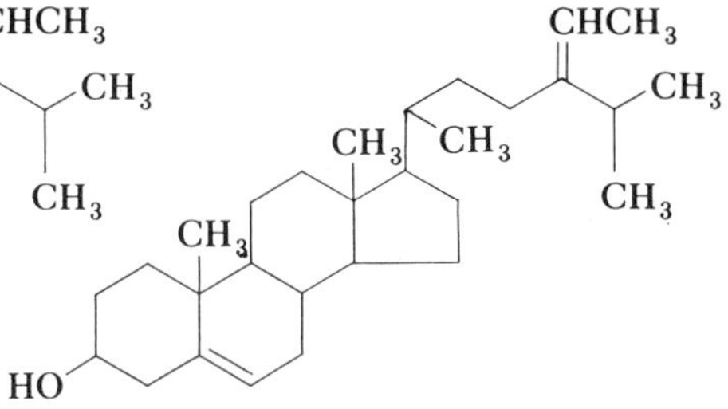

Sargasterol

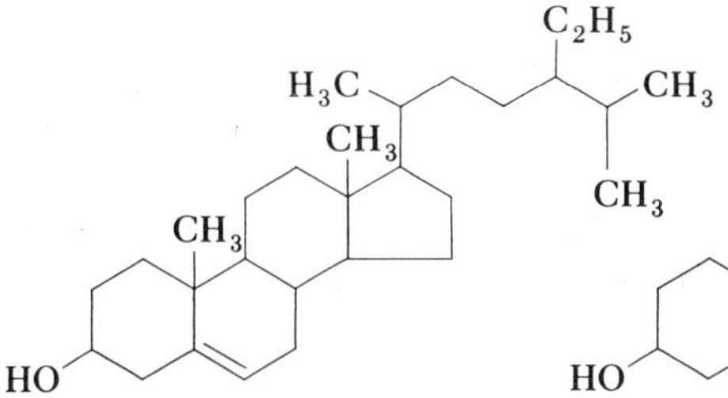

β-Sitosterol

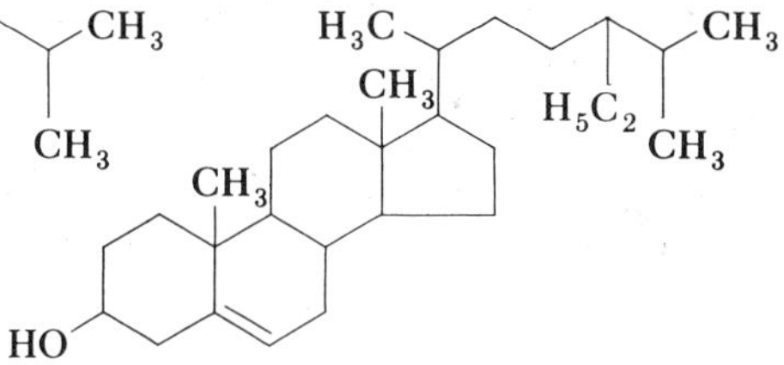

γ-Sitosterol (Clionasterol)

FIGURE 2.14. C_{29} STEROLS RELATED TO CHOLESTEROL.

Δ^5-cholesten-3β-ol, or, named with reference to the parent hydrocarbon of stigmasterol, Δ^5-stigmasten-3β-ol. It is probably the most common sterol in plants. The main commercial sources of β-sitosterol are sugar cane wax, tall oil, and cotton seed oil. C_{28} and C_{29} sterols are only absorbed to a minor extent by most animals and are usually excreted unchanged. β-Sitosterol is hydrogenated to 24β-ethylcoprostan-3β-ol in their intestines. γ-Sitosterol (Figure 2.14) is the principal sterol of soybean oil, but it also occurs in many other vegetable oils. It is one of the most widely distributed sterols in marine vertebrates, and was called clionasterol before its identity with γ-sitosterol was recognized. Toads also secrete γ-sitosterol through their skin glands. The 24-ethylenecholesterol, fucosterol (Figure 2.14), occurs in algae, particularly in the

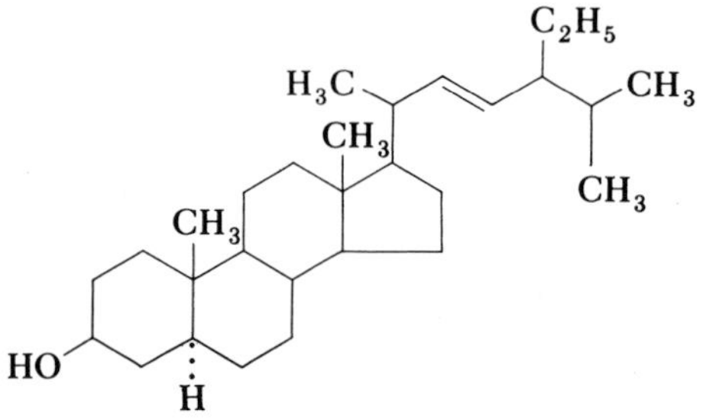

FIGURE 2.15. 5-DIHYDROSTIGMASTEROL.

Phaeophyceae. The fucosterol content parallels the fat content of the algae; fucosterol is higher in those growing in shallow water than in deep water. It is highest in the fall and lowest in the spring. The 20-epimer of fucosterol, sargasterol (Figure 2.14), has been discovered in *Sargassum* algae.

The sterols in Figure 2.16 are epimeric at C-24. The α-epimer, chondrillasterol, has been isolated from both a sponge (*Chondrilla*

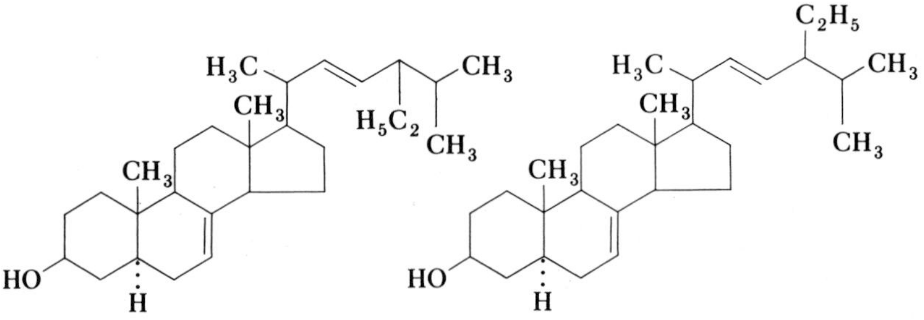

Chondrillasterol   α-Spinasterol

FIGURE 2.16. Δ⁷-C₂₉ STEROLS.

nucula) and an alga (*Scenedesmus obliquus*). The β-epimer, α-spinasterol, occurs in spinach, alfalfa, and other plants.

6. Analysis

Some of the analytical methods applicable to the sterols in this chapter have already been mentioned under cholesterol. The isolation procedures are the same in principle, but in some instances, e.g. in the case of stigmasterol, advantage may be taken of the insolubility of the acetate tetrabromide.

Complicated mixtures from natural sources are sometimes freed of nonalcoholic substances by the use of alkali-soluble derivatives of the sterols. Sterol sulfates, hemiphthalates, and hemisuccinates are easily prepared and separated from lipide-soluble contaminants by solvent partition.

Saturated sterols can be separated from unsaturated ones by the Anderson-Nabenhauer method. When a mixture of saturated and unsaturated sterols in carbon tetrachloride is treated with acetic anhydride and concentrated sulfuric acid, the unsaturated sterols form colored products, which can be removed with alkali, leaving the saturated steroids in the organic solvent.

The resolution of sterol mixtures is often a very difficult problem, requiring the preparation of various derivatives and repeated recrystallization. Adsorption chromatography, notably on alumina, may frequently effect separation, provided there is sufficient structural difference between the components to result in differences in adsorbability, solubility, or both. Thus, cholestan-3β-ol and coprostanol are readily separated from each other by alumina chromatography. The A/B *trans*-sterols (cholestanol) are more strongly adsorbed than the corresponding A/B *cis*-sterols (coprostanol). In the case of sterols epimeric at a hydroxyl group the axial epimer is generally less strongly adsorbed than the equatorial one. Thus, cholestan-3α-ol (a) is eluted before cholestan-3β-ol (e), and coprostan-3β-ol (a) before coprostan-3α-ol (e). Δ^7-Stenols are more strongly adsorbed than Δ^5-stenols, and cholesterol can be separated from lathosterol by adsorption chromatography. The *p*-phenylazobenzoates of sterols, being colored, have the advantage that the progress of the chromatographic process can be followed visually. Iodine[131]-labeled derivatives can be traced by suitable counting equipment. The sterols with conjugated double bonds may be detected on the chromatographic column in ultraviolet illumination. The 5,7-diene system absorbs strongly around 280 mμ.

Δ^7-Stenols react faster than Δ^5-stenols to give a color in the Liebermann-Burchard reaction. The "fast-acting" sterols, which include 7-hydroxysterols, can be detected in sterol mixtures by performing the color reaction at 0°C instead of at room temperature. Two other color tests should be mentioned in addition to those given in Chap. I, p. 16. In the Tortelli-Jaffé reaction a solution of bromine in chloroform is pipetted under the solution of the sterol in glacial acetic acid. A green color at the interface of the two solutions indicates the presence of a double bond at C-8 ($\Delta^{8(14)}$, Δ^7, and $\Delta^{8(9)}$). The Rosenheim reaction is carried out by adding a few drops of aqueous trichloroacetic acid solution to the sterol, dissolved in chloroform. If the B ring contains a system of conjugated double bonds, a red color appears which changes to blue.

The optical rotation of steroids and particularly of sterols is very useful in the identification of known steroids as well as in the determination of the structure of new ones. A system of classifying sterols according to their optical rotation has been proposed by Bergmann. It is based on the fact that strong negative rotation, together with the ultraviolet absorption around 280 mμ is characteristic of sterols containing a conjugated system of double bonds in ring B, that sterols with isolated double bonds show an intermediate negative rotation, and that sterols with a single double bond show a low negative rotation. In the absence of double bonds the rotation is slightly positive, but steroids containing an 8,9-double bond are even more positive. The method of molecular rotation differences was extensively developed by Barton. The difference between the molecular rotation of a steroid and that of the parent hydrocarbon is due to the rotation contribution of the functional groups in the steroid. Except for steroids with conjugated double bonds, this difference is characteristic of the position and orientation of the substituents and is an additive physical property. Thus, the position and configuration of substituents can be deduced by comparison of molecular rotation differences for pairs of epimers at a given center in a given series of steroids. The determination of optical rotation at a series of wavelengths, or rotatory dispersion, introduced into the steroid field by Djerassi, has further extended the usefulness of this tool in structure determination.

III

Vitamin D Group

1. Photoisomers

WHEN $\Delta^{5,7}$-STEROLS ARE EXPOSED to ultraviolet radiation, they undergo a series of rearrangements. Those known as provitamins D form antirachitic substances, vitamins D. The photochemical reactions are illustrated in Figure 3.1, which shows the conversion of ergosterol (provitamin D_2) to ergocalciferol (vitamin D_2). The substance marked X is an unstable intermediate, which is in reversible photolytic equilibrium with ergosterol, lumisterol, previtamin D_2 (not to be confused with the previously mentioned provitamin D_2), and tachysterol. R stands for the C_9H_{17} side chain. Lumisterol differs from ergosterol only in the inversion of the asymmetric centers at C-9 and C-10, but in the other photoisomers the 9,10-bond is broken and they may be referred to as 9,10-$seco$ergosterols (Latin $secare$, to cut). As Velluz has shown, previtamin D_2 can be isolated only if the irradiation is carried out below 25°C. As indicated by X-ray measurements, spectroscopic and chemical evidence, previtamin D_2 is a geometric isomer of tachysterol with respect to the 6,7-double bond, which is cis in the former and $trans$ in the latter case. Treatment of previtamin D_2 with iodine, a typical cis-$trans$ catalyst, converts it to tachysterol. The reverse transformation can be effected by ultraviolet irradiation ($h\nu$ in Figure 3.1). Without further irradiation previtamin D_2 is rearranged to vitamin D_2 by warming to 65°C (Δ in Figure 3.1). The 5,7-diene system in ergocalciferol is $trans$-oriented with respect to the single 6,7-bond (s-$trans$ or transoid), but the 6,10-diene system is cis oriented with respect to the single 5,10-bond (s-cis, or cisoid). Tachysterol (Greek $tachys$, fast), having

34

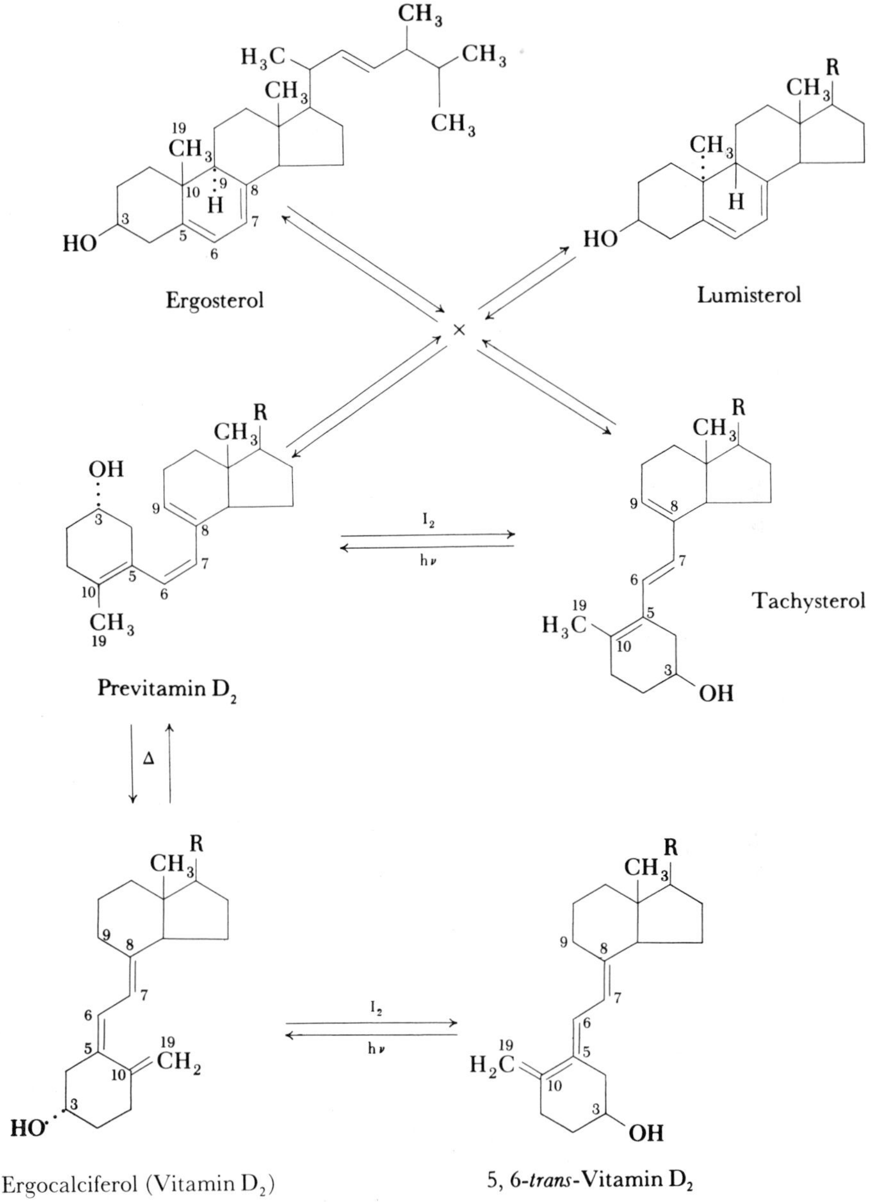

FIGURE 3.1 COMPOUNDS RELATED TO ERGOCALCIFEROL

a cisoid arrangement with respect to the 7,8-bond without *cis*-oriented blocking substituents at C_6 and C_9, reacts rapidly with citraconic anhydride and other dienophile reagents; whereas ergocalciferol reacts more slowly and previtamin D_2 not at all. The most effective wavelength for the production of vitamin D is 280 mμ. Irradiation with light of higher wavelengths favors the formation of lumisterol, and shorter wavelengths increase the yield of tachysterol. Over-irradiation produces the so-called Suprasterols I and II, which are isomeric with lumisterol and ergosterol in C-9 and C-10. When treated with iodine, vitamin D_2 is converted to the 5,6-*trans*-vitamin D_2 (Figure 3.1). The reaction is reversed by irradiation, as in the case of the isomerization of previtamin D_2 to tachysterol.

Reduction of tachysterol with lithium in liquid ammonia produces dihydrotachysterol (Figure 3.2). The orientation of the methyl group at C-10 is still unknown.

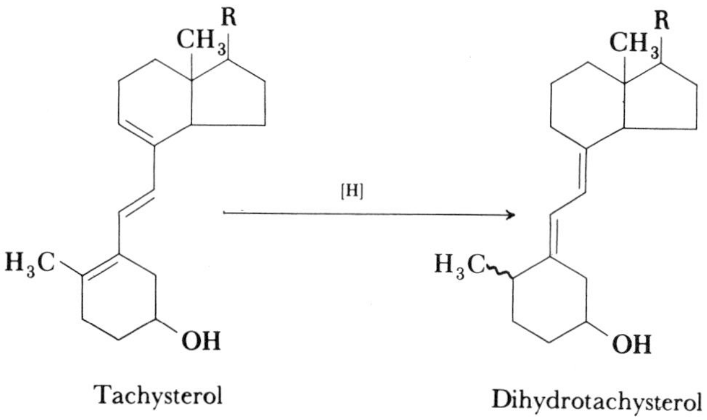

FIGURE 3.2. REDUCTION OF TACHYSTEROL

The first crystalline antirachitic irradiation product of ergosterol was named vitamin D_1 in Germany and calciferol in England. It was later found to be a molecular compound consisting of vitamin D_2 and lumisterol. The name calciferol has been retained for vitamin D_2, but we shall use the more specific name ergocalciferol. The irradiation of 7-dehydrocholesterol produces vitamin D_3, also called cholecalciferol (Figure 3.3), and a series of

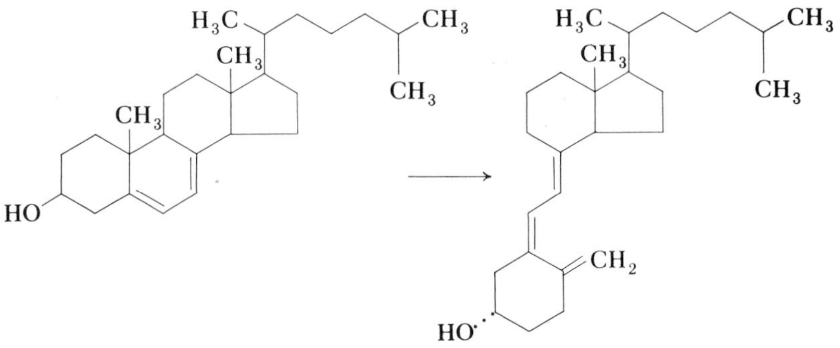

7-Dehydrocholesterol   Cholecalciferol (Vitamin D_3)

FIGURE 3.3. CHOLECALCIFEROL FROM 7-DEHYDROCHOLESTEROL

photoisomers analogous to those described for ergosterol. To distinguish their names, subscripts must be added (e.g. tachysterol$_2$ and tachysterol$_3$). Other sterols containing a 5,7-diene system undergo similar photochemical reactions to give vitamin D analogs of varying biological activity.

2. Biological Activity

Rickets is a disease of higher animals, characterized by a failure to mineralize newly formed osteoid tissue and cartilage matrix. As a result soft, uncalcified bone is produced, which is easily deformed when subjected to stresses such as the gravitational force. In infants the skull and chest, in the walking child or young animal the long bones, especially the legs are deformed. The growing ends of the bones (metaphyses and costochondral junctions) are enlarged, and in severe cases fractures may occur and result in dwarfism. Growth is generally depressed and the tooth enamel may also be affected.

The disease can be prevented or cured by the vitamins of the D group. The activity of these vitamins is expressed in international units, which are equivalent to U.S.P. units, rat units D_3, and chick units D_3. One international unit of vitamin D activity is defined as the activity of 0.025 γ of vitamin D_3. While the potency of vitamin D_3 is equal to that of vitamin D_2 in rats, ergocalciferol has only 1-3 per cent of the activity of cholecalciferol in chicks. Vitamin D_3 may also be more active in humans than vitamin D_2. The side chains of vitamin D_2, vitamin D_3, and other members of the vitamin D group are shown in Figure 3.4 where R stands for the ring system.

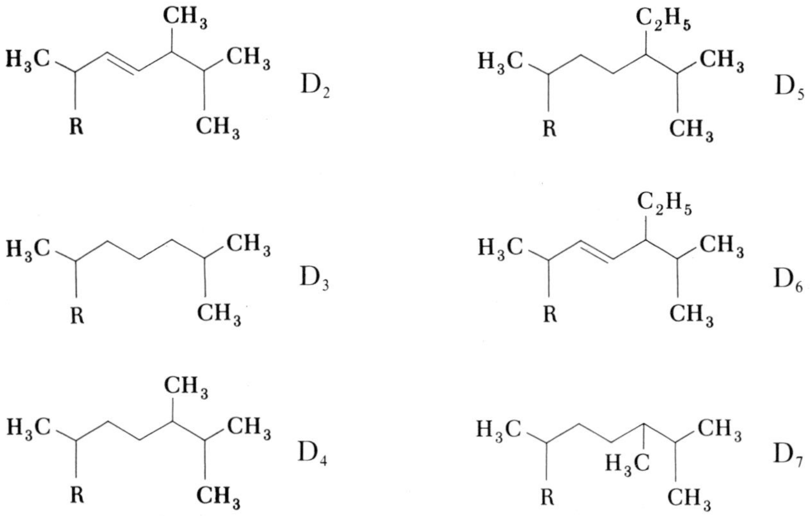

FIGURE 3.4. SIDE CHAINS OF VITAMINS D

Of the photoisomers of vitamin D_2 described in the foregoing section all are inactive except tachysterol, which has a weak activity. Dihydrotachysterol$_2$ is low in antirachitic activity, but increases the serum calcium level by mobilizing bone salts. Under the trade name A.T. 10 (Antitetany Compound 10) it is used for the treatment of idiopathic and hypoparathyroid tetany. Dihydrotachysterol$_3$ is twice as active as A.T. 10 in raising the serum concentration of calcium.

While the suprasterols are only slightly toxic, the irradiation of ergosterol in alcohol solution produces some material of unknown constitution which is quite toxic. It has been called toxisterol or, because it has an absorption maximum at 248 mμ, Substance 248, and is also antirachitically inactive.

The 3-epimers of ergocalciferol and of cholecalciferol have only one-twentieth of the antirachitic activity of the "natural" vitamins. Their 3-keto-, 3-thio-, 3-chloro-, and 3-bromoderivatives are inactive. The 22,23-epoxide of vitamin D_2, prepared by activation of 22,23-oxidoergosterol has a low activity. When 22-dihydroergosterol is activated, vitamin D_4 (Figure 3.4) is obtained, which has an activity intermediate between vitamin D_2 and vitamin D_3. However, vitamin D_7 (Figure 3.4), obtained by irradiation of 7-dehydrocampesterol, which differs from D_4 only in the configuration of the C-28 methyl group has only one-tenth of the biological activity of vitamin D_2. "Vitamins" D_5 and D_6, derived from 7-dehydro-β-sitosterol and 7-dehydrostigmasterol, respectively, have an ethyl group on the C-24 carbon of vitamins D_2 and D_3 and are practically inactive. It is not surprising, therefore, that more radical changes in the side chain abolish the biological activity completely. Thus, when the chain is shortened to the cholanic acid (cf. Chap. VI, p. 81) analog, as in the photochemical activation of 3β-hydroxy-$\Delta^{5,7}$-choladienic acid, or removed, as in the irradiated $\Delta^{5,7}$-androstadiene-3,17-diol, inactive products are obtained.

The sea mussel *Mytilus edulis* contains a provitamin, which was indirectly identified as $\Delta^{5,7,20}$-cholestatrien-3β-ol. Another compound, tentatively designated as D_m, occurs in the ribbed mussel *Modiolus demissus*. Considerable interest has been aroused by the announcement of Bills in 1926 that pure cholesterol acquired antirachitic activity when refluxed in an inert solvent with Floridin. The compound, having an absorption maximum at 250 mμ, has been designated as "Ketone 250" and shows one-tenth of the activity of vitamin D_3. It is present in fish liver oil and soybean oil and forms a lipide-soluble calcium enolate, having the same antirachitic potency as vitamin D_3. Another vitamin, prepared by the same method from $\Delta^{2,4,2',4'}$-3,3'-bischolestatetraene, has also been named vitamin D_7.

3. Nutrition

Owing to the difficulties involved in the isolation and purification of the vitamins D, relatively little is known about the distribution of individual vitamins in nature, and the active compounds are usually referred to as vitamin D. Plant tissues, with the possible exception of the *Sargassum* algae and some edible mushrooms, contain no vitamin D. While the formation of vitamin D from provitamin D in the floating algae by sunlight is not surprising, mushrooms may be capable of synthesizing vitamin D in the dark.

In animals vitamin D is derived either from the diet or from the insolation of provitamin D in the skin. Dietary vitamin D may be present as such or produced by irradiation of provitamins in the food. The richest source of vitamin D in the diet is the liver oil of certain fish. It contains cholecalciferol, largely in the form of esters, but perhaps also other vitamins D. The vitamin D content varies with the species of fish and with the oil content of the liver. While the liver oil of the oriental tuna contains about 45,000 I.U. per g, cod liver oil contains only 100 I.U. per g and the sturgeon liver contains almost no vitamin D. In the winter when the oil content of the fish livers is low, their vitamin D content is high, but in summer the oil content is high and the vitamin D content is low. The vitamin A content of fish liver oils varies with their vitamin D content. With increasing age of the fish both increase. The origin and function of the large stores of vitamin D in fish is not clear. Their diet is certainly rich in vitamin D, consisting of algae, plankton, invertebrates, and other fish. However, there are indications that they can maintain their vitamin D stores on a vitamin D-free diet in the dark, and deep-sea fish obviously do not depend on insolation.

Other dietary sources of vitamin D include animal skins, eggs, milk, and butter. The vitamin D content of milk and butter depend on the season and rations of the cows. Irradiation of the cows or milk produces cholecalciferol; whereas ergocalciferol is found in the milk after feeding the animals irradiated ergosterol.

Skin sterols are rich in 7-dehydrocholesterol, which on irradiation by the sun is converted to cholecalciferol. The distribution and origin of 7-dehydrocholesterol have already been discussed in Chap. II, p. 23. Cholecalciferol is absorbed directly from the skin or ingested. Animals lick their fur in "neatening" their body, and it is difficult to make rats vitamin D deficient if they are exposed to light and allowed to lick their fur. Birds ingest the preen gland oil in preening their feathers. The feet of birds are also rich in 7-

dehydrocholesterol, and irradiation of their feet is an effective means of preventing rickets.

The irradiation of food containing ergosterol or other provitamins D is an effective method of incorporating vitamin D in the diet. The distribution of ergosterol in nature has already been discussed in Chap. II, p. 27. Steenbock has patented the irradiation of foods with ultraviolet light, and considerable royalties from it have accrued to the Wisconsin Alumni Research Foundation. In the industrial process vegetable oils containing provitamins are exposed to ultraviolet irradiation in a shallow, moving layer. Milk is now fortified by addition of vitamin D, rather than by irradiation.

Irradiated ergosterol can be used as a vitamin supplement for human consumption. However, the poultry industry requires cholecalciferol, which is manufactured by partial synthesis of 7-dehydrocholesterol and subsequent ultraviolet irradiation. The recommended daily allowance of vitamin D for human nutrition is 400 I. U. The vitamin is required by growing children, but not by adults, who apparently can get along on the amounts present in the ordinary mixed diet and the amount synthesized by irradiation of the skin. In pregnancy and lactation, when there is a drain on the calcium reserves of the body, vitamin D supplements of 400–1000 I.U. per day are beneficial. Tanning of the skin seems to decrease the effectiveness of solar irradiation. In the treatment of rickets 1000 units of vitamin D per day is commonly used, but larger doses at greater intervals may be given. The excess vitamin D is stored in the liver, kidneys, and walls of the intestine and a small portion of the administered vitamin is excreted by way of the feces. Normal absorption of vitamin D is contingent on normal fat absorption and on the presence of bile salts.

Excessive doses of vitamin D produce a hypervitaminosis. The amounts which will produce toxic symptoms vary widely with individuals. Very small amounts of vitamin D have been reported to be toxic in some cases, but generally the toxic dose is about 1000 times the therapeutic dose. Hypervitaminosis D manifests itself in a decalcification of the bones, an increase in the blood levels of calcium and phosphorus and deposition of calcium phosphate in various organs, e.g. in the kidneys and vascular system. Parathyroid atrophy has been observed in dogs as a consequence of the hypercalcemia.

Children will develop rickets if they are deficient in vitamin D, even with an optimal intake of calcium and phosphorus, but rats can be made rachitic only if they are fed a diet in which the calcium/phosphorus ratio is unfavorable, usually too high. In rickets the product of calcium × phosphorus concentration in the blood is low. The serum inorganic phosphate is always decreased, but the calcium level may be normal, owing to increased parathyroid activity. The serum alkaline phosphatase is elevated, perhaps due to leakage of phosphatase from the bones. The intestinal contents become more alkaline, and the fecal excretion of calcium and phosphate, but especially of the former, is increased. Vitamin D increases the calcium and phosphate absorption and restores the mineral balance. It may also have a direct effect on the tissues by increasing the activity of alkaline phosphatase. This would result in an increase in both the calcium and phosphorus absorption from the intestine and calcium phosphate deposition in the metaphysis. The citric acid concentration in rachitic bones is also low. Citric acid has some therapeutic and prophylactic effect in rickets, perhaps by virtue of the fact that it may form a complex with calcium in the intestine and promote calcium absorption. Rats are capable of absorbing large amounts of calcium and phosphate even in advanced rickets, and this may well explain their resistance to vitamin D deficiency.

4. Analysis

Cholecalciferol may be isolated from fish liver by liquefication with alkali. The oil which separates is saponified in the process. Distribution between 90 per cent methanol and petroleum ether leaves the vitamin A in the alcohol layer, while vitamin D is concentrated in the petroleum ether layer. Digitonin precipitates 3β-hydroxysteroids, but lumisterol and the *seco*sterols are not precipitated. Further purification may be obtained by alumina chromatography, especially of the 3,5-dinitrobenzoate or by molecular distillation. The enrichment of fish liver oils by molecular distillation was an important industrial process for the preparation of vitamin A and D concentrates until the advent of the cheaper synthetic vitamin A.

The optical rotation is a convenient measure for following the progress of the irradiation of ergosterol. It changes from negative to positive during the process. Another tool, which has been of great value in the early phases of vitamin D research, is the ultraviolet absorption. Ergosterol exhibits an absorption maximum of 282 mμ in ethanol, while ergocalciferol shows a maximum at 265 mμ. Ultraviolet absorption is still an important tool in the determination of the structure of steroids containing chromophoric groups. Applied to the vitamin D field, it may be used, e.g. to distinguish between cisoid and transoid systems. The former have a lower molecular extinction than the latter.

Chemical methods of determining vitamin D are generally inferior to biological methods with respect to both sensitivity and specificity. Purified concentrates of vitamin D can be assayed chemically by measuring the intensity of the yellow color produced on addition of antimony trichloride in chloroform, the green color produced by dichlorohydrin and acetyl chloride in chloroform, and the violet color with aluminum chloride in ethanol. There is also a titrimetric method based on the liberation of iodine from a solution of iodine trichloride in carbon tetrachloride. Promising micro methods are becoming available, which are based on the separation of sterols by paper chromatography, notably reversed phase partition chromatography, and may precede the chemical determination.

In the biological methods the therapeutic or prophylactic effects of test doses on animals fed a rachitogenic diet are evaluated. The ratio of activities in rats and chicks permits a distinction between ergocalciferol and cholecalciferol. There are a number of ways in which the antirachitic activity may be estimated. The bones of the test animals may be ashed and the ash content determined by weighing. It is also possible to evaluate X-ray pictures of the skeleton by comparison with standard X-ray pictures. In the line test the calcification of long bones is visualized histochemically and the line between the epiphysis and diaphysis (rachitic metaphysis) is evaluated. The vitamin D content of test doses can also be determined from their effect on rat growth. A more recent test uses the injection of P^{32} into rats after the administration of the test dose. After ten days the fore-paws are placed under a Geiger counter and the count is interpreted by reference to a standard graph.

IV

Steroid Sapogenins
and Alkaloids

1. Structure of Sapogenins

MANY PLANTS YIELD water-soluble extracts which are surface-active
and foam like soap solutions. The saponins (Latin *sapo*, soap) are
generally glycosides in which the C-3 hydroxyl group of terpenoid
or steroidal aglycones is combined with a chain of sugars. Pentacyclic triterpene (C_{30}) sapogenins are widely distributed in the
plant kingdom. Figure 4.1 shows some examples of these genins. It
is apparent that the four isoprene units forming rings A, B, and C
are arranged in the same manner as the corresponding units in
squalene. The first two genins in Figure 4.1 are representative of
the oleanane series. Soyasapogenols have been biosynthesized in
soybean seedlings from radioactive mevalonic acid. In this plant
they occur together with stigmasterol and sitosterols. Glycyrrhetic
acid is the genin in glycyrrhizic acid. The latter was isolated
from licorice root and is of interest because of its reported desoxy-
corticosterone-like activity in animals. α-Amyrin has been isolated
from elemi resin and lupeol from the lupine plant. Lupeol has
also been found to occur together with lophenol (Chap. II, p. 22).
α-Amyrin and lupeol are representative of the ursane and lupane
series, respectively.

The basic structure of steroid sapogenins is shown in Figure 4.2.
They are internal ketals of 16,27-dihydroxy-22-ketosteroids (right
side of Figure 4.2) with 27 carbon atoms and contain two hetero-
cyclic rings. Ring E is a 5-membered (furane) and ring F a 6-
membered (pyrane) oxygen heterocycle. The rings are joined at

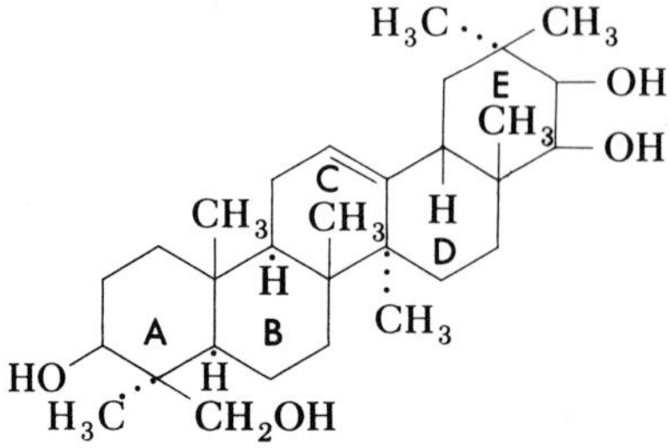

Soyasapogenol A

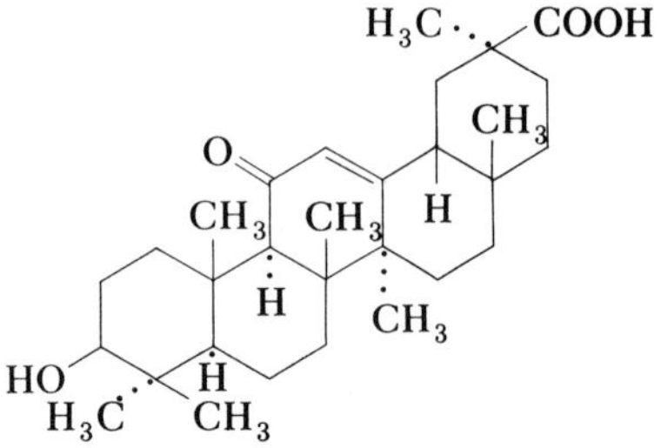

Glycyrrhetic Acid

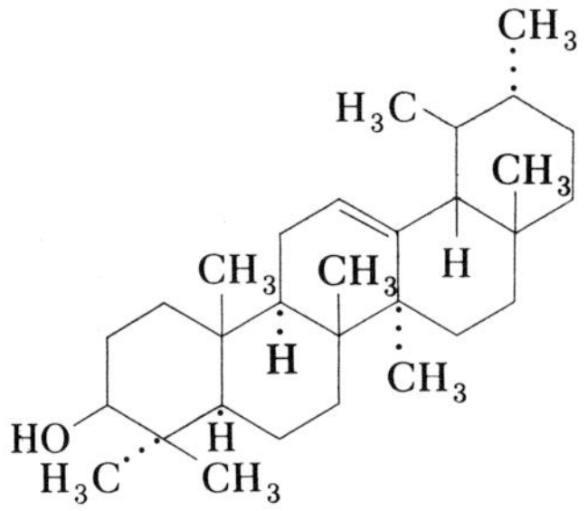

α-Amyrin

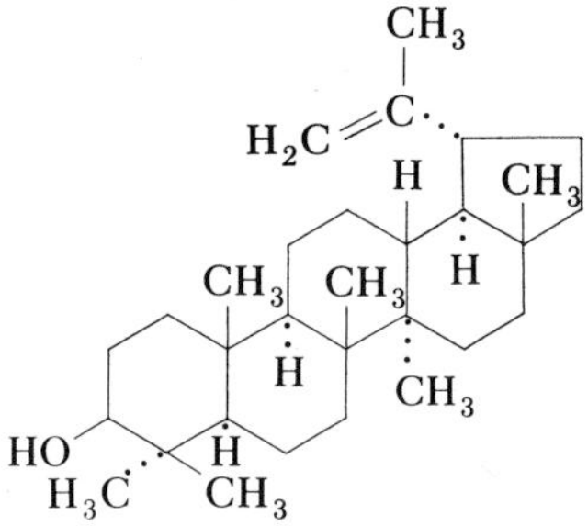

Lupeol

FIGURE 4.1. TRITERPENE SAPOGENINS.

C-22 in spiroketal fashion, and the basic structure or parent "hydrocarbon" is therefore called spirostane. The stereochemical problems connected with the spiroketal side chain are very complex, and some of the fine points are still to be settled.

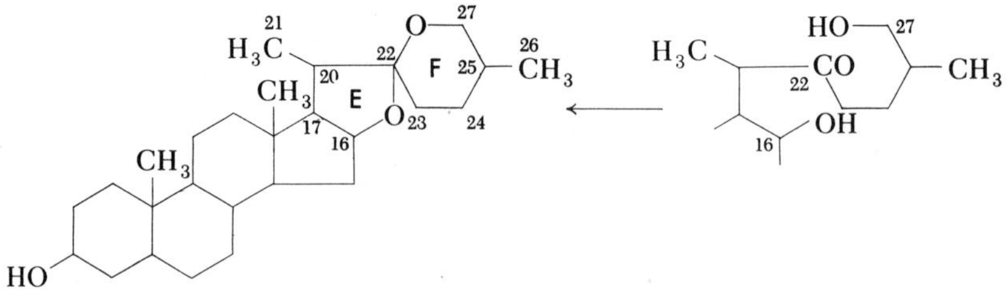

FIGURE 4.2. STEROID SAPOGENIN.

Figure 4.3 is a conformational formula of a steroid sapogenin. The compound shown has an A/B *trans* junction, but A/B *cis*-fused sapogenins are also common. The C-3 hydroxyl group is almost invariably β-oriented. The carbon-oxygen bond at C-16 and the 17,20 carbon-carbon bond are also β-oriented. The methyl group at C-20 has the same orientation as that in cholesterol and is now designated as β-oriented. The pyrane oxygen is located behind the plane of ring E. Formerly it was believed that the

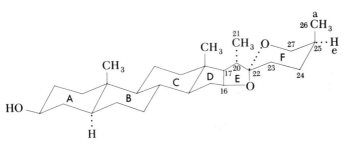

FIGURE 4.3. STEROID SAPOGENIN. (CONFORMATIONAL FORMULA).

steroid sapogenins belong to two series, isomeric at C-22. The sapogenins with the oxygen behind the plane of the E ring were grouped in the "a series" and those with the oxygen in front of it in the "b series." Recent work has shown that probably all natural sapogenins have the same configuration at C-22, and that the difference between the two series is due to isomerism at C-25. The methyl group at C-25 may be either axial (a and β), as shown, or equatorial (e and α) to the pyrane ring. It was previously designated as either L (axial) or D (equatorial).

Figure 4.4 gives an example of two sapogenins differing only in the configuration at C-25. For the sake of convenience we shall indicate the axial methyl group at C-25 by a full line and the equatorial methyl group by a broken line in these and subsequent formulae. Both tigogenin and neotigogenin belong to the 5α-series (A/B *trans*), but tigogenin is the 25α isomer and belongs, according to some textbooks, to the iso series, while neotigogenin is the 25β isomer and belongs to the normal or neo series. We shall avoid the names normal and iso series, since they have also been

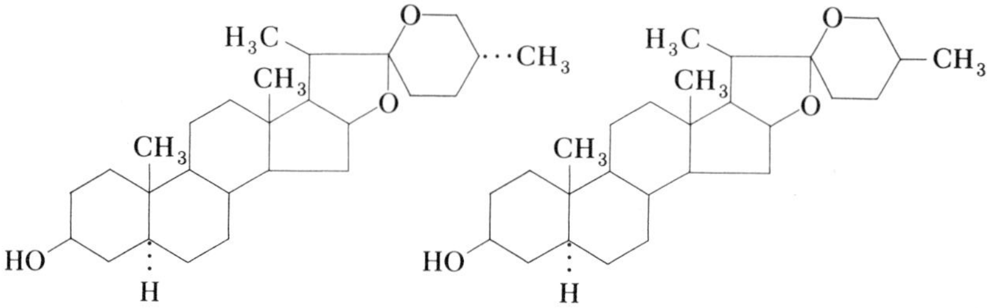

Tigogenin (25α)   Neotigogenin (25β)

FIGURE 4.4. 5α-SAPOGENINS.

used to designate the 22b and 22a series, respectively, but instead
we shall use trivial names and refer to the β and α configuration at C-25. The systematic name of tigogenin is 5α, 25α-spiro-
stan-3β-ol, while neotigogenin is 5α, 25β-spirostan-3β-ol. The
trivial names often have obscure origins, e.g. rockogenin was
named after Rocky (nickname of Prof. Whitmore), and in some
cases a trivial name has been given to a sapogenin known under
another trivial name in an impure state, e.g. the names cor-
relogenin and gentrogenin have been suggested for neobotogenin
and botogenin, respectively.

2. Characteristics of Sapogenins and Saponins

The detergent properties of saponins make them useful as soap
substitutes, since they are nonalkaline and are not precipitated
by hard water, and as foaming agents in fire extinguishers. They
also have the property of forming molecular compounds with
cholesterol and other 3β-hydroxysteroids. When injected into the
blood stream, they are hemolytic, because they combine with the
cholesterol in the red cell membranes. The hemolytic effect can be
counteracted *in vitro* by addition of cholesterol. Saponins are
toxic to cold-blooded animals, perhaps owing to their detergent
properties, and can be used as fish poison. Fish killed by saponins
are edible, since ingested saponins are not absorbed. However,
large quantities of saponins irritate the intestinal mucosa and
may produce vomiting. Saponins also irritate the nasal membranes

and cause sneezing. They are unimportant constituents of various crude drugs. The most important use of sapogenins is as starting materials for the synthesis of steroid hormones. A large industry is engaged in the isolation of sapogenins from plants and their conversion to other steroids. The function of saponins in plants is still unknown, but it has been observed that seeds of pea and corn absorb water more rapidly in their presence and that steroidal saponins exert a marked stimulatory effect on the growth of pea embryos.

Steroid saponins are found in relatively large quantities in the Liliaceae (e.g. *Yucca*), Amaryllidaceae (e.g. *Agave*), and Dioscoreaceae (e.g. *Dioscorea*). The wild yam *Dioscorea tokoro* Makino contains, among others, the three Δ^5-sapogenins shown in Figure 4.5. While it is tempting to postulate a biochemical relationship between the open ring structure of kryptogenin and the closely related spiroketal structures of diosgenin and yamogenin, no experimental basis for such a hypothesis exists at the present time. Dios-

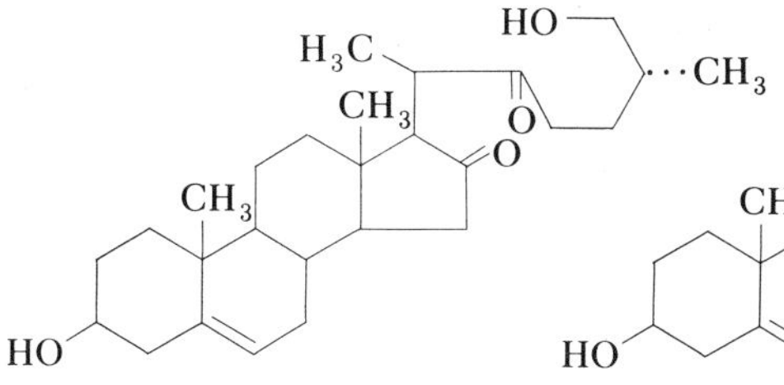

Kryptogenin 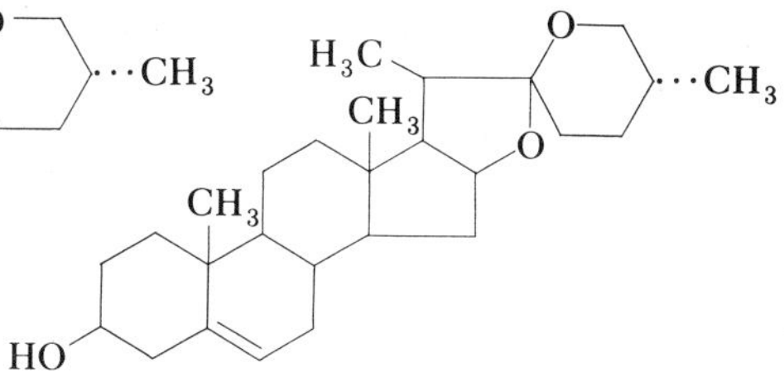   Diosgenin

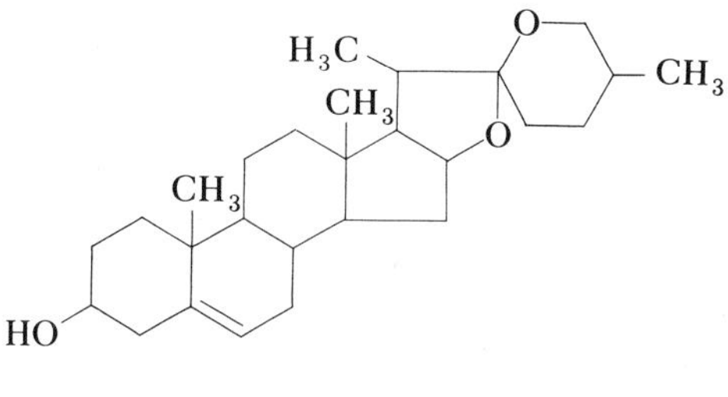

Yamogenin

FIGURE 4.5. Δ^5-SAPOGENINS.

genin occurs as dioscin, a glycoside with 1 glucose and 2 rhamnose units, and in combination with 1 rhamnose and 2 glucose units as gracillin in *Dioscorea* species. As the glucoside trillin and the diglucoside trillarin, it also occurs in *Trillium erectum* (bethroot). The presence of a Δ^5-double bond in diosgenin makes it especially valuable as a starting material for the synthesis of progesterone and other hormones containing the Δ^4-3-keto group in the molecule. The abundance of yams in the Mexican jungle has been largely responsible for the rise of the Mexican hormone industry.

Reduction of the 5,6-double bond of diosgenin and yamogenin gives rise to 5α- and 5β-sapogenins. The formulae of the 5α-sapogenins tigogenin and neotigogenin have been presented in Figure 4.4. Tigogenin was first isolated from *Digitalis* leaves, where it occurs in the form of tigonin, a glycoside containing 2 mols of glucose, 2 mols of galactose, and 1 mol of xylose per mol of tigogenin. It also occurs in *Chlorogalum pomeridianum* as the glycoside amolonin (3 glucose, 1 galactose, and 2 rhamnose), together with neotigogenin. The analogous 5β-sapogenins are smilagenin (25α) and sarsasapogenin (25β), whose structure is shown in Figure 4.6. Both genins occur in *Smilax ornata* and in Radix

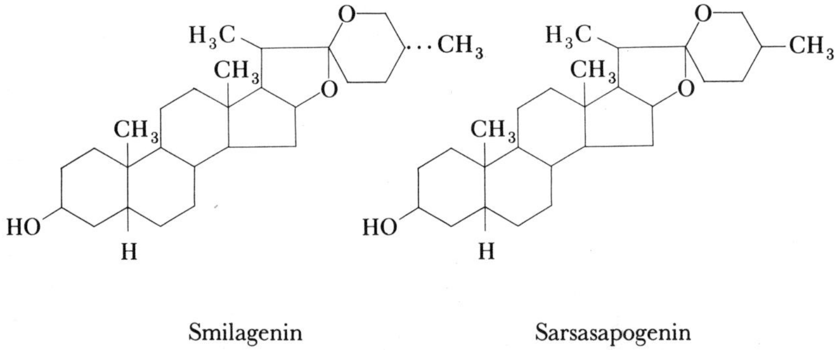

Smilagenin   Sarsasapogenin

FIGURE 4.6. 5β-SAPOGENINS.

sarsaparilla. However, the Jamaican sarsaparilla yields smilagenin, whereas the Vera Cruz variety contains sarsasaponin, a glycoside consisting of 1 mol of rhamnose and 2 mols of glucose per mol of sarsasapogenin.

A large number of sapogenins have been discovered and de-scribed by Marker, and the demand for synthetic hormones has been a powerful stimulus to further research in this area. Sapo-genins have been isolated which carry additional oxygen functions on carbon atoms 1, 2, 5, 6, 12, and 15 in various combinations. Those with an oxygen function attached to ring C were of great interest as starting materials for 11-oxygenated hormones such as cortisone. A readily available sapogenin of this kind is hecogenin (Figure 4.7), which is 5α, 25α-spirostan-3β-ol-12-one. It was first isolated from *Hechtia texensis*, but also occurs in *Agave sisalana* (sisal). As a by-product of the sisal industry (in East Africa and Haiti) it is especially cheap and abundant. Another interesting sapogenin is digitogenin (Figure 4.7). The glycoside digitonin contains 2 glu-cose, 2 galactose, and 1 xylose units and occurs in *Digitalis lanata* and *D. purpurea*. As mentioned above (cf. also Chap. I, p. 15),

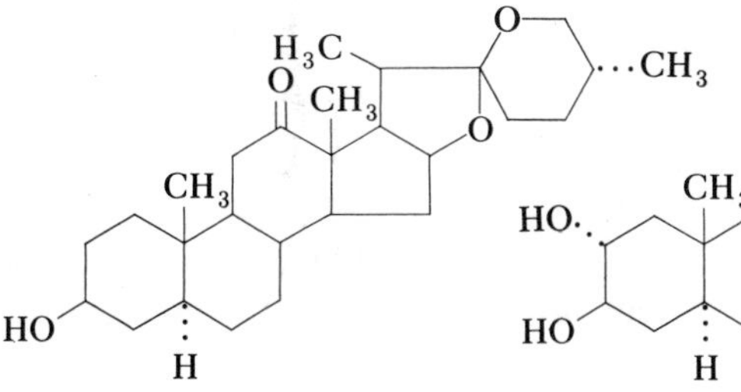

Hecogenin 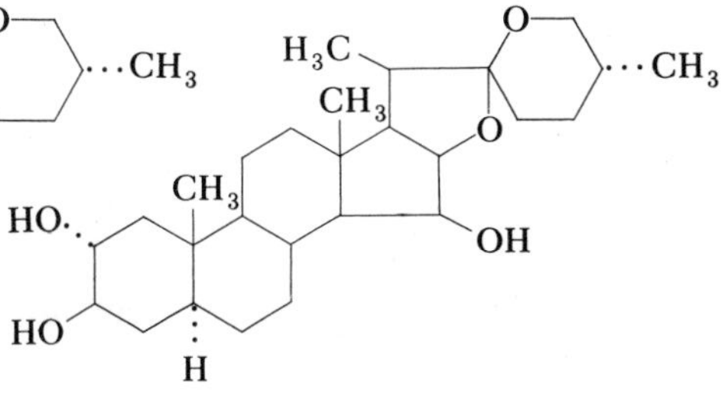   Digitogenin

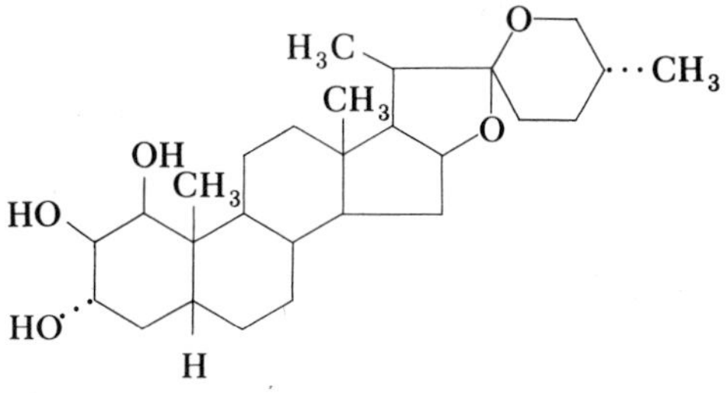

Tokorogenin

FIGURE 4.7. OXYGENATED SAPOGENINS.

digitonin is used as a reagent for the precipitation of 3β-hydroxy-steroids. Other sapogenins in this genus are the previously mentioned tigogenin, and also gitogenin (5α, 25α-spirostane-2α, 3β-diol) and neochlorogenin (5α, 25β-spirostane-3β, 6α-diol). *Yucca schottii* contains yuccagenin (25α-Δ⁵-spirostene-2α,3β-diol) in the roots, kammogenin (25α-Δ⁵-spirostene-2α,3β-diol-12-one), in addition to smilagenin, in the flowers, and neomanogenin (5α, 25β-spirostane-2α,3β-diol-12-one) in the fruits. Tokorogenin (Figure 4.7) (from *Dioscorea tokoro*) is of interest because of the unusual 3α-hydroxyl group.

Sapogenins have not been found in animals so far, with one possible exception. Ox bile has yielded two substances, whose structure is presented in Figure 4.8. These compounds are unusual in having both a 3α-hydroxyl group and an additional hydroxyl group in the side chain. Cholegenin contains two furane rings instead of one furane and one pyrane ring. The biological significance of these compounds is unknown. However, since they are found in the bile of British, but not American cattle, they may well be of dietary origin.

Saponins are readily extracted from plant material with hot water or alcohol and may be precipitated from solution by the addition of lead salts or ether. The aqueous solution can also be extracted with benzene to remove fatty material, and the saponins can then be extracted with butanol, leaving proteins and carbohydrates in the aqueous phase. Acid or enzyme hydrolysis yields the sapogenins, which may be converted to acetates and purified by

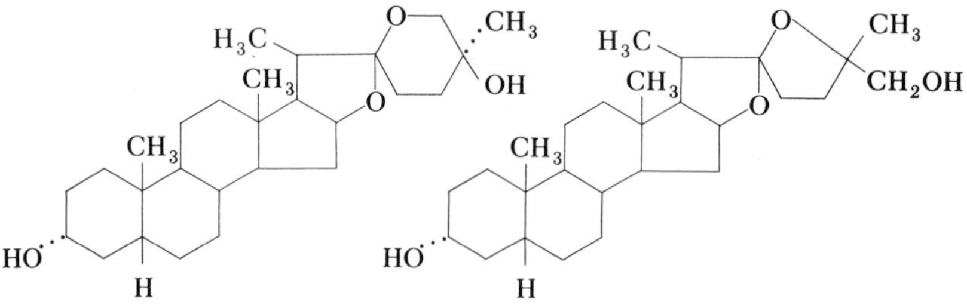

Isocholegenin   Cholegenin

FIGURE 4.8. SAPOGENINS IN OX BILE.

alumina chromatography. It is also possible to use the molecular compounds with 3β-hydroxysteroids or with amyl alcohol for the isolation of saponins, but most of these compounds are more soluble than the cholesterol digitonide.

Sapogenins give color tests with various reagents such as sulfuric acid, antimony trichloride, trichloroacetic acid, and a number of aromatic aldehydes. These tests are not specific for sapogenins, but in some cases individual sapogenins can be differentiated by such color reactions, especially in conjunction with paper chromatography. The hemolysis of red blood cells by saponins can be used as a sensitive and relatively specific guide in isolation work. The hemolytic effect of sapogenins has been suggested as a specific detection method in paper chromatography. The infrared spectrum of sapogenins shows several strong absorption bands between 1350 and 875 cm^{-1}, characteristic of the spiroketal side chain. In the 25β-series the absorption at 920-915 cm^{-1} is more intense than that at 899-894 cm^{-1}, whereas the reverse is true of the 25α-series of sapogenins.

3. *Solanum* Alkaloids

Plants of the genus *Solanum* produce glycoalkaloids which are in many ways similar to saponins. They contain the same types of sugars as the saponins, they are also surface-active and hemolytic, and they also form molecular compounds with cholesterol and related steroids. However, they are toxic when ingested and have a basic character due to the presence of a nitrogen atom in the molecule. The *Solanum* alkaloids or alkamines, as the genins are called, are C_{27} steroids, which can be divided into two classes.

The first class comprises the nitrogen analogs of the sapogenins and is represented by solasodine and tomatidine (Figure 4.9). Solasodine has the same structure as diosgenin (Figure 4.5), except for the fact that NH is substituted for O in the F ring. It is significant that diosgenin and solasodine have been found to occur together in at least one plant source, the fruits of *Solanum xanthocarpum*. The berries of the shrub *S. sodomeum* (Dead Sea apple) contain the solasodine glycosides solasonine (1 rhamnose, 1 galactose, 1 glucose) and solasodamine (2 rhamnose, 1 galactose, 1 glu-

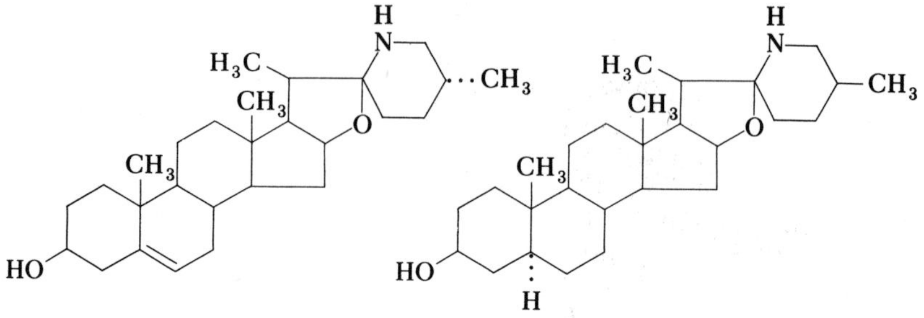

Solasodine   Tomatidine

FIGURE 4.9. *SOLANUM* ALKALOIDS I.

cose). Solamargine (2 rhamnose, 1 glucose) is the solasodine glycoside of *S. marginatum.*

The leaves of bittersweet (*S. dulcamara*) have yielded the
glycoside soladulcine, which contains the genin soladulcidine.
Soladulcidine is 5α-solasodan-3β-ol; i.e., the nitrogen analog of
tigogenin (Figure 4.4), which has also been isolated from bitter-
sweet.

Tomatidine is the nitrogen analog of neotigogenin and, again,
both genins have been found to occur together in the leaves of the
primitive red currant tomato (*Lycopersicon pimpinellifolium*). Tomatidine was first isolated in the course of an investigation of the anti-
biotic effect of tomato leaf extracts. It has some fungistatic and
bacteriostatic effect, and it is also true that tomatidine-containing
plants are not attacked by potato beetles, but it is perhaps of
greater interest as a potential raw material for steroid syntheses.
Tomatine, the xylosido-glucosido-glucosido-galactoside of tomatidine, occurs in all varieties of *Solanum lycopersicum* (tomato). As
the fruits ripen their tomatine content decreases, while the concentration in the leaves increases. Unfortunately, the tomatine content of the varieties of tomatoes used commercially in the United
States is not very high.

The second class of *Solanum* alkaloids comprises C_{27} steroids
containing a condensed ring system and tertiary nitrogen and is
represented by solanidine and demissidine (Figure 4.10). The
orientations at C-20, 22, and 25 are probably all β. Solanidine
was first isolated from the poisonous leaves of the black night-
shade (*S. nigrum*), but occurs in many *Solanum* species. *Solanum*

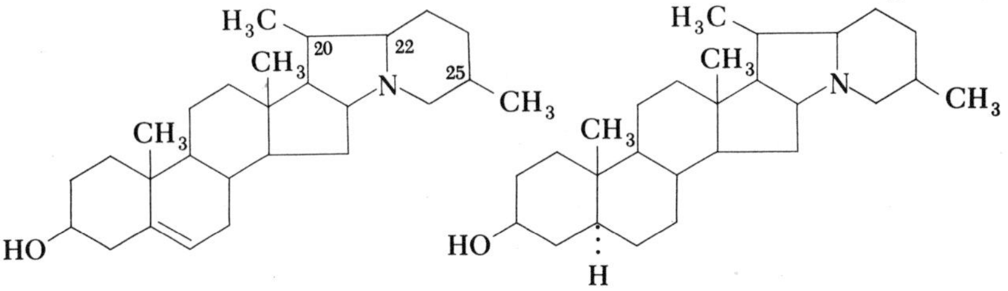

Solanidine   Demissidine

FIGURE 4.10. *SOLANUM* ALKALOIDS II.

tuberosum (potato) contains a mixture of glycosides, called solanines, in which solanidine is combined with various sugars. α-Solanine contains a rhamnosido-galactosido-glucose (solanose), β-solanine contains galactose and glucose, and γ-solanine only galactose. The solanine content of different potato varieties is different and varies from year to year. During the last two-thirds of its growth the plant transfers the solanine from the leaves to the berries and roots, but potato tubers do not contain enough solanidine to be toxic unless they are sprouting. Potato sprouts are the richest source of the alkamine. In addition to solanidine, potato plants also contain a number of other Δ^5-steroids: β-sitosterol, stigmasterol, yamogenin, and 5-dehydrotomatidine (the nitrogen analog of yamogenin). The chaconines are solanidine glycosides, containing 1 glucose and 0-2 rhamnose units, which occur not only in *S. chacoense* but also in *S. tuberosum*.

The leaves of *S. demissum*, a potato species which grows wild in South America, and some other *Solanum* species contain demissine, the xylosido-glucosido-glucosido-galactoside of demissidine. Considerable interest has been aroused by the fact that demissidine-containing species are not attacked by the larvae of the potato beetle, and breeding experiments have been undertaken to produce beetle-resistant potato varieties.

Two alkamines have been isolated from the rhizomes of *Veratrum album* which chemically belong to the *Solanum* alkaloids. They are rubijervine (12α-hydroxysolanidine) and isorubijervine (18-hydroxysolanidine). The names are derived from the Spanish word *hierba*, herb, and from the red color reaction with concentrated sulfuric acid.

The *Solanum* alkamines give both the characteristic alkaloid and the steroid color tests. Marquis reagent (sulfuric acid and formaldehyde) gives a purple color, Mayer's reagent (mercuric iodide) gives a precipitate, etc. Solasodine, but not solanidine, in alcohol solution gives a greenish yellow fluorescence with sulfuric acid. The glycosides form precipitates with cholesterol, as previously mentioned, and the reaction can be used for separating or differentiating the alkaloids from their glycosides. In animal tests large doses of certain *Solanum* alkaloids produce parenchymatous nephritis and hemoglobinuria, followed by nervous paralysis and cardiac arrest.

4. Kurchi Alkaloids

The bark of the kurchi shrub (*Holarrhena antidysenterica*) has long been used as a remedy for amoebic dysentery in India. Various Indian and African species of *Holarrhena* contain esters or glycosides of a series of C_{21} alkamines, called the kurchi alkaloids. Kurchi bark contains four types of alkaloids, three of which are repre-

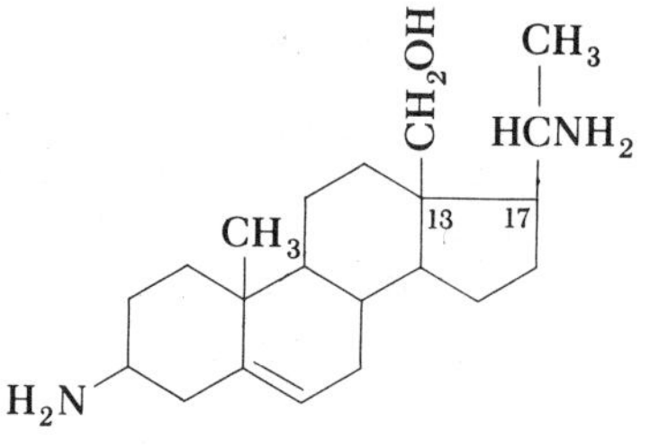

Holarrhimine 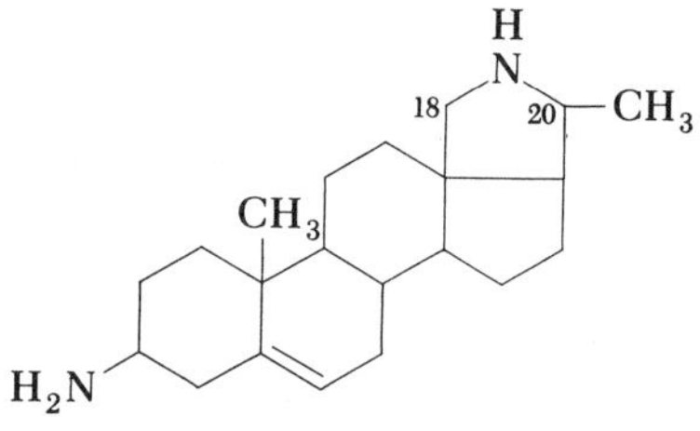   Conarrhimine

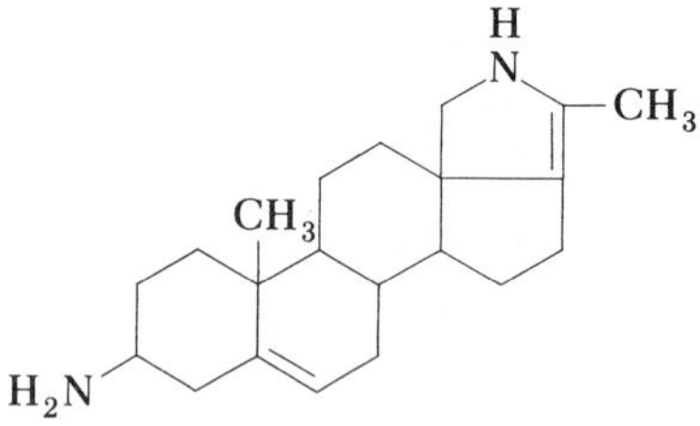

Conkurchine

FIGURE 4.11. KURCHI ALKALOIDS.

sented in Figure 4.11. The fourth type is related to kurchamine, which has not yet been completely characterized.

Holarrhimine is a C_{21} steroid (the D ring has been written "upside down" for convenience) with amino groups at C-3 and C-20 and a methylol group at C-13. The amino group at C-3 is β-oriented in holarrhimine, but α-oriented in another kurchi alkaloid, holarrhidine. Various *N*-methyl substituted holarrhimines have also been isolated. *Funtumia labifolia*, which belongs to the Apocynaceae, contains funtumidine, a 3α-aminosteroid with 21 carbons.

In conarrhimine the nitrogen atom at C-20 forms a pyrrolidine ring. Again, various *N*-methyl substituted conarrhimines are known. The trimethyl substituted conarrhimine, conessine, is the most abundant kurchi alkamine and forms the starting material of a synthetic process for the production of 18-hydroxylated steroid hormones. 12β-Hydroxyconessine (holarrhenine) has been found in *Holarrhena congolensis* in the form of an ester, holarrhetine (Figure 4.12). Holafrine is the corresponding ester of 12β-hydroxy-

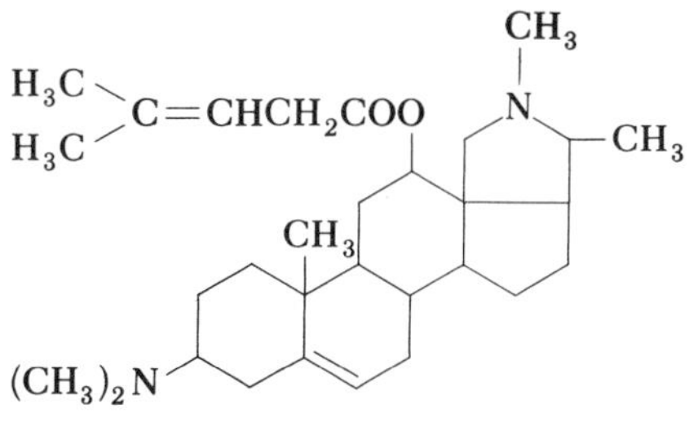

Holarrhetine

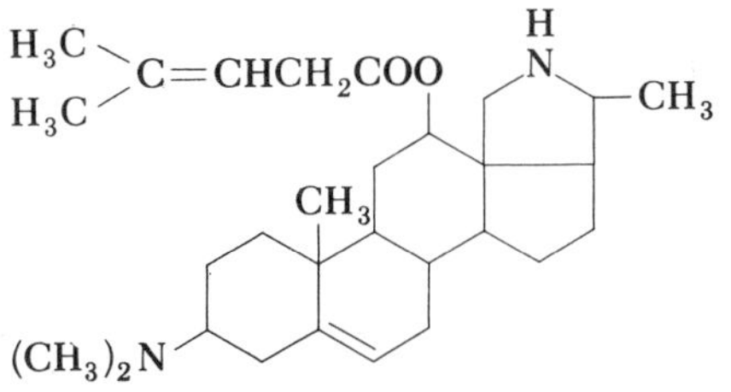

Holafrine

FIGURE 4.12. ESTERS OF KURCHI ALKALOIDS.

conessimine. In both cases the acid involved is pyroterebic acid, which appears to be, at least formally, related to isoprene.

The last group of kurchi alkaloids is related to conkurchine (Figure 4.11), a 17,20-dehydroconarrhimine. In conessidine the amino group of conkurchine is monomethylated.

5. *Veratrum* Alkaloids

Veratrum plants belong to the Liliaceae. The alkaloids occur in the roots and rhizomes of *V. viride*, the green or American "hellebore," and of the closely related *V. album*, the white or European "hellebore," but in the seeds of the Central American *V. sabadilla*. They are not steroids, strictly speaking, since they contain a 5-membered C ring and a 6-membered D ring. Figure 4.13 shows the structure of two representatives of this group, veratramine and jervine. Veratramine contains an aromatic D ring and a hydroxyl group at C-23, whereas jervine contains a conjugated 11-keto group and a 5-membered E ring, formed by the 17,23-epoxide. Veratramine was first isolated from the roots of

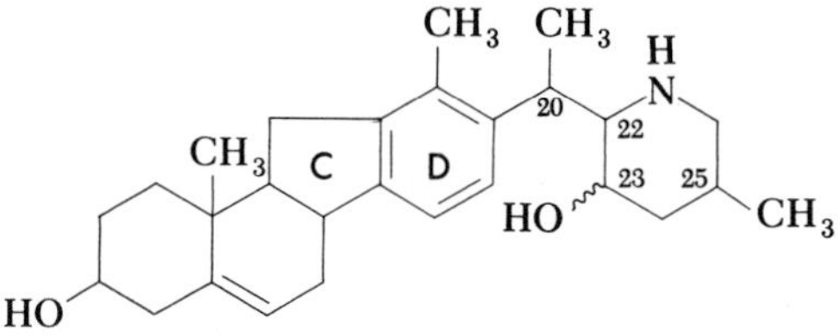

Veratramine

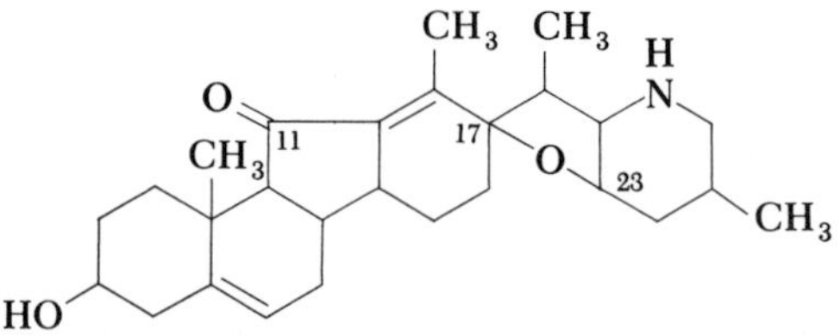

Jervine

FIGURE 4.13. *VERATRUM* ALKALOIDS.

V. album as the glucoside and jervine also occurs in *V. album* and *V. viride* roots.

A number of alkamine esters of germine (Figure 4.14) have been found in the rhizomes of *V. album* and *V. viride*. Germine is a 3,4-α-ketol, which forms a hemiketal with a 9α-hydroxyl group. In the plant, germine occurs as the ester of α-methylbutyric acid (protoveratridine), of both α-methylbutyric and α-hydroxy-

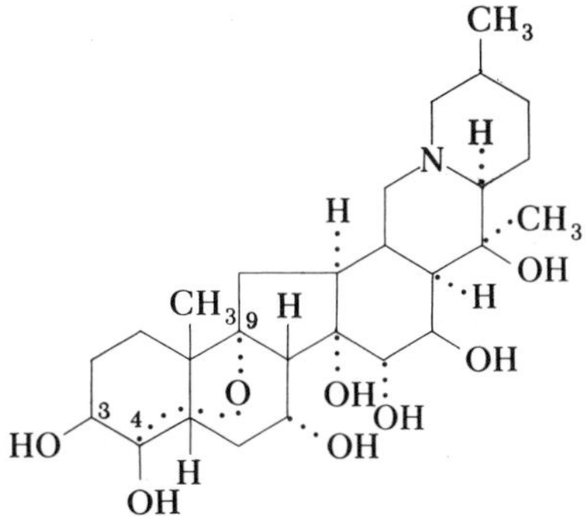

FIGURE 4.14. GERMINE.

α-methylbutyric acid (germerine), and of acetic, α-methylbutyric, as well as α-hydroxy-α-methylbutyric acid (germitrine). The co-occurrence of acetic acid, branched chain C_5 acids, and a steroid-like structure is not surprising in view of their biogenetic relationship (cf. Chap. I, p. 9). Cevagenine has a structure similar to that of germine and occurs in the form of esters with angelic acid (cevadine) and veratric acid (veratridine) in the seeds of *V. sabadilla*. *Fritillaria* corms also contain alkamines of this group, e.g. sipieimine, and have been used as the drug *si-pei-mu* in China for a long time.

The *Veratrum* alkaloids stimulate the sensory nerve endings, and, in contact with the skin, they produce a prickling sensation. They act on the mucous membranes of the nose to induce sneezing. Taken internally, *Veratrum* alkaloids and particularly their esters intensify and prolong the contraction of striated muscles and act on the pulmonary stretch receptors to produce respiratory depression. The circulatory effects are of greatest interest. The alkaloids have a

positive inotropic action on the heart and produce brady-
cardia and, in large doses, cardiac arrythmias and eventually
ventricular tachycardia and fibrillation. Like the cardiac glycosides, *Veratrum* alkaloids increase the work performance of the fail-
ing heart. The hypotensive effect of the alkamines is mediated
through the nervous system (reflex inhibition of vasomotor centers)
and it is used in the treatment of essential and malignant hypertension and of eclampsia. Kerosene solutions of *Veratrum* alkaloids
have also found some use as insecticides. The fundamental effect on
excitable tissues appears to be the increase in potassium leakage
from the cells together with an interference with sodium extrusion.

The isolation of the steroid alkaloids from plants is carried out
by the usual methods employed in the alkaloid field, i.e., with
acids or acidified alcohol or by solvent extraction after liberation
of the alkamines by alkali. Veratramine is precipitated by digitonin; whereas jervine is not. Concentrated sulfuric acid gives a
red color and green fluorescence with cevadine and a red color and
blue fluorescence with veratridine. Methods for the separation of
steroid alkaloids, based on partition chromatography, have been
worked out. Solvent systems containing acids or buffered stationary
phases have proved to be most useful for the basic steroids.

V

Cardiac Glycosides

1. Cardenolides

PLANTS OF SEVERAL families contain glycosides of C_{23} steroids with potent cardiac activity. The genus *Digitalis* (Scrophulariaceae) is of major medicinal importance, and galenical preparations of *Digitalis lanata* and *D. purpurea*, the common foxglove, have been used for generations. In addition to inactive saponins (cf. Chap. IV, p. 51) and digitanol glycosides (cf. Chap. 'V, p. 77) digitalis contains a mixture of cardiac-active glycosides. *D. lanata* is a richer source of cardiac glycosides than *D. purpurea*. In the former they are more concentrated in the leaves than in the seeds; whereas the reverse is true in the latter species.

On hydrolysis of the mixture of cardiac-active digitalis glycosides ("digilanide substance") in *D. lanata*, one obtains mainly the three aglycones shown in Figure 5.1. One important feature of their structure, which appears in all cardiac aglycones, is the 14β-hydroxyl group (*cis*-fusion of rings C and D). Another characteristic feature is the α,β-unsaturated γ-lactone ring. The cardiac aglycones containing this butenolide ring are collectively named cardenolides. Digitoxigenin may be systematically designated as 3β,14β-dihydroxy-5β-cardenolide, gitoxigenin as 3β,14β,16β-trihydroxy-5β-cardenolide, and digoxigenin as 3β,12β,14β-trihydroxy-5β-cardenolide. These three cardenolides occur in digitalis as the glycosides lanatoside (or digilanide) A, B, and C, in which the aglycones digitoxigenin, gitoxigenin, and digoxigenin, respectively, are linked to 2 molecules of digitoxose, 1 molecule of acetyldigitoxose, and one molecule of glucose. The acetyl group can be removed by mild alkaline hydrolysis and the glucose unit may be removed enzymatically. Deacetylation of the

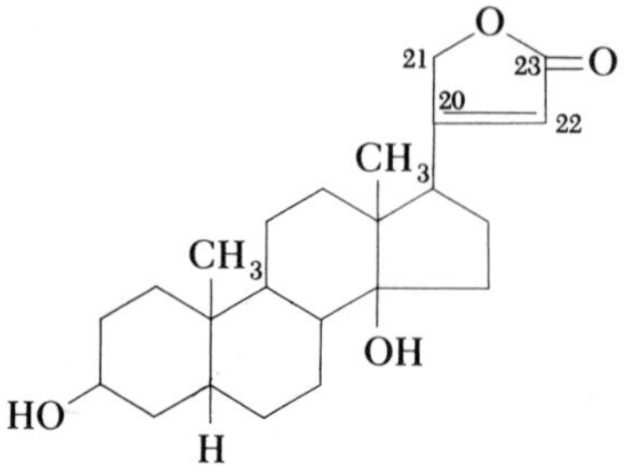

Digitoxigenin

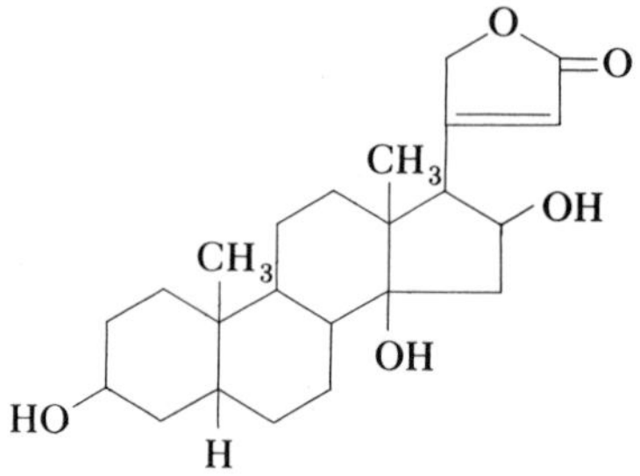

Gitoxigenin

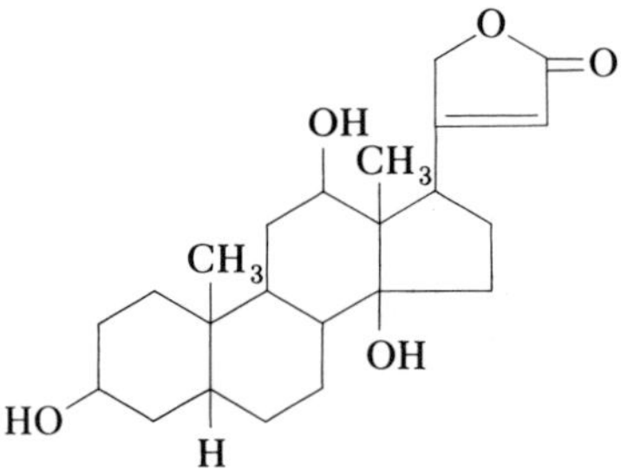

Digoxigenin

FIGURE 5.1. DIGITALIS CARDENOLIDES.

lanatosides produces the corresponding purpurea glycosides (des-acetyllanatosides or desacetyldigilanides), while removal of the glucose unit gives the acetyl derivatives of the digitoxose triosides. Combination of the two hydrolytic procedures yields the digo-toxose triosides digitoxin, gitoxin, and digoxin.

Other glycosides of cardenolides also occur in nature. In addition to glucose and rhamnose, which are widely distributed in nature, they contain C_6 sugars which have not yet been found in other natural sources. These may be 2,6-desoxysugars, such as digitoxose, 6-desoxy-3-methoxysugars, such as digitalose and thevetose, or 2,6-desoxy-3-methoxysugars, such as oleandrose. The structures of some of these sugars are shown in Figure 5.2 in the Fischer projection. The glycosidic linkage is always β in the case of the D-sugars and α in the case of L-sugars.

Digitalinum verum is a glycoside yielding one mol of digitalose and one mol of glucose per mol of gitoxigenin; gitorin is a gitoxigenin glucoside, and strospeside is a gitoxigenin digitaloside. Thevetin is a glycoside yielding one mol of thevetose and two mols of glucose per mol of digitoxigenin. This glycoside occurs in the fruit of *Thevetia neriifolia* (be-still nut). An enzyme in the nut (thevetiobiase) hydrolyzes the glucosidic linkage and produces neriifolin, the digitoxigenin thevetoside.

Figure 5.3 shows three cardenolides related to gitoxigenin. Oleandrigenin is the 16β-acetoxy analog and gitaloxigenin the 16-

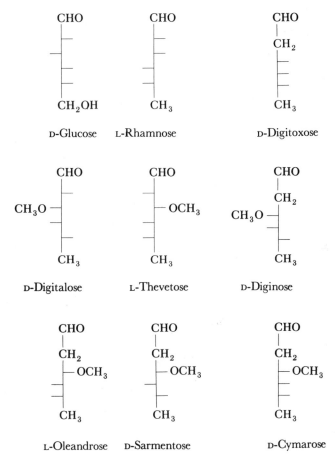

FIGURE 5.2. SOME SUGARS IN CARDIAC GLYCOSIDES.

formyl derivative, while in adonitoxigenin the C-19 methyl group is oxidized to an aldehyde group. The 16-oxygenated cardenolides appear in various species and may, perhaps, constitute a link between this group of steroids and the sapogenins. Oleandrigenin, combined with oleandrose, forms the glycoside oleandrin, found in *Nerium oleander*, an Apocynacea. *Nerium odorum* contains

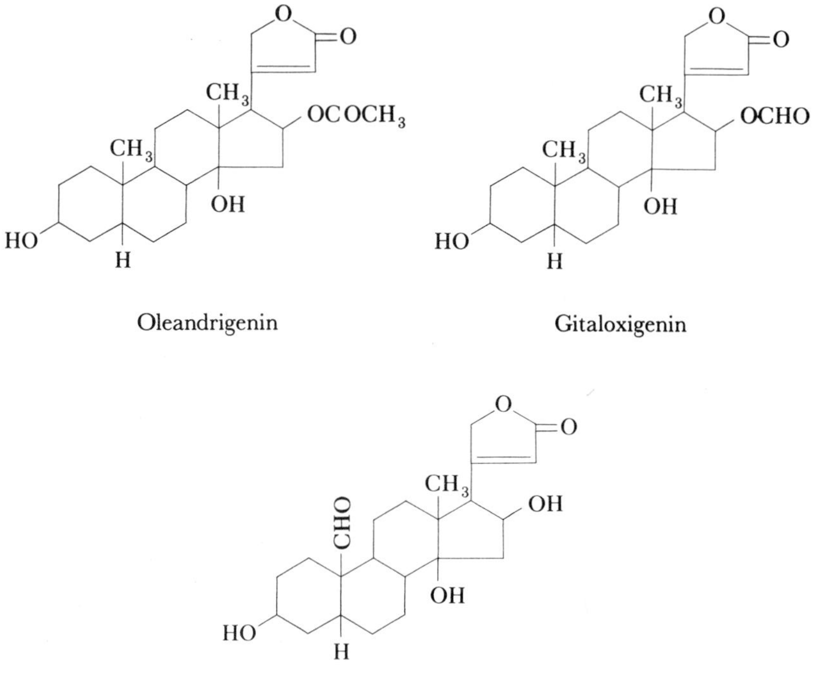

Oleandrigenin   Gitaloxigenin

Adonitoxigenin

FIGURE 5.3. CARDENOLIDES RELATED TO GITOXIGENIN.

oleandrin in the leaves, but odorosides (digitoxigenin and uzarigenin [cf. Figure 5.4] glycosides) in the bark. Gitaloxin, a digitalis glycoside, on mild hydrolysis gives three mols of digitoxose per mol of gitaloxigenin. The herb of *Adonis vernalis*, a Ranunculacea, contains adonitoxin, the adonitoxigenin rhamnoside.

In the cardenolides discussed so far rings A and B are *cis*-fused. 5α-Cardenolides (Figure 5.4) occur in certain genera. Uzarigenin

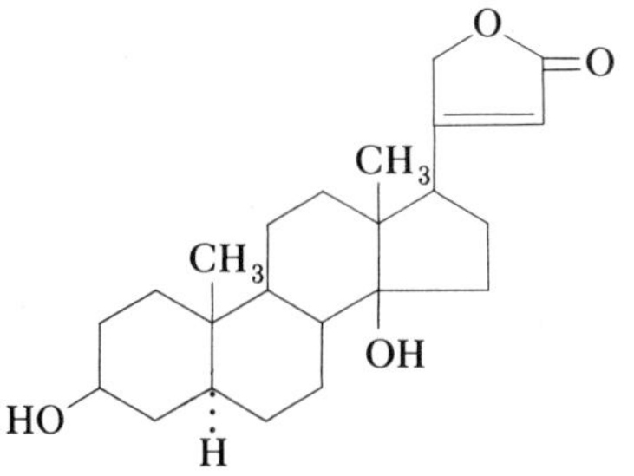

Uzarigenin

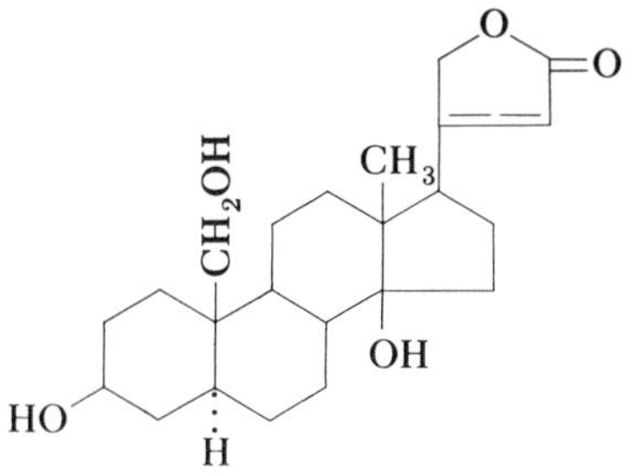

Coroglaucigenin

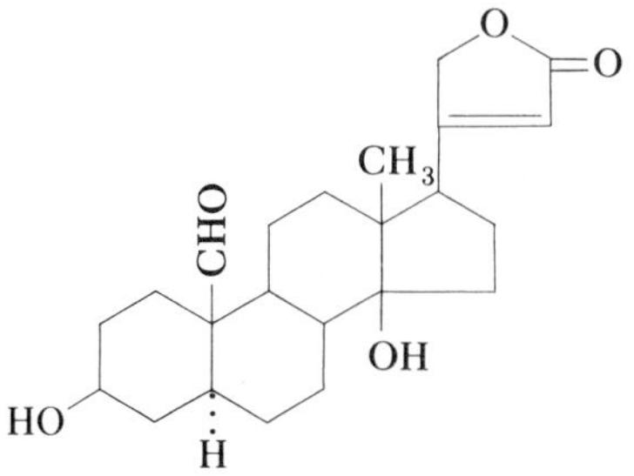

Corotoxigenin

FIGURE 5.4. 5α-CARDENOLIDES.

is the 5α-analog of digitoxigenin. In addition to uzarigenin, uzara root contains its 3α-epimer, urezigenin, the only known 3α-cardenolide. In coroglaucigenin and corotoxigenin the C-19 methyl group is oxidized to the alcohol and aldehyde group, respectively. These aglycones have been found in *Coronilla glauca*, a Papilionacea, but frugoside, a coroglaucigenin glycoside also occurs in the seeds of the Asclepiadaceae *Gomphocarpus fruticosus* and *Xysmalobium undulatum*; glycosides of corotoxigenin are also present in *Strophanthus Boivinii*, an Apocynacea. The Asclepiadaceae contain a great variety of cardenolides. The glycosides in the latex of *Calotropis procera* are acid-resistant. Under drastic conditions they yield methyl- and hydroxymethylreductinic acid (Figure 5.5).

Seeds of the genus *Strophanthus* have long been used by African aborigines for the preparation of arrow poisons. The cardiac

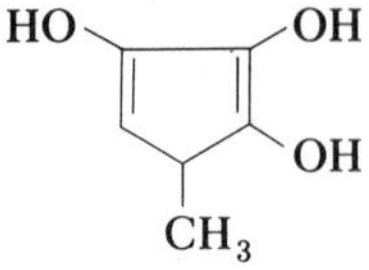

Methylreductinic Acid 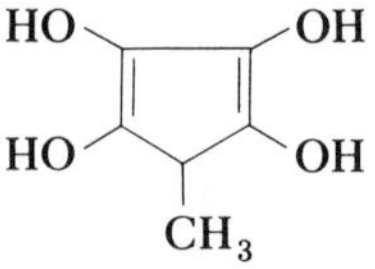   Hydroxymethylreductinic Acid

FIGURE 5.5. METHYL- AND HYDROXYMETHYLREDUCTINIC ACIDS.

glycosides in these seeds have been intensively investigated by Reichstein. Figure 5.6 shows three cardenolides which usually occur together in various *Strophanthus* seeds. They all contain a 5β-hydroxyl group and differ only in the state of oxidation at C-19. Periplogenin derives its name from the genus *Periploca* (Asclepiadaceae), in which it was first found. It occurs there as the gly-

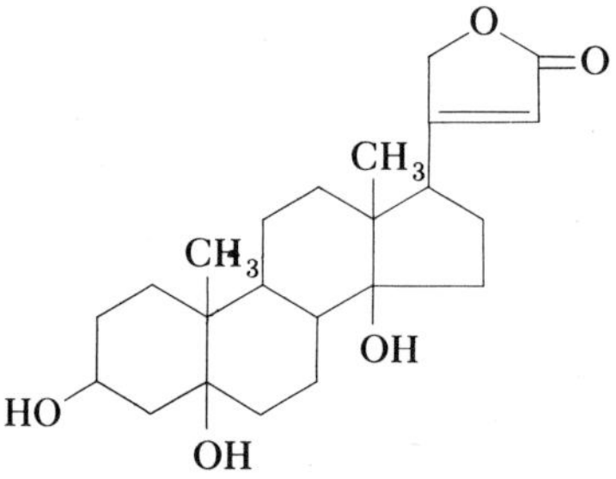

Periplogenin

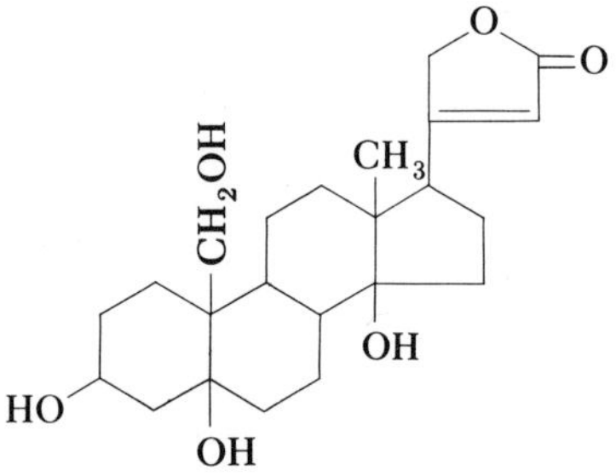

Strophanthidol

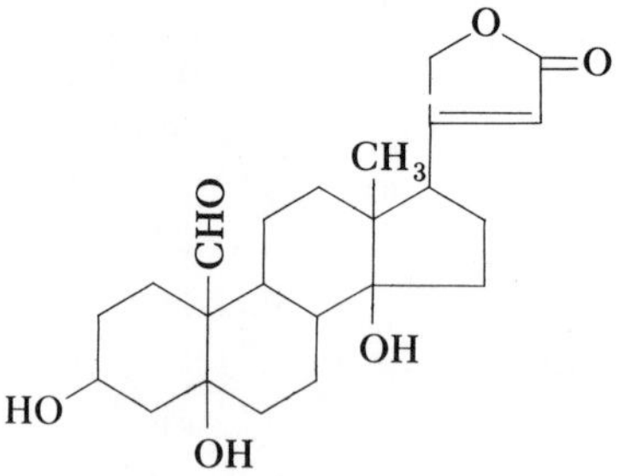

Strophanthidin

FIGURE 5.6. 5β-HYDROXYCARDENOLIDES.

coside periplocin, linked to one cymarose and one glucose unit. Extracts of various *Strophanthus* seeds contain the periplogenin cymaroside, periplocymarin, and the periplogenin digitaloside, emicymarin. The strophanthidol cymaroside is called cymarol. The rhamnoside convallotoxol occurs in the leaves of *Convallaria majalis* (lily-of-the-valley). The rhamnoside of strophanthidin, occurring in the same source, is called convallatoxin. The chief source of strophanthidin is *S. kombé*, where it occurs in combination with strophanthotriose (1 cymarose and 2 glucose units) as the glycoside k-strophanthoside. Treatment of this glycoside with α-glucosidase from yeast gives the strophanthobioside (1 cymarose and 1 glucose unit) k-strophanthin-β. Incubation of the latter with strophanthobiase from seeds of *S. Courmontii* then yields cymarin, the strophanthidin cymaroside.

News of the occurrence of an 11-oxygenated cardenolide, sarmentogenin (Figure 5.7), in African *Strophanthus* species

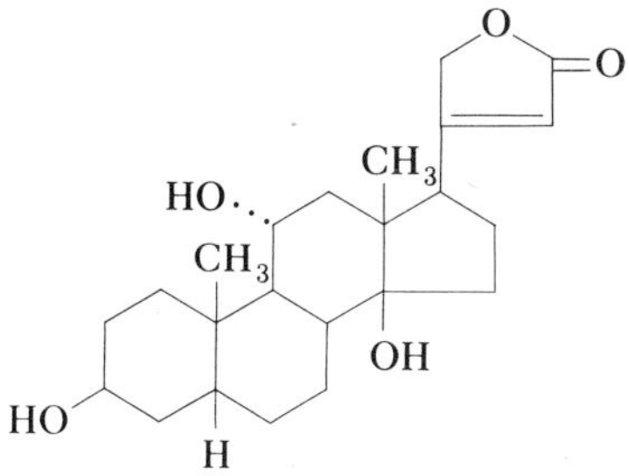

Sarmentogenin

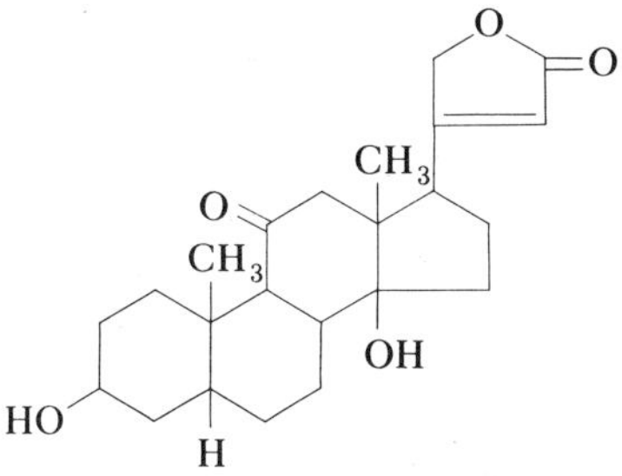

Desarogenin

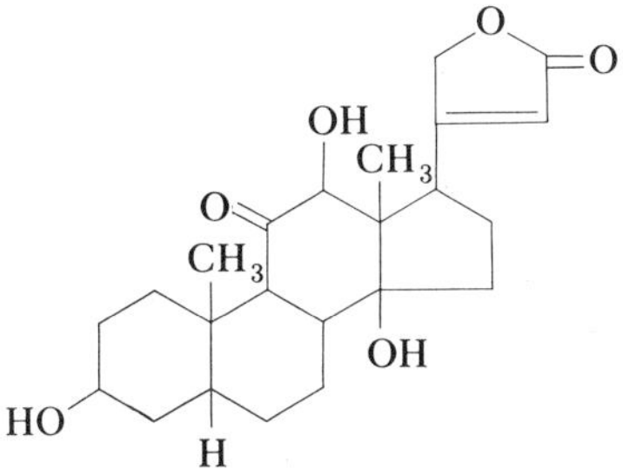

Sarmutogenin

FIGURE 5.7. 11-OXYGENATED CARDENOLIDES.

caused considerable excitement during the early attempts to secure raw materials for the partial synthesis of adrenocortical hormones. Several countries sent expeditions to Africa to locate a sarmentogenin-rich species. Sarmentogenin was found in a variety of *Strophanthus sarmentosus* which could not be readily distinguished botanically from other varieties. However, it was possible to group the varieties on the basis of their chemical composition into 4 classes: 1. a sarmentogenin-producing variety, which contains sarmentocymarin (sarmentogenin sarmentoside) and sarnovide (sarmentogenin digitaloside), 2. a sarmutogenin-producing variety, containing sarmutoside (sarmutogenin [cf. Figure 5.7] sarmentoside) and musaroside (sarmutogenin digitaloside), 3. a sarverogenin-producing variety, containing sarveroside (sarverogenin [cf. Figure 5.8] sarmentoside) and panstroside (sarvero-

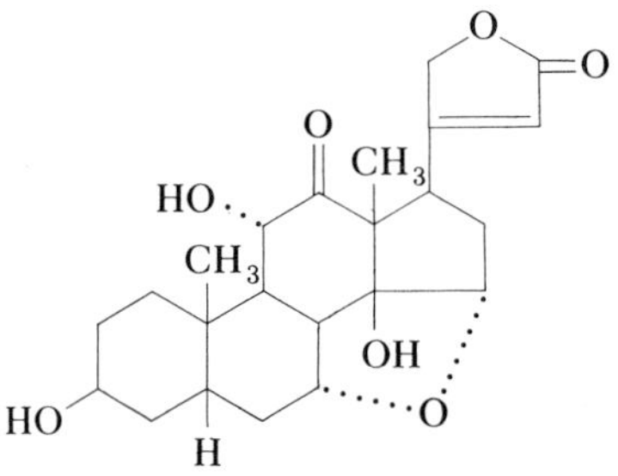

Sarverogenin 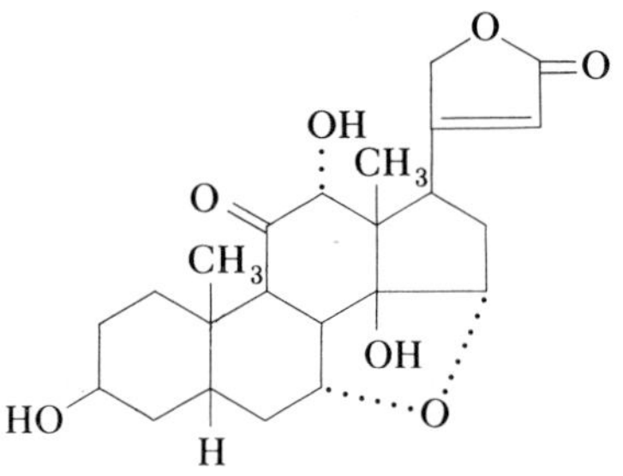   Inertogenin

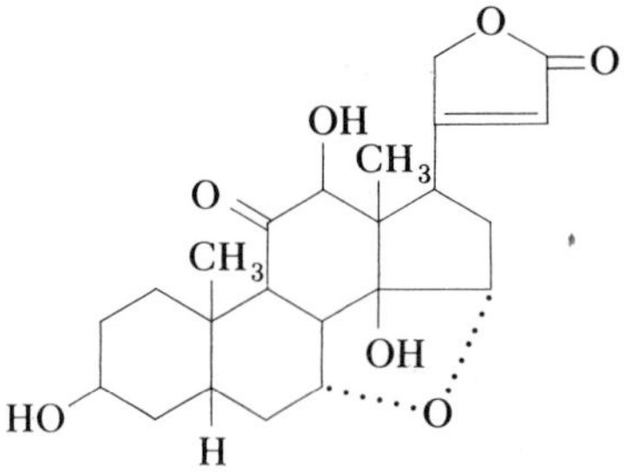

Leptogenin

FIGURE 5.8. CARDENOLIDES OXYGENATED IN C-11 AND C-12.

genin digitaloside), and 4. a variety poor in cardiac glycosides. In addition to genetic factors, the age of the plants, their location, and weather conditions influence the glycoside composition of the seeds. Desarogenin, an 11-dehydrosarmentogenin (cf. Figure 5.7), occurs in *S. Vanderijstii.*

Figure 5.8 shows the structures of three cardenolides which are found together in various *Strophanthus* seeds. They contain oxygen functions on both C-11 and C-12 and are interconvertible in the laboratory and perhaps also in the plants. An oxygen bridge probably extends from C-7 to C-15. The diginoside of sarverogenin is called intermedioside, that of inertogenin inertoside, and that of leptogenin leptoside. The most highly oxygenated cardenolide,

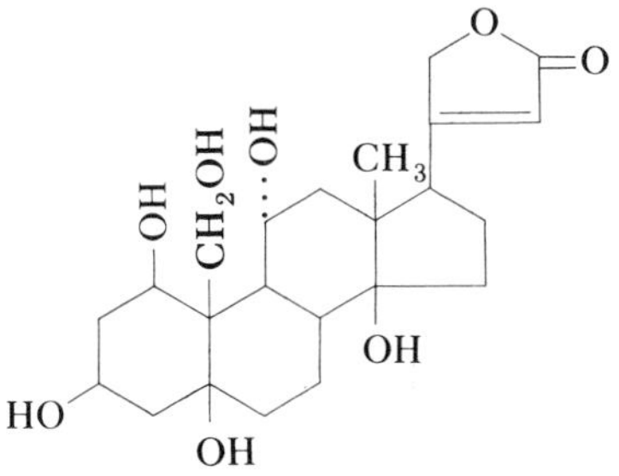

FIGURE 5.9. OUABAGENIN.

ouabagenin (Figure 5.9), is an important drug in cardiac therapy. It was first isolated from the bark and root of the African ouabaio tree (*Acokanthera sp.*), but is now obtained from *S. gratus*, an unusually rich source. It occurs as the rhamnoside ouabain (g-strophanthin) in *Acokanthera* and *Strophanthus* (both Apocynaceae).

2. Bufadienolides

Cardiac-active genins with 24 carbon atoms occur in the roots of plants in the lily and buttercup families as well as in toad venoms. In addition, the toxic secretion of the skin glands of the toad, particularly of the parotid glands, may contain the biogenetically related sterols cholesterol, ergosterol, and γ-sitosterol, as well as pressor amines (bufotenines, adrenaline). The structural formulae of three of the cardiac-active bufogenins (Latin *bufo*, toad) are shown in Figure 5.10. They are characterized by the 20,22-unsaturated lactone ring and, like the cardenolides, by the presence of the 14β-hydroxyl group. In analogy to the cardenolides they are called bufadienolides, and they may be given analogous systematic names, e.g. bufalin is 3β,14β-dihydroxy-5β-bufadieno-lide. Bufalin is the digitoxigenin analog in the bufadienolide series, bufotalin is the analog of oleandrigenin, and gamabufotalin the sarmentogenin analog.

There is some evidence that toads synthesize bufogenins from cholesterol. In the venom bufadienolides occur either free or in the form of conjugates (bufotoxins), in which the C-14 hydroxyl group of the steroid is esterified with suberylarginine (Figure 5.11). The gamabufotalin ester is called gamabufotoxin (Japanese

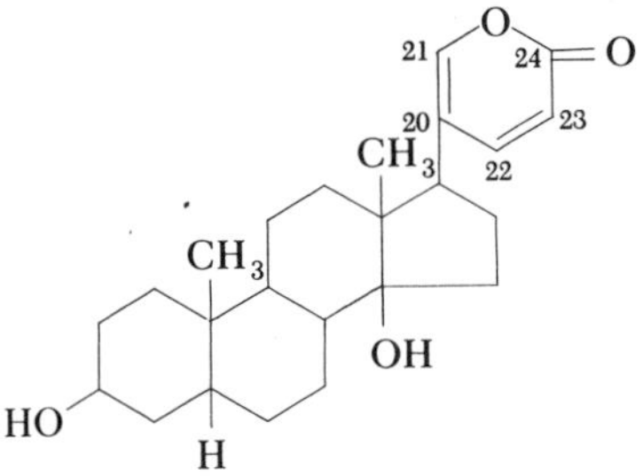

Bufalin

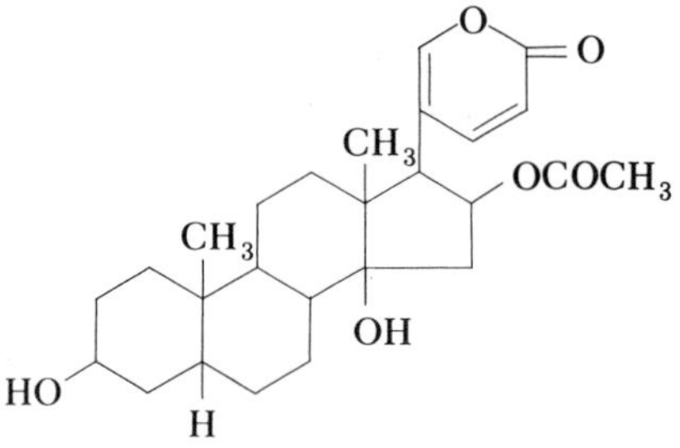

Bufotalin

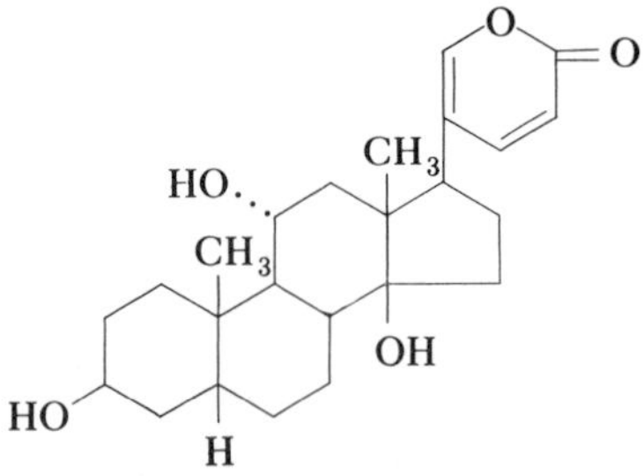

Gamabufotalin

FIGURE 5.10. 5β-BUFADIENOLIDES.

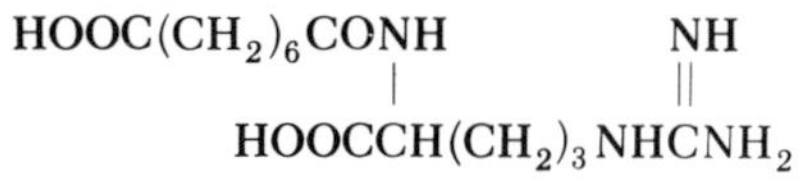

HOOC(CH$_2$)$_6$CONH   NH
                           | ||
      HOOCCH(CH$_2$)$_3$NHCNH$_2$

FIGURE 5.11. SUBERYLARGININE.

gama, toad), which has been found in the skin of *Bufo vulgaris formosus*. Bufalin and bufotalin are among the active principles in the Chinese drug *ch'an su* (*senso* in Japan), which is prepared from the skin of *Bufo bufo gargarizans*.

Bufadienolide analogs of periplogenin, strophanthidol, and strophanthidin are presented in Figure 5.12. Telocinobufagin and bufotalidin have been found in the European toad (*Bufo bufo bufo*). Bufotalidin has also been isolated from the rhizome of the Christmas rose (*Helleborus niger*), where it was named hellebrigenin.

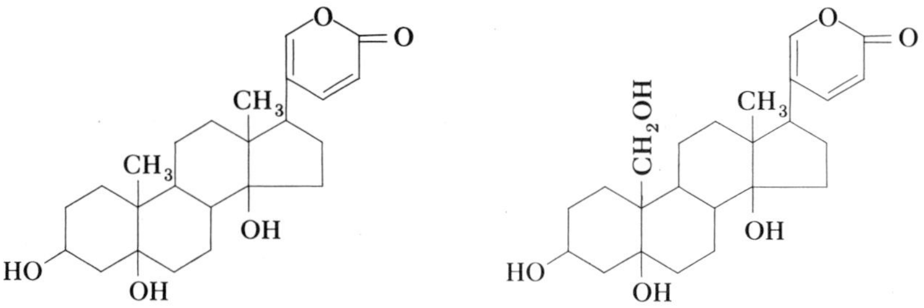

Telocinobufagin

Hellebrigenol

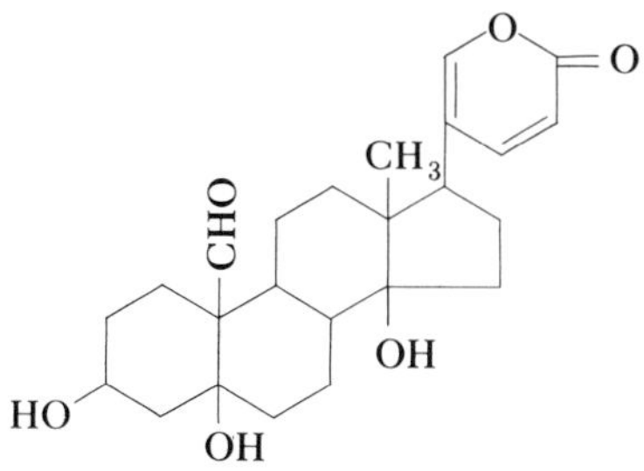

Bufotalidin, Hellebrigenin

FIGURE 5.12. 5β-HYDROXYBUFADIENOLIDES.

Hellebrigenol and hellebrigenin occur in the plant as the rhamnosides. As in the case of the cardenolides, in the plant the sugars are linked to the C-3 hydroxyl group of the bufadienolides.

Several plants belonging to the Liliaceae, notably the genera *Bowiea* and *Scilla* (*Urginea*) contain bufadienolides. The name scilladienolides has been proposed for these cardiac-active aglycones. Two aglycones occurring in the bulbs of white squill (*Scilla maritima*) are presented in Figure 5.13. Scilliglaucosidin was also found in *Bowiea* bulbs. They contain a 4,5-double bond and carry either a —CH₃ or —CHO group on C-10. Natural scillarenin glycosides include glucoscillaren A (1 rhamnose and 2 glucose units), scillaren A (1 rhamnose and 1 glucose), and proscillaridin A (1 rhamnose). Red squill, which belongs to the same species, contains a different cardiac glycoside, scilliroside. The latter is the glucoside of scillirosidin, the third aglycone in Figure 5.13. It dif-

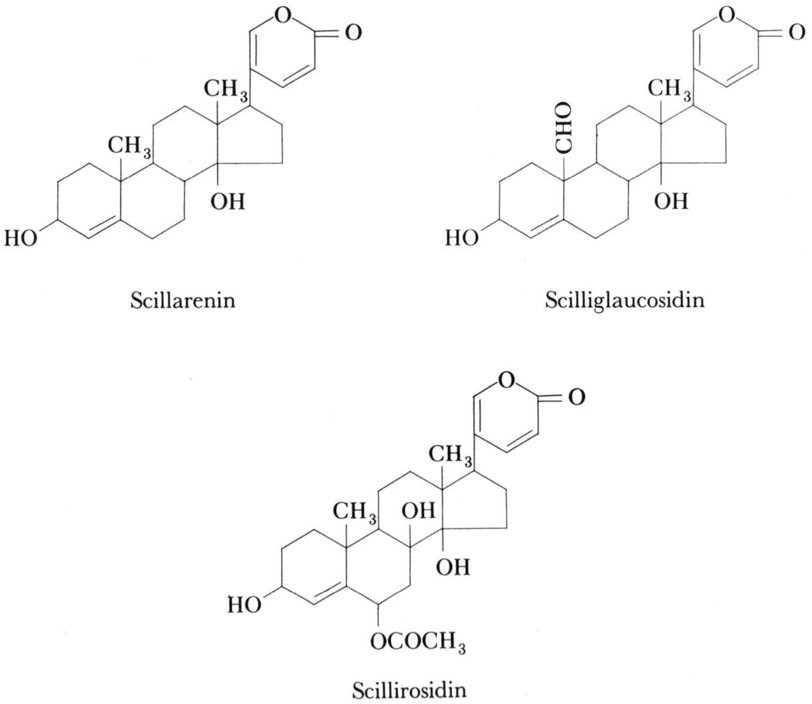

Scillarenin

Scilliglaucosidin

Scillirosidin

FIGURE 5.13. Δ⁴-BUFADIENOLIDES.

fers from scillarenin in having an additional hydroxyl group at C-8 and an acetoxy group at C-6. The bulbs of *Bowiea volubilis* contain bufadienolides with *trans*-fused A/B rings. Bovoside A, isolated from *Bowiea*, is the thevetoside of bovogenin A (Figure 5.14). Bufadienolides and cardenolides have not been found together in

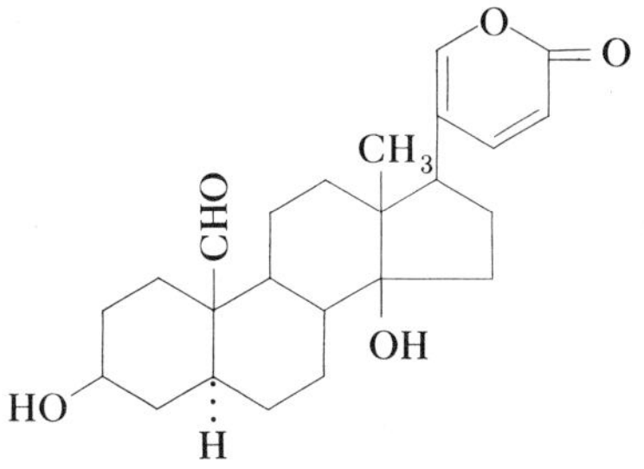

FIGURE 5.14. BOVOGENIN A.

the same plant genus. However, some genera belonging to the same family (e.g. the Liliaceae) may elaborate bufadienolides (e.g. *Bowiea* and *Scilla*), while others may contain cardenolides (*Convallaria* and *Rhodea*).

3. Pharmacology

Although much work has been done on the relation between chemical structure and pharmacological activity of cardiac glycosides, notably by Chen, only a few generalizations can be made. Both the unsaturated lactone ring and the 14β-hydroxyl group (or C/D *cis*-juncture) are necessary for biological activity. The β-configuration at C-17 is likewise required, the 17-iso-(or *allo*-) derivatives being totally inactive. There is no definite difference between the effectiveness of cardenolides and bufadienolides. However, while the monoglycosides of bufadienolides are less active than their aglycones, the cardenolides are generally less active than their monoglycosides. The conjugated toad venoms are either less potent than the steroids or equally potent. Rhamnosides appear to have a higher activity than the corresponding thevetosides.

There are large species differences in the response to cardiac poisons. In comparison with the cat dose, the lethal dose is about twice as great for rabbits and about 60 times as great for rats. Frogs are suitable test animals, but toads are practically immune to cardiac poisons. While extracts of *S. kombé* seeds are about equally toxic to cats and dogs, digitoxin is much less active in dogs than in cats. Red squill is a rather specific poison for rats.

Cardiac glycosides, either in purified form or as galenical preparations, are used in medicine under a variety of trade names. Digitalis is still the most popular drug in congestive heart failure. Injectable tinctures are used for prompt initial digitalization and powdered leaf tablets for maintenance doses. The dose is expressed in international units. An international unit is equal to a U.S.P. unit and corresponds to 100 mg of digitalis powder or 1 ml of tincture of digitalis, bioassayed in pigeons. The therapeutic dose varies from case to case and must be individually adjusted.

Cardiac glycosides have a bitter taste. They act directly and specifically on the heart muscle to increase the force of systolic contraction and improve the cardiac output. Cardiac glycosides stimulate the vagal endings and decrease the heart rate. By depressing auriculoventricular conduction they relieve auricular fibrillation. Large doses produce nausea, salivation, blurred vision, diarrhea, and muscle weakness. In contrast to small doses, overdoses increase the heart rate, reduce the output, produce fibrillations, and finally stop the heart in systole. The action of cardiotonic agents is slow, cumulative, and long lasting.

Experiments with radioactive cardiac glycosides, produced by growing *Digitalis* plants in an atmosphere of radioactive carbon dioxide, have shed some light on the metabolism of cardenolides. They are absorbed in the gastro-intestinal tract and metabolized in the liver. There is no evidence for a preferential accumulation in the heart muscle. Metabolites are excreted both in the urine and stool over a long time, especially in older individuals. 12-Hydroxy-digitoxin has been isolated from rat urine following digitoxin administration. Microorganisms (*Fusarium lini*) are also known to introduce a 12β-hydroxyl group into cardiac aglycones.

The mode of action of cardiac glycosides is not well understood. Szent-Györgyi's school has proffered evidence that cardiac glycosides as well as desoxycorticosterone and progesterone decrease the intracellular potassium content of the muscle fiber. This may bring about the increase in contractility of the actomyosin system. There are various indications that cardiac glycosides may indeed be involved in ion transport phenomena by inhibiting the active transport of sodium and potassium across the cell membrane. Digitalis promotes a loss of body potassium and has a qualitatively similar effect to desoxycorticosterone in prolonging the life of adrenalectomized animals. It is also known that potassium counteracts the arrythmias produced by digitalis and that calcium potentiates the effect of digitalis.

4. Analysis

The isolation of cardiac glycosides from plant material is complicated by the fact that plant tissues may contain enzymes which hydrolyze the glycosides. Also, allomerizing enzymes in seeds invert the configuration at C-17 to yield 17-isoaglycones. To prevent hydrolysis, a cold ammonium sulfate solution may be used for the extraction of digitalis leaves. This treatment precipitates the enzymes and permits recovery of the glycosides by solvent extraction of the aqueous solution. In the work-up of seed material defatting by petroleum ether precedes the extraction of hydrolytic enzymes by cold water and extraction of glycosides by alcohol. The alcohol treatment inactivates the allomerizing enzymes. After precipitation of tannins with lead hydroxide, the glycosides may be hydrolyzed or further purified. The isolation of toad poisons is somewhat simpler. The venom can be expressed and dried and the bufotoxins subsequently extracted by solvents.

Chromatographic methods are extremely useful for the separation of individual glycosides and genins. Adsorption chromatography on alumina is suitable for the less polar compounds, but neutral alumina must be used, since alkali can produce a variety of artifacts. Partition chromatography is eminently suitable for the separation of more polar compounds. It may be carried out on a preparative scale on columns of diatomaceous earth and other inert carriers or on a microscale on filter paper. The solvent systems used depend on the particular problem and include mixtures of chloroform, methanol, and water or water-saturated butanol for the separation of more highly polar glycosides, and two-phase organic solvent systems such as chloroform/formamide and propylene glycol/toluene for the less polar glycosides and aglycones. For the detection of cardiac glycosides and aglycones in paper chromatograms treatment with trichloroacetic acid, antimony trichloride, or some of the color reactions listed below may be used.

The glycosides may be hydrolyzed by enzymes obtained from aqueous plant extracts or snail intestinal juice, or by acid hydrolysis. Since they are also sensitive to acid, mild hydrolytic conditions must be used. Glycosides of 2-desoxysugars are more easily hydrolyzed than those of sugars with a 2-hydroxyl group. In the latter case treatment with hydrogen chloride in acetone at room temperature for a period of one to two weeks (Mannich-Siewert method) is effective.

A number of color reactions have been described, some of which are also suitable for quantitative analysis of cardiac glycosides. The Keller-Kiliani test is specific for glycosides containing 2-desoxysugars. When they are dissolved in glacial acetic acid containing a trace of ferric chloride and when concentrated sulfuric acid is layered beneath the solution, the acetic acid layer turns blue. Sulfuric acid (84 per cent) alone gives various colors with cardiac glycosides and aglycones. The Legal test is carried out by adding alkali to a solution of the genin and sodium nitroprusside in pyridine. A red color indicates the presence of the butenolide ring in the genin. The reduction of silverdiammine ion (Tollens test) is also due to the presence of the α,β-unsaturated lactone ring. Other tests for cardenolides include the Baljet reaction (orange color with alkaline picrate), the Raymond test (purple color with m-dinitrobenzene and methanolic potassium hydroxide) and the Kedde modification of the latter test (purple color with 3,5-dinitrobenzoic acid and alkali). Bufadienolides do not give all of these reactions. A reagent containing p-dimethylaminobenzaldehyde in sulfuric acid is used for paper chromatography. Bufadienolides may be differentiated from cardenolides by their ultraviolet absorption spectra. The coumalin ring absorbs around 300 mμ, while the butenolide ring gives rise to an absorption maximum at 217 mμ.

In the bioassay of cardiotonic substances, the toxicity, rather than the therapeutic effect, is determined. In the Hatcher test they are intravenously infused into cats and the mean lethal dose (LD_{50})

is obtained; i.e., the mean dose in mg per kg required to kill half of the test animals. In the frog test the material is injected into the lymph sac until the frog heart stops in systole. While chemical methods may ultimately replace bioassays for routine analyses, there is a continued need for animal tests, since it is not possible to predict the cardiotonic activity of newly isolated substances on the basis of their chemical structure.

5. Digitanol Glycosides

A number of glycosides of C_{21} steroids have been isolated from various *Digitalis* species by Tschesche and other workers; these are collectively known as digitanol glycosides. Figure 5.15 shows the

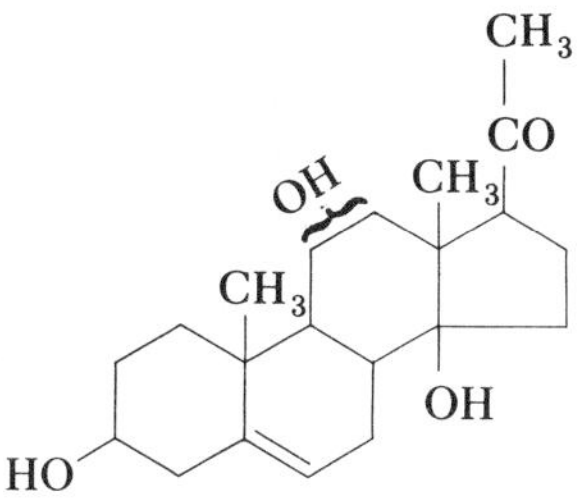

Digipurpurogenin 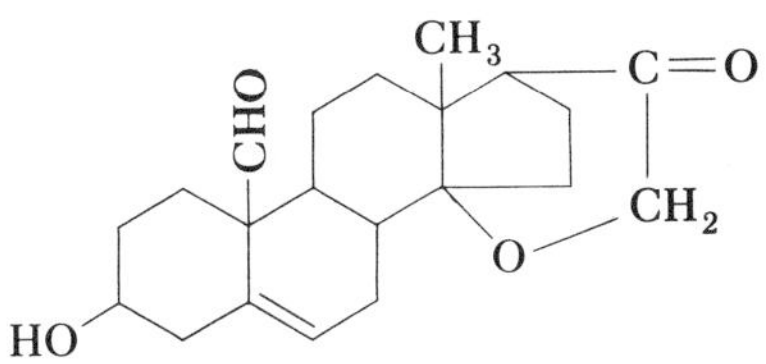   Diginigenin

FIGURE 5.15. DIGITANOL GENINS.

structure of two of the genins, digipurpurogenin and diginigenin. Both compounds have the C/D *cis*-juncture characteristic of cardiac aglycones and a 5,6-double bond. Digipurpurogenin contains a secondary hydroxyl group, located at either C-7, C-11, or C-12. In diginigenin the oxygen at C-14 forms a cyclic ether with the C-21 carbon, and the C-10 carbon carries a —CHO group instead of a —CH$_3$ group. Digifologenin (not shown) is 2β-hydroxydiginigenin.

The digitanol glycosides have no cardiotonic activity, but they are of great biogenetic interest. Diginigenin, containing a C-19 aldehyde group, may constitute a precursor of estrogens. Estrogens (cf. Chap. X, p. 156) contain an aromatic A ring, which is presumably formed from ring A saturated steroids via a C-19 aldehyde. It has been known for some time that estrone and estriol occur in plants, but their origin is still obscure.

Digipurpurogenin has been isolated as the tridigitoxoside digipurpurin, diginigenin as the diginoside diginin and as the digitaloside digitalonin. Digifologenin is combined with diginose in digifolein and with oleandrose in lanafolein. In this case the oleandrose belongs to the D-series; whereas oleandrose in the cardiotonic glycosides belongs to the L-series.

VI

Bile Acids

1. Coprostane Derivatives

THE BILE OF VERTEBRATES contains a class of steroids, the bile acids and alcohols, which, according to Haslewood, reflects the position of the animals on the evolutionary scale. Alcohols with 27, 28, or possibly 29 carbons occur as sulfates in the bile of elasmobranch fishes, but not in animals higher than the amphibians. The bile alcohols are derivatives of coprostane or bufostane (24-methyl-coprostane) of incompletely known constitution. Tentative structures of three representatives of this group of steroids are shown in Figure 6.1. All three have α-hydroxyl groups on C-3, 7, and 12, which is quite characteristic of bile acids and alcohols. However, ranol, a C_{27} pentahydric alcohol isolated from the bile of the frog *Rana temporaria*, does not seem to have the same arrangement of hydroxyl groups. Tetrahydroxycoprostane and pentahydroxybufostane occur, together with cholesterol, in the bile of toads. Since the bile of hibernating toads is especially rich in these polyalcohols, it is assumed that the bile alcohols are intermediates of the arrested cholesterol metabolism of these animals. α-Scymnol, which occurs in the bile of sharks (e.g. *Scymnus borealis*) and rays, is most likely a 24,25-epoxide and may be a biochemical progenitor of C_{24} bile acids.

In teleostean fishes, amphibians, and reptiles coprostane derivatives with a terminal carboxyl group have been found. These coprostanic acids occur in the bile in conjugation with taurine. Figure 6.2 shows examples of the C_{27} bile acids and of a taurine conjugate. $3\alpha,7\alpha,12\alpha$-Trihydroxycoprostanic acid occurs in crocodilian bile and in the bile of the American bull frog, *Rana catesbeiana*. Taurine

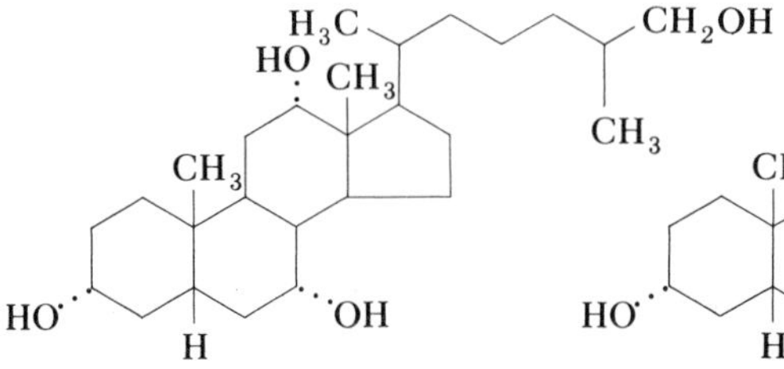

Tetrahydroxycoprostane 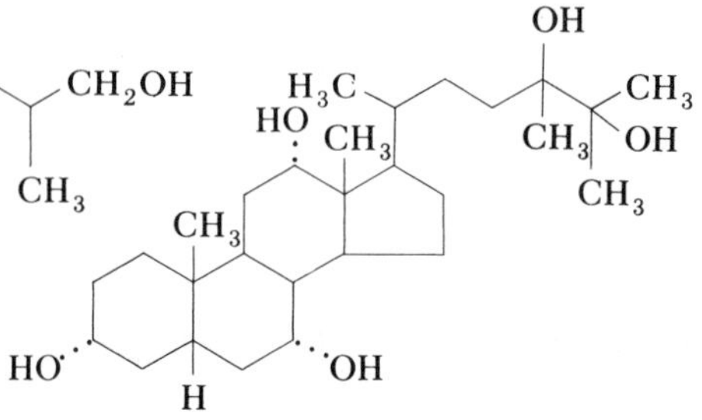   Pentahydroxybufostane

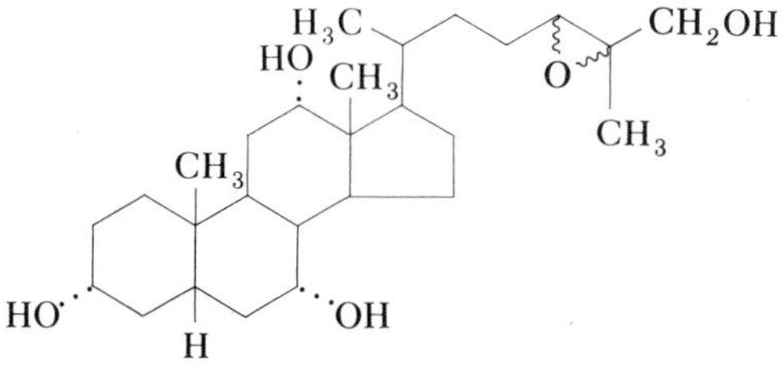

α-Scymnol

FIGURE 6.1. BILE ALCOHOLS.

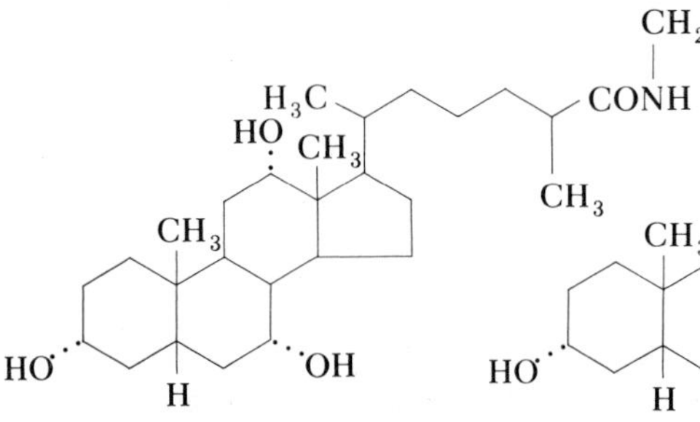

Taurine Conjugate of   Tetrahydroxycoprostanic Acid
Trihydroxycoprostanic Acid

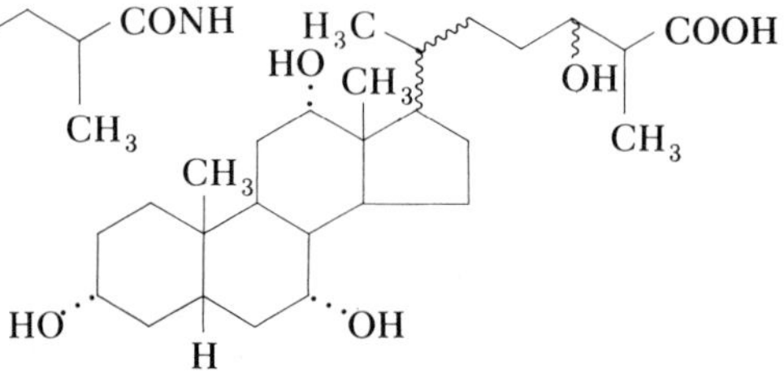

FIGURE 6.2. C$_{27}$ BILE ACIDS.

is attached to the bile acids by a peptide linkage. The bile of the gigi fish contains a 3α,7α,12α,24ξ-tetrahydroxycoprostanic acid, isomeric at either C-17 or C-20.

2. Cholanic Acids

The bile of more "modern" vertebrates contains derivatives of a C_{24} acid, cholanic acid (Figure 6.3), in which the A and B rings are *cis*-fused. Allocholanic acid (5α) derivatives which have occasionally been reported must be considered as artifacts. Most bile acids have a 3α-hydroxyl group, but 3β-hydroxycholanic acid derivatives also occur in nature. The systematic names of bile acids are formed by indicating the position of ring substituents in prefixes. Thus cholic acid (Figure 6.4) is named $3\alpha,7\alpha,12\alpha$-trihydroxy-cholanic acid. Trivial names of bile acids are often derived from the Greek or Latin names of the species from which they were first isolated.

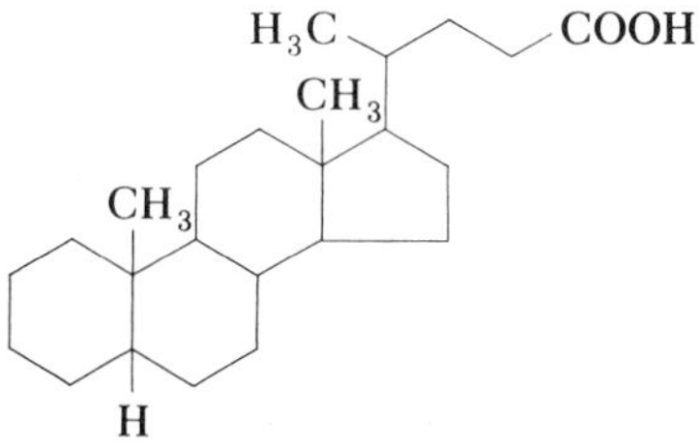

FIGURE 6.3. CHOLANIC ACID.

In the bile, the cholanic acids are conjugated with either glycine or taurine. Figure 6.4 gives the formulae and names of the cholic acid conjugates. Conjugation with glycine seems to be confined to the highest class of vertebrates, the Mammalia. At the alkaline pH of the bile the conjugates, which are stronger acids than the bile acids, are actually present in the form of the anion and are referred to as bile salts.

Structures of some C_{24} bile acids are shown in Figure 6.5 and Figure 6.6, where R stands for the C_5 side chain. For other structural formulae cf. Figure 6.9. Lithocholic acid (Greek *lithos*, stone) was first isolated from gallstones of cattle, and concrements of calcium lithocholate have been found in pigs. The acid occurs in the bile of various mammals and has occasionally been found in small amounts in human bile. Lithocholic acid and the epimeric isolitho-cholic acid have been isolated from human feces. Chenodesoxy-

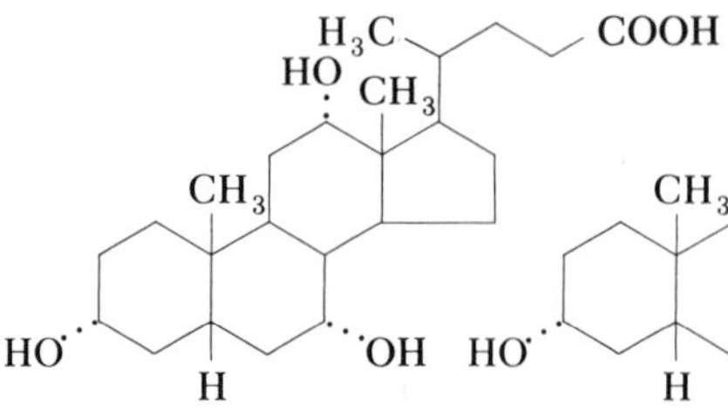

Cholic Acid

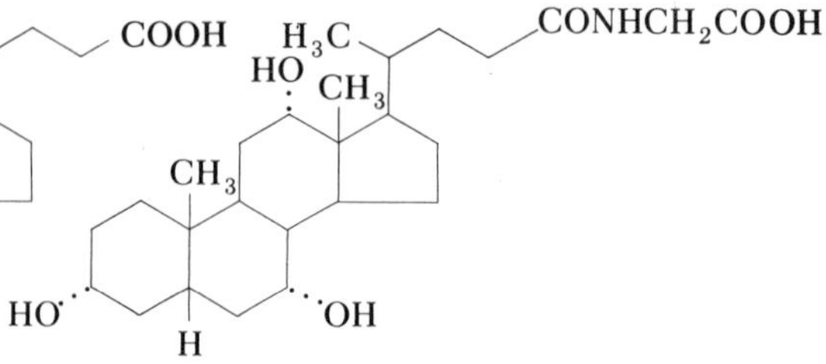

Glycocholic Acid

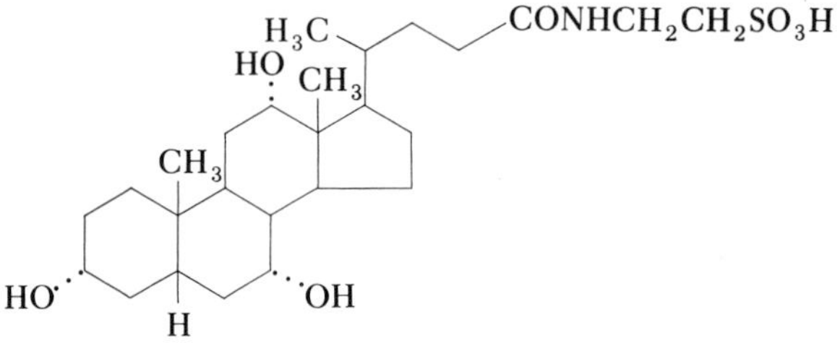

Taurocholic Acid

FIGURE 6.4. CONJUGATION OF CHOLIC ACID.

cholic acid was first isolated from goose bile and later from a variety of birds and fish. Wieland, who first found it in human bile, proposed the name anthropodesoxycholic acid, but this name has not found general acceptance. In decreasing order of relative amounts human as well as ox bile contains cholic acid, desoxycholic acid, chenodesoxycholic acid, and lithocholic acid. In human bile, chenodesoxycholic acid is often the principal bile acid. Rat bile contains largely cholic acid and some chenodesoxycholic acid. 12-Ketolithocholic acid was first isolated from ox bile as a molecular compound with chenodesoxycholic acid. Desoxycholic acid and 12-ketolithocholic acid have also been isolated from human feces. Desoxycholic acid forms choleic acids (cf. Sec. 4, p. 90). In the laboratory, it can be converted to the carcinogen methylcholanthrene (cf. Chap. I, p. 14). It has a bitter taste, while cholic acid is bitter-sweet and lithocholic acid is tasteless. Both cholic and desoxycholic acid have some commercial value as starting materials for the synthesis of adrenocortical hormones.

The occurrence of some bile acids has been thought to be re-stricted to a relatively small number of species. However, as meth-ods of isolation are improved, it is likely that some of these ideas will have to be revised. Structures of some of the C_{24} bile acids are shown in Figure 6.5 and Figure 6.6, but even some of the struc-tures, e.g. that of α-lagodesoxycholic acid, are doubtful. Ursodes-oxycholic acid was first isolated from the bile of bears (Latin *ursus*) but has more recently been found in coypu and rat bile. α-Lagodes-

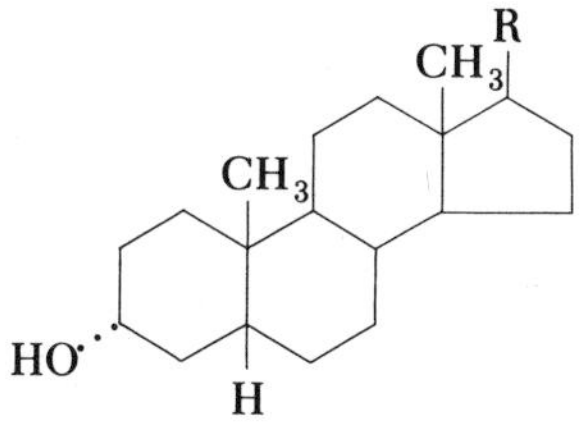

Lithocholic Acid

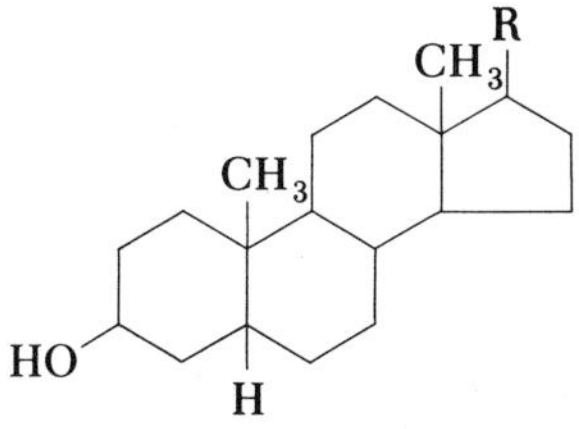

Isolithocholic Acid

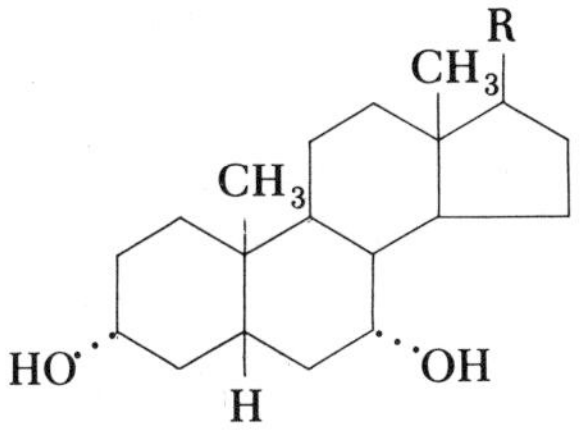

Chenodesoxycholic Acid

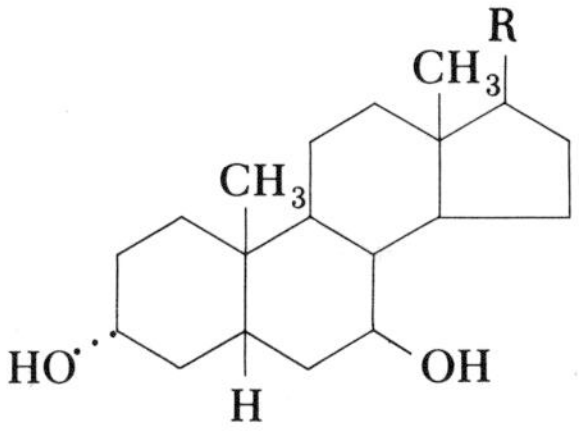

Ursodesoxycholic Acid

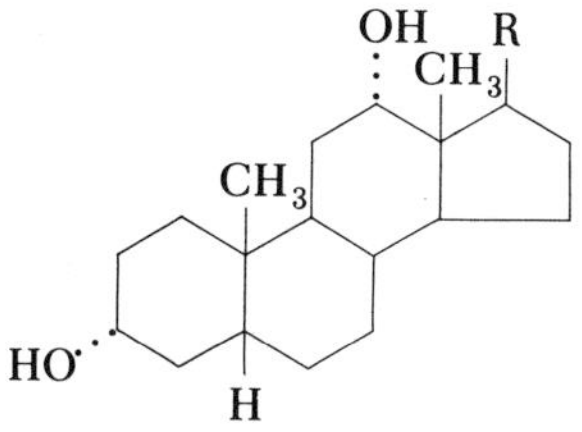

Desoxycholic Acid

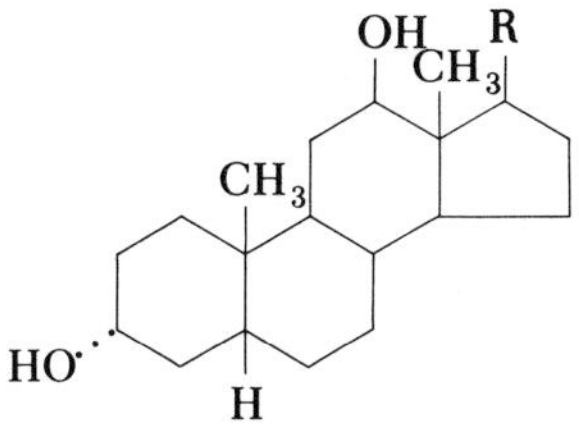

α-Lagodesoxycholic Acid

FIGURE 6.5. C_{24} BILE ACIDS I.

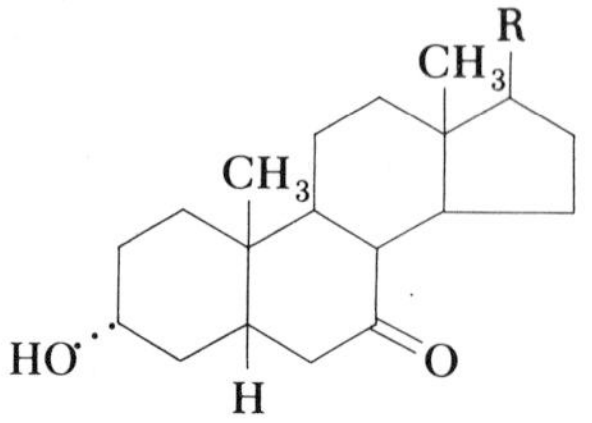

7-Ketolithocholic Acid 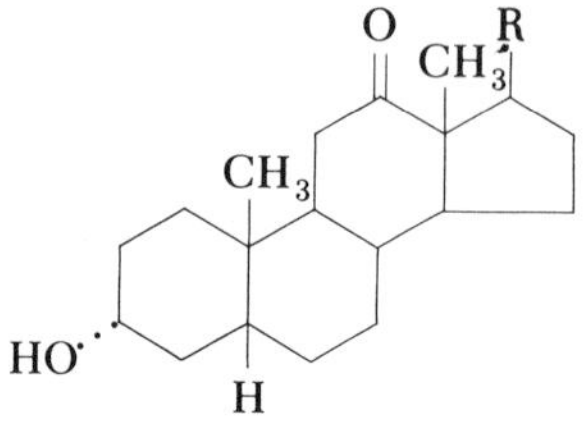   12-Ketolithocholic Acid

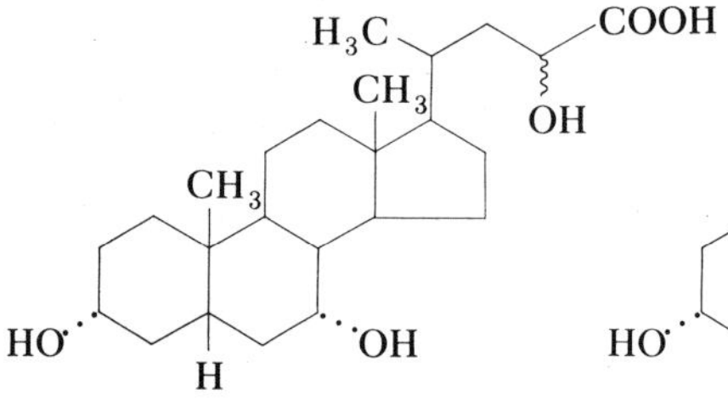

β-Phocaecholic Acid 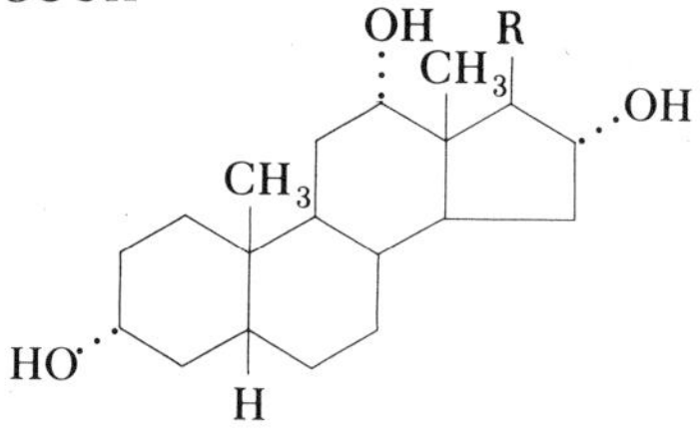   Pythocholic Acid

FIGURE 6.6. C$_{24}$ BILE ACIDS II.

oxycholic acid and its 3β-epimer, β-lagodesoxycholic acid, have so far been found only in rabbit (Greek *lagos*) bile, 7-ketolithocholic acid in the coypu, a rodent raised for its fur (nutria), β-phocaecholic·acid in the seal (*Phoca hispida*) and walrus, and pythocholic acid only in snakes belonging to the Boidae (boas and pythons).

3. Biogenesis and Metabolism

There can be no doubt nowadays that bile acids are an end-product of cholesterol metabolism. The first demonstration of the conversion of cholesterol to bile acids was given by Bloch, *et al.* in 1943, who injected deuterated cholesterol into a dog and recovered labeled cholic acid. It was found subsequently that rats given 4-C[14]-cholesterol excreted radioactive bile acids, while the radioactivity of 27-C[14]-cholesterol was recovered largely from the expired air. These results indicate that the ring system of cholesterol remains intact, while the isopropyl group of the side chain is removed. The conversion of cholesterol to cholic acid involves reduction of the double bond, hydroxylation in the ring, and degradation of the side chain. Details of these reactions are still missing. However, much has been learned about their sequence by administering radioactive precursors to bile fistula rats and identifying their metabolic products.

Results of such studies, carried out largely in the laboratory of Bergström, are summarized in Figure 6.7. Arrows in this as well as subsequent figures indicate metabolic conversions which have been observed, dotted arrows reactions presumed but not observed, and double lines through arrows reactions that do not occur: Cholesterol is converted to lithocholic acid, chenodesoxycholic acid, and cholic acid. While the intermediate steps have not yet been tested, it is known that 7α-hydroxyepicholesterol, $3\alpha,7\alpha$-dihydroxycoprostane, and $3\alpha,7\alpha,12\alpha$-trihydroxycoprostane give rise to cholic acid. Also, $3\alpha,7\alpha$-dihydroxycoprostanic acid yields chenodesoxycholic acid, and $3\alpha,7\alpha,12\alpha$-trihydroxycoprostanic acid yields cholic acid. However, cholic acid is not formed from $3\alpha,7\alpha$-dihydroxycoprostanic acid, 3β-hydroxy-Δ^5-cholenic acid, lithocholic or chenodesoxycholic acid. It may be concluded therefore that the 12-hydroxylation of the ring system must precede the degradation of the side chain. $3\alpha,7\alpha$-Dihydroxycoprostane can be further hydroxylated, but once the side chain is oxidized no hydroxyl group can be introduced into the 12α-position. The relative extent to which 12-hydroxylation or degradation of the side chain without 12-hydroxylation occurs in the animal may be regulated by thyroid function. Hyperthyroid rats secrete more chenodesoxycholic acid than cholic acid, while in the hypothyroid state they produce almost exclusively cholic acid.

The metabolism of bile acids varies with animal species. In contrast to the other species examined so far only the rat is capable of introducing a hydroxyl group into the 7α-position of bile acids. Rat liver preparations convert desoxycholic acid to cholic acid (Figure 6.8). Bacteria in the intestines of various species are capable of performing the reverse reaction, the removal of the 7α-hydroxyl group from cholic acid. Desoxycholic acid in the bile is probably entirely of bacterial origin. It is absent from the bile of newborn babies and rapidly disappears from the bile of rabbits

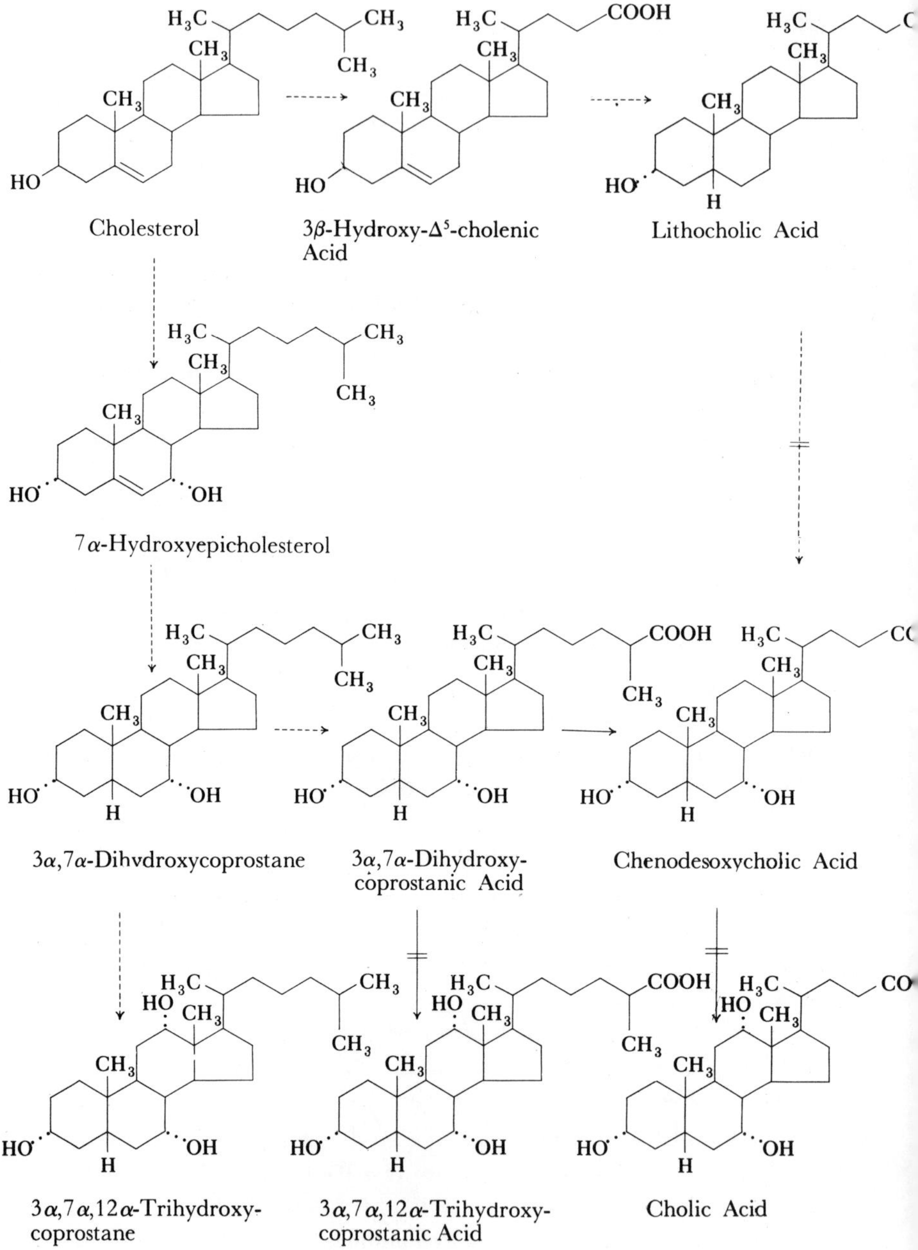

FIGURE 6.7. BIOGENESIS OF BILE ACIDS.

when a bile fistula is made. Bacteria can also oxidize the 12α-hydroxyl group of desoxycholic acid to a keto group. These reactions are summarized in Figure 6.8, where R stands for the C_5 side chain.

Figure 6.9 illustrates some metabolic reactions of chenodesoxycholic acid. In pigs this acid is hydroxylated in the 6α-position to

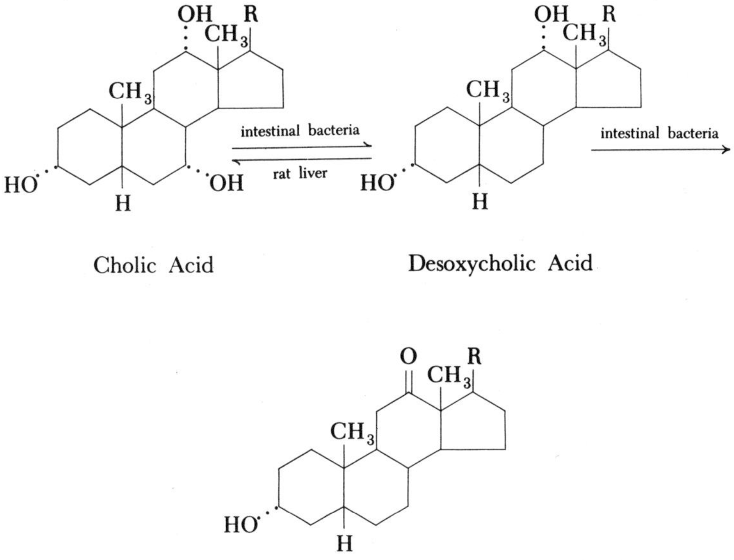

Cholic Acid

Desoxycholic Acid

12-Ketolithocholic Acid

FIGURE 6.8. METABOLISM OF DESOXYCHOLIC ACID.

give hyocholic acid. Microorganisms in the intestines of various species can again remove the 7α-hydroxyl group and produce hyodesoxycholic acid. Rats have the ability to convert chenodesoxycholic acid into both α- and β-muricholic acids (Latin *murinus*, pertaining to the mouse). This involves not only the introduction of a 6β-hydroxyl group, but in the case of β-muricholic acid also inversion of the asymmetric center at C-7. It has been shown that, at least in the case of cholic acid (Figure 6.10), intestinal bacteria are responsible for the inversion, which proceeds *via* the 7-ketone. Germ-free rats cannot accomplish this reaction. ω-Muricholic acid

α-Muricholic Acid   Chenodesoxycholic Acid   β-Muricholic Acid

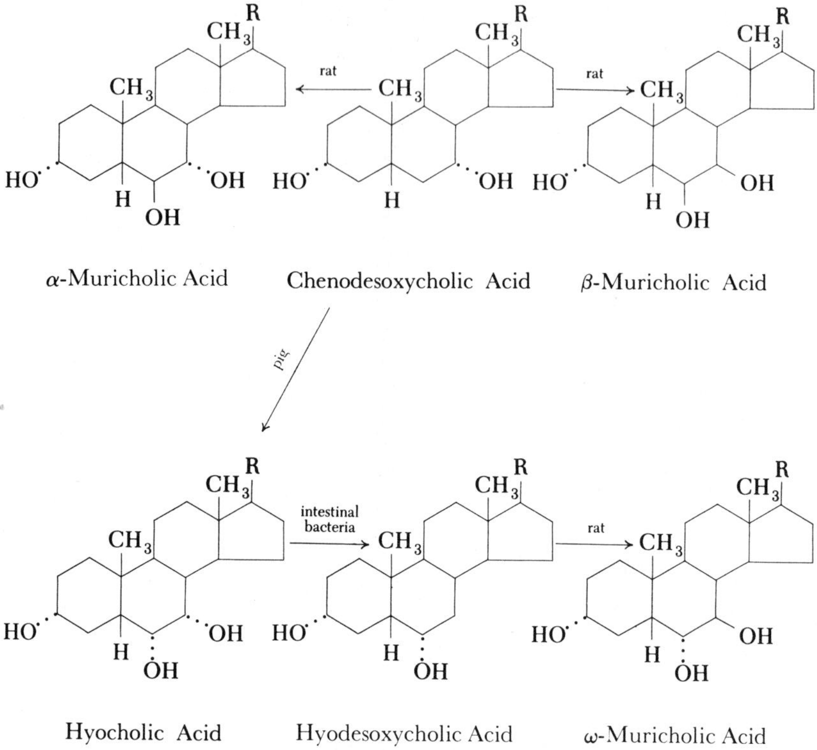

Hyocholic Acid   Hyodesoxycholic Acid   ω-Muricholic Acid

FIGURE 6.9. METABOLISM OF CHENODESOXYCHOLIC ACID.

(Figure 6.9) was isolated from the urine of surgically jaundiced rats after the administration of hyodesoxycholic acid.

The conjugation of bile acids has been studied *in vitro* by use of liver microsome preparations. These contain an enzyme which

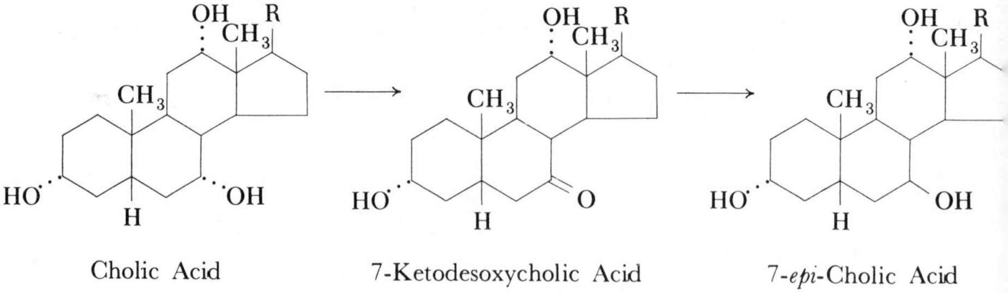

Cholic Acid   7-Ketodesoxycholic Acid   7-*epi*-Cholic Acid

FIGURE 6.10. BACTERIAL METABOLISM OF CHOLIC ACID.

activates cholic acid. In the presence of ATP, cholic acid forms cholyl CoA (Figure 6.11). A second enzyme brings about the conjugation with taurine or glycine. Rabbit liver conjugates cholic acid exclusively with glycine, chicken liver only with taurine, and

Cholic acid + ATP + HSCoA → cholyl SCoA + AMP + PP

Cholyl SCoA + taurine → taurocholic acid + HSCoA

FIGURE 6.11. CONJUGATION OF CHOLIC ACID.

rat liver produces both conjugates, although more taurocholate than glycocholate. In the intact animal the conjugates are hydrolyzed by enzymes in the intestinal flora and only germ-free animals excrete conjugated bile acids in the feces.

4. Physiology

The bile salts are formed in the liver, collected in the biliary passages, stored and concentrated in the gallbladder, and intermittently discharged into the common bile duct. Bile is an alkaline secretion, which contains, in addition to the bile salts, cholesterol, lecithin, and bile pigments, especially bilirubin. In the duodenum the bile helps to neutralize the gastric chyme and to emulsify the dietary lipides. Although bile acids have an effect on the pH optimum of pancreatic lipase, the evidence for an activating effect on this enzyme is contradictory. It is certain, however, that the bile salts, consisting of a hydrocarbon portion and polar group, have a powerful detergent effect and promote the contact between the lipase and the substrate. They are not indispensable in this respect, since the soaps formed are also detergents. The dispersion of lipides in the gut enables the intestinal mucosa to absorb them. Bile salts are important in the absorption of cholesterol (cf. Chap. I, p. 10) and of fat-soluble vitamins. In biliary obstruction there may be symptoms of vitamin K deficiency. Two other biologically important properties of bile acids are their hemolytic effect and their antibacterial activity.

The discovery of the choleic acids by Wieland and Sorge in 1916 started much speculation about their possible physiological significance. Briefly, desoxycholic acid, but no other bile acid except the synthetic apocholic ($\Delta^{8(14)}$-desoxycholic) acid, has the ability to form coordination or inclusion compounds with fatty acids, hydrocarbons, cholesterol, etc. The number of desoxycholic acid molecules involved depends on the chain length of the fatty acid. Formic acid does not give a choleic acid. Acetic acid combines with desoxycholic acid in a mol ratio of 1:1. Propionic acid requires 3 molecules of desoxycholic acid; fatty acids with 4-8 carbon atoms, 4 molecules; those with 9-14 carbon atoms, 6 molecules; and higher fatty acids, 8 molecules of desoxycholic acid. In branched chain fatty acids and hydrocarbons the longest chain determines the mol ratio. Since choleic acids form water-soluble salts, it was believed that they may be important in fat transport. While it is true that the absorption of certain substances in the form of choleic acids is improved (e.g. camphor ingested as the choleic acid, codechol), choleic acids probably have very little physiological importance. Desoxycholic acid occurs in the bile in the form of conjugates, but the conjugates do not form choleic acids. Moreover, the more abundant cholic acid does not form adducts with fatty acids.

As previously indicated, the relative extent of conjugation with glycine and taurine depends on the species. Glycine conjugates occur only in mammals. Rabbit bile contains almost exclusively glycodesoxycholic acid, while rat bile contains no glycine conjugates. In man and pig glyco-conjugation predominates, but in cattle variable proportions of the two modes of conjugation have been observed. The proportion of taurine conjugates can be increased in man by the ingestion of taurine, but glycine ingestion has no effect.

The conjugated bile acids are rapidly and effectively reabsorbed from the gut and transported to the liver *via* the portal system without reaching the lymphatic circulation. In obstructive jaundice bile acids appear in the peripheral circulation and in the urine. The enterohepatic circulation of bile acids regulates their hepatic synthesis. Drainage of the bile through a fistula increases the bile acid production, and simultaneous infusion of bile salts into the common duct above the fistula depresses the rate of synthesis. It is estimated that about three-fourths of the body cholesterol is catabolized to bile acids and eventually removed by way of the feces. The half-life of cholic acid has been estimated at 2.8 days and the pool size at 3.58 g. Experiments with germ-free rats have shown that the half-life of cholic acid depends on the intestinal bacteria. It is 2 days in normal, but 11.4 days in germ-free rats.

5. Analysis

For the isolation of conjugated bile acids the bile is freed of mucin, evaporated, and extracted with alcohol. On repeated precipitation with ether and redissolving in alcohol the sodium salts of the conjugates are obtained. The free bile acids are isolated after alkaline hydrolysis of the bile. They are precipitated by the addition of acid and then dissolved in alcohol. Their barium salts are also alcohol-soluble. After removal of fatty material with petroleum ether, the bile acids may be separated by a variety of methods. When the mixture is dissolved in ether and extracted with hydrochloric acid of different concentrations, some separation is obtained, but more efficient fractionation is achieved by countercurrent distribution.

The convenient and highly efficient separation methods of partition chromatography are gradually replacing adsorption chromatography of the esters in biochemical research on bile acids. Reversed phase partition chromatography on hydrophobic Supercel columns has been especially valuable in the study of radioactive metabolites of bile acids or their conjugates. Elution patterns are obtained by radiochemical assay and by titration of the effluent with base. In ordinary partition chromatography on columns or filter paper, acetic acid is usually incorporated into the solvent system to repress the ionization of the bile acids and to increase their solubility, but alkaline solvent systems are also suitable for the separation of bile acids in the form of their anions. Color reagents for paper chromatography include antimony trichloride, phosphoric acid, and phosphomolybdic acid.

A number of color tests have been developed which are more or less specific for bile acids. Some of these are now of minor interest. Cholic acid, dissolved in ethanol and treated with a few drops of iodine solution gives on warming a blue color in transmitted light and needles which appear yellow in reflected light. This test (Mylius reaction) is not given by lithocholic or desoxycholic acid. The Hammarsten test is carried out by adding cholic acid to 25 per cent hydrochloric acid. A violet color appears, which on heating changes to yellow. Yamasaki modified the test by heating with concentrated hydrochloric acid and observing the absorption spectroscopically. Bile acids having hydroxyl groups on carbons 3, 7 and 12, on 3, 6 and 12, or on C-3 and C-12 and a double bond in ring B absorb between 560 and 590 mμ. Cholic acid and its conjugates give a green fluorescence with concentrated sulfuric acid. The ultraviolet absorption spectra of bile acids treated with sulfuric acid are a valuable aid in their identification. In the Pettenkofer reaction a solution of sucrose or furfural is added to the test solution. On addition of concentrated sulfuric acid and warming a red color appears which changes to bluish red in several days. The Pettenkofer reaction and the Liebermann-Burchard reaction (Chap. I, p. 16) form the basis of some of the quantitative methods for the determination of bile acids.

VII

Progesterone

1. Synthesis

FIGURE 7.1 SHOWS THE structural formulae of two C_{21} hydrocarbons, pregnane and allopregnane, as well as the formula of progesterone. Pregnane is the C_{21} analog of coprostane (A/B *cis*), and allopregnane is the C_{21} analog of cholestane (A/B *trans*). The systematic names of C_{21} steroids are derived from these two parent hydrocarbons. Thus, progesterone is Δ^4-pregnene-3,20-dione. The Δ^4-3-keto group is a characteristic feature of the majority of steroid hormones. Progesterone, the progestational hormone, occupies a key position in the biosynthesis as well as in the industrial preparation of steroid hormones.

Among the most important industrial starting materials for the partial synthesis of progesterone and the adrenocortical hormones are the sapogenins diosgenin and hecogenin (cf. Chap. IV, p. 50). The process is outlined in Figure 7.2. Treatment with acetic an-

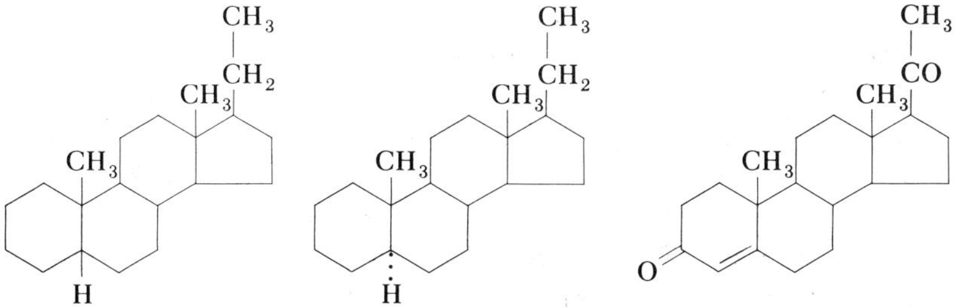

| Pregnane | Allopregnane | Progesterone |

FIGURE 7.1. C_{21} STEROIDS.

93

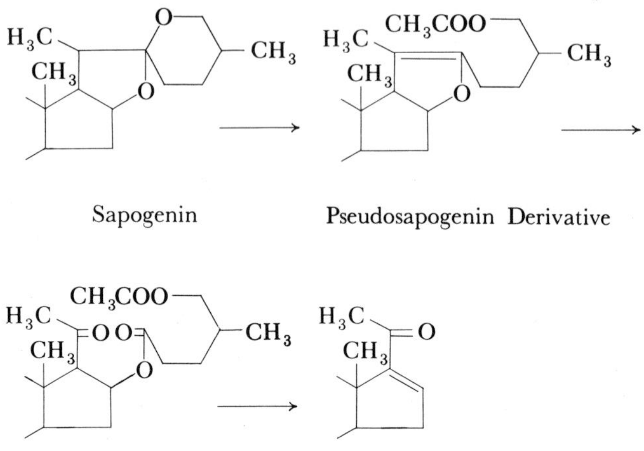

Sapogenin   Pseudosapogenin Derivative

Pregnane Derivative

FIGURE 7.2. SYNTHESIS FROM SAPOGENINS.

hydride converts the sapogenin to the diacetate of the so-called pseudosapogenin, which is oxidized to a diketone by chromic acid. Hydrolysis of this intermediate gives the corresponding pregnane derivative, which is readily converted to progesterone or other C_{21} steroids. A similar process has been applied to the nitrogen analogs of sapogenins, tomatidine and solasodine (cf. Chap. IV, p. 54), but has not been employed industrially as yet. Other economical routes for the synthesis of progesterone start from the Δ^{22}-sterols ergosterol and stigmasterol (cf. Chap. II, ‚p. 28). This process is illustrated for ergosterol in Figure 7.3. After conversion of the 3β-hydroxy-5,7-diene to the Δ^4-3-ketone by appropriate oxidation and reduction, the side chain is cleaved at the 22,23-double bond by ozonization. This treatment leads to the C_{22} acid. The name bisnorcholanic acid indicates that it contains two carbon atoms less (bisnor) than cholanic acid. The C-22 carbon is subsequently removed to give the 20-ketone, progesterone. The preparation of C_{21} steroids from C_{24} bile acids (cf. Chap. VI, p. 82) involves the removal of 3 carbon atoms from the side chain by the Miescher degradation.

In the animal body progesterone is synthesized by degradation of cholesterol. This was first demonstrated by Bloch and coworkers, who fed deuterated cholesterol to a pregnant woman and isolated labeled pregnanediol, the chief metabolite of progesterone (cf. Sec. 2, p. 98), from her urine. More direct evidence has been obtained by *in vitro* studies. When human placenta was perfused with radioactive cholesterol, radioactive progesterone was recovered from the perfusate. It was also shown that "pregnenolone"

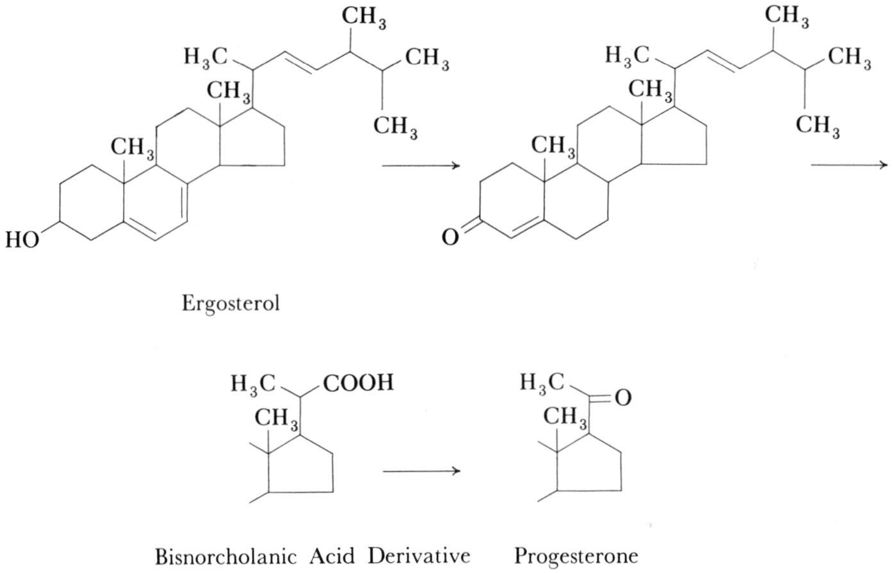

Ergosterol

Bisnorcholanic Acid Derivative   Progesterone

FIGURE 7.3. SYNTHESIS FROM ERGOSTEROL.

(Δ^5-pregnen-3β-ol-20-one, cf. Figure 7.4) is an intermediate in the reaction. Incubation of this steroid with placental, testis, corpus luteum, and adrenal tissue yields progesterone, in addition to other products. These tissues contain enzyme systems which convert Δ^5-3β-hydroxysteroids to Δ^4-3-ketosteroids. An enzyme called 3β-hydroxy dehydrogenase is specific for Δ^5 or A/B-*trans* 3β-hydroxy-steroids, requires DPN, and does not appear to promote the reverse reaction. The enzyme system which cleaves isocaproic acid from the cholesterol side chain (Figure 7.4) has not been adequately purified. It occurs in adrenals, testes, and ovaries and appears to require ATP and DPN. It is quite likely that the cleav-

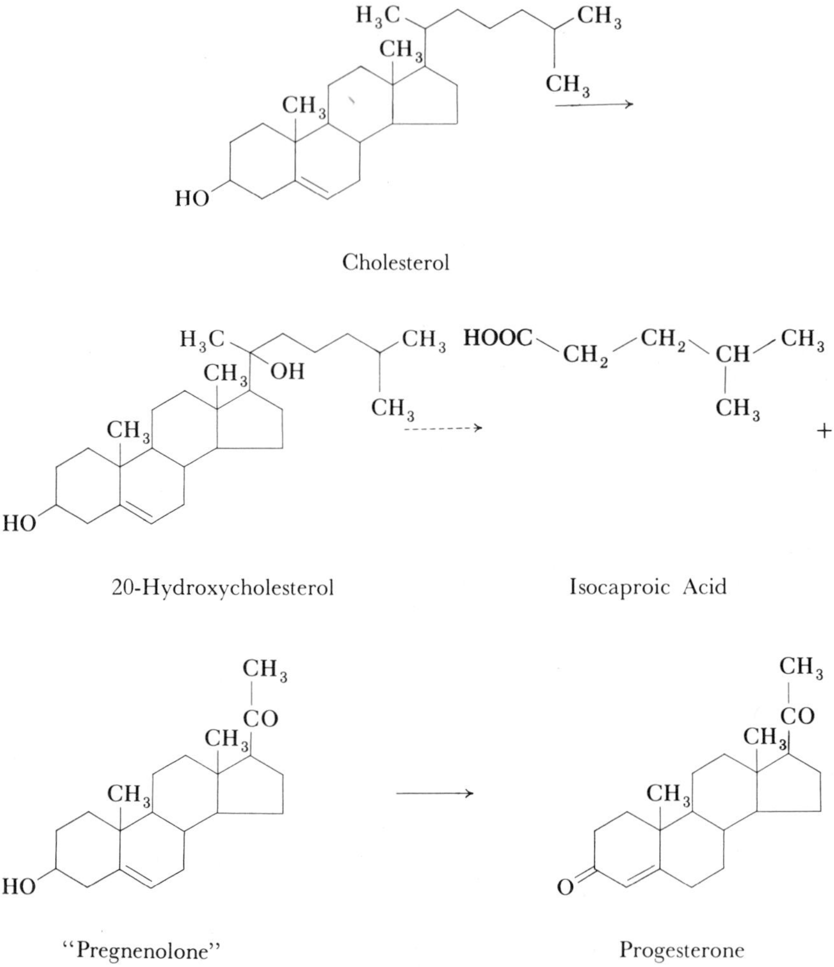

Cholesterol

20-Hydroxycholesterol   Isocaproic Acid

"Pregnenolone"   Progesterone

FIGURE 7.4. BIOGENESIS OF PROGESTERONE.

age involves 20-hydroxylation of cholesterol. 20-Hydroxycholes-
terol has been tentatively identified as an intermediate in this
conversion on the basis of experiments in which radioactive cholesterol was incubated with homogenates of beef adrenals. Progesterone has been isolated from corpus luteum, placenta, and adrenal
tissue, but not from testes. However, the progesterone precursor
pregnenolone has been found in hog testes, and bulls excrete large
amounts of the progesterone metabolite pregnanediol while steers

do not. It is quite likely that testes also synthesize progesterone, although they do not store the hormone.

2. Metabolism

Administered progesterone is converted in the animal body,
mainly by the liver, but perhaps also in the kidneys, to various
metabolites which can be recovered from the excreta. While the
feces are the chief excretory route in rats, the urinary excretion
is believed to predominate in the human organism. After the administration of radioactive progesterone during increased production of progesterone in the body, in the luteal phase or during
pregnancy, 20-40 per cent of the administered radioactivity may be
recovered from the urine of women. From the bile of a woman with
a bile fistula 40 per cent of the administered radioactivity has
been recovered.

Figure 7.5 outlines the metabolism of progesterone in human
subjects. Reduction of the 20-keto group of progesterone by
placental tissue yields both Δ^4-pregnen-20α-ol-3-one (OH on the
right in the projection formula) and Δ^4-pregnen-20β-ol-3-one
(OH on the left). With the exception of these two compounds and
progesterone all steroids shown in Figure 7.5 have been isolated
from human pregnancy urine. The reduction of the 4,5-double
bond is mediated by one of two enzyme systems. In one case
pregnane-3-20-dione is formed, in the other allopregnane-3,20-
dione. In the human organism, reduction to pregnane derivatives predominates. Also, the 3-keto group is preferentially reduced to a 3α-hydroxyl group. The most abundant metabolite
of progesterone in human pregnancy urine is pregnane-3α,20α-
diol, usually referred to as pregnanediol. In the course of
pregnancy the proportion of "pregnanolone" (pregnan-3α-ol-20-
one) in the urine increases. These two compounds and "allo-
pregnanediol" (allopregnane-3α,20α-diol) make up the bulk of
the steroid mixture which is usually determined as urinary pregnanediol. They are the only metabolites whose origin from progesterone has been definitely established, but there is little doubt
that the other steroids shown in Figure 7.5 have a similar origin.
The metabolites with a 3α-hydroxyl group are largely excreted

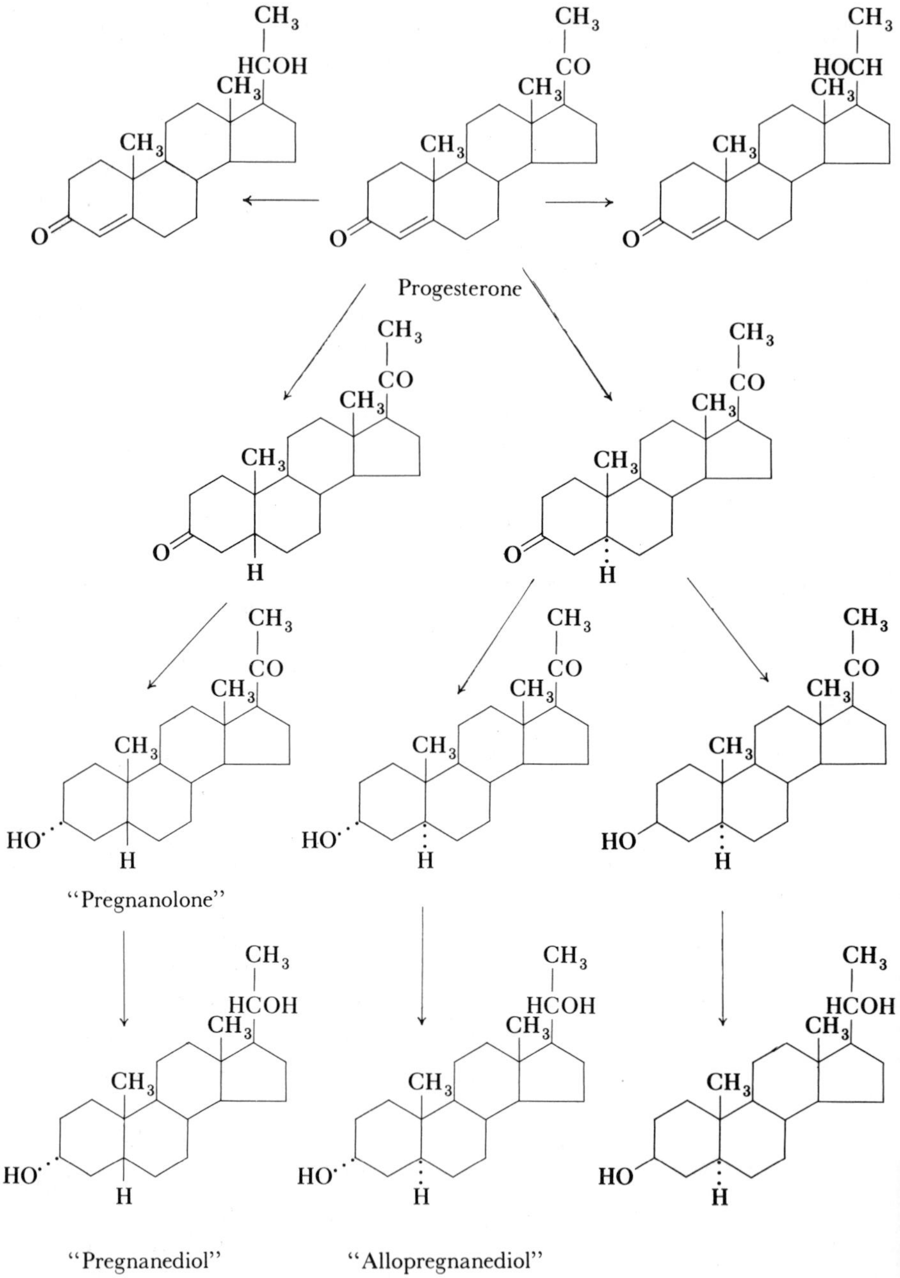

FIGURE 7.5. METABOLISM OF PROGESTERONE.

in the form of the glucosiduronates (glucuronides). Conjugation occurs in the liver. The structural formula of pregnanediol sodium glucosiduronate is shown in Figure 7.6. Man and dog are the only species known to excrete pregnanediol as the glucosiduronate, although various species including the chimpanzee are known to excrete pregnanediol. The rhesus monkey, a species which is used in various pharmacological tests because it is considered to be closely related to the human species, does not excrete pregnanediol, even after the administration of progesterone.

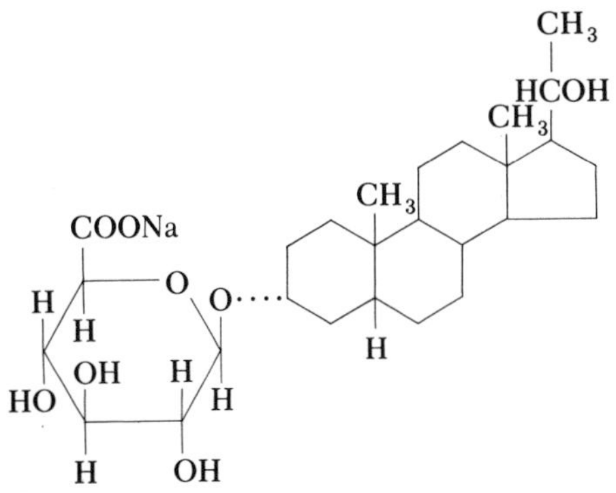

FIGURE 7.6. PREGNANEDIOL SODIUM GLUCOSIDURONATE.

Adrenal tissue contains hydroxylating enzymes capable of introducing OH groups into progesterone in specific positions and orientations. Experiments with purified tissue fractions, incubated with either H_2O^{18} or O_2^{18} have shown that the steroid does not undergo dehydrogenation and subsequently hydration, but that it is directly oxidized to the hydroxylated derivative. Only molecular oxygen and TPNH are required for the enzymatic hydroxylation. A number of hydroxylation reactions have been demonstrated by perfusion of surviving beef adrenals or by incubation of adrenal tissue preparations with progesterone. Some of these are shown in Figure 7.7. The 11β-hydroxylase was found to occur in adrenal mitochondria, while the 17α- and 21-hydroxylases are concentrated in the microsome fraction. Hydroxylation at C-21 produces desoxycorticosterone. Combinations of hydroxylation reactions give rise to other adrenocortical hormones (Chap. VIII, p. 112).

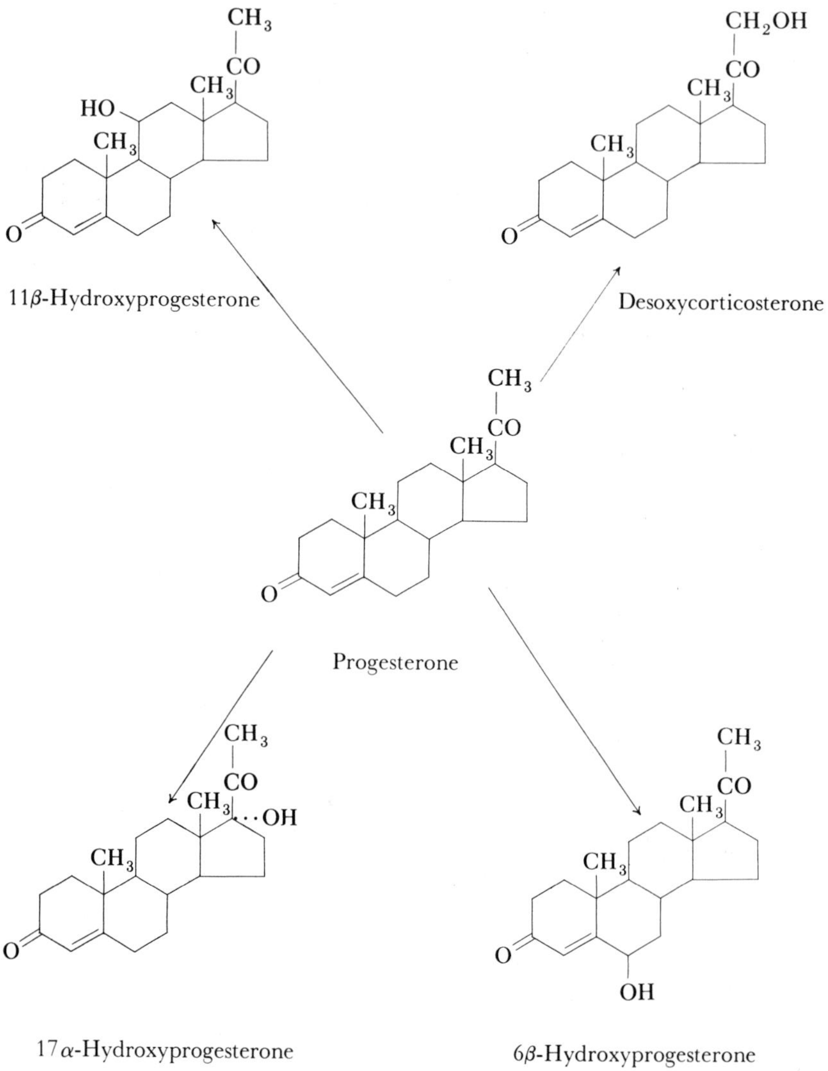

FIGURE 7.7. ADRENAL HYDROXYLATION OF PROGESTERONE.

Microorganisms, particularly the filamentous fungi, but also bacteria and protozoa, are very adept in modifying steroids. Compared to the enzymes in mammalian tissues, microbial enzymes are more vigorous and more versatile in their action on steroids. By growing the organisms on steroid-containing media, they may be induced to perform—on substrates that they have not previously encountered—reactions which have been difficult or impossible to accomplish in the laboratory. A notable example is the introduction of an oxygen function into the steroid nucleus at C-11. In 1952 Peterson and Murray reported that *Rhizopus nigricans* converts progesterone to 11α-hydroxyprogesterone in high yields. This discovery not only solved the problem of synthesizing 11-oxygenated adrenocortical hormones from a plentiful starting material, but also initiated an extensive investigation of microbiological transformations of steroids. Many microorganisms, including a bacillus (*Bacillus cereus*), are now known to be capable of hydroxylating steroids in the 11α-position. The 11β-hydroxylation is carried out by *Curvularia lunata*, 21-hydroxylation by *Ophiobolus herpotrichus*, and 6β-hydroxylation by various species of *Mucor, Helicostylum, Penicillium, Cephalothecium,* and *Streptomyces.* In fact, all hydroxylation reactions observed in mammalian tissues, except 6α- and 18-hydroxylation, have been demonstrated in some microorganism. Moreover, microorganisms can carry out hydroxylations and other reactions which have not yet been observed in mammalian tissues. While the introduction of a 17-hydroxyl group is apparently inhibited by the presence of a 21-hydroxyl group in the case of tissue enzymes, a fungus such as *Cephalothecium roseum* can hydroxylate desoxycorticosterone to 17α, 21-dihydroxyprogesterone (desoxycortisol). Another strain of this organism has been found to convert progesterone to 11α,17α-dihydroxyprogesterone, and in many instances two reactions are carried out simultaneously on the substrate. Thus, *Curvularia lunata,* mentioned above, actually produces a variety of steroids including 11β,21-dihydroxyprogesterone (corticosterone) from progesterone. Generally, fungi which hydroxylate in the 11β-position also hydroxylate in 14α, whereas 11α-hydroxylating fungi do not. It is also interesting that certain fungi introduce a 6β-hydroxyl group into Δ⁴-3-ketosteroids, but a 7β-hydroxyl group into 3β-hydroxysteroids. Other microbiological transformations will be discussed in subsequent chapters.

3. Endocrinology

Judging from the low urinary excretion of pregnanediol (about 1 mg or less per day), children, men, and women—either after menopause or in the follicular phase of their menstrual cycle—do not produce much progesterone. Under the influence of the pituitary gonadotropins the corpus luteum produces progesterone during the secretory phase. The pregnanediol excretion then gradually rises to a level of about 5 mg per day. Progesterone is required for the maintenance of pregnancy. It prepares the uterus for the implantation of the fertilized ovum by inducing specific changes in the uterine mucosa. If conception does not occur, the corpus luteum and the progesterone-induced changes regress, and part of the endometrium is sloughed off (menstruation). If conception has occurred, the corpus luteum persists and continues to produce progesterone.

A functioning corpus luteum is not required after the first trimester of pregnancy, since the placenta contributes the major share of the progesterone by this time. The pregnanediol excretion rapidly rises during the second trimester, and before delivery 60-100 mg of pregnanediol may be excreted per day. The urinary progesterone excretion is too low to be estimated, but with recent technical improvements progesterone has been measured in blood and shown to reach a level of 10 γ per 100 ml during the second half of the gestation period. Pregnanediol determinations have no particular value as a pregnancy test, since the excretion is rather low and variable in the early stages of pregnancy. Some use has been made of pregnanediol determinations in cases of threatened abortion, but unless the urinary levels are followed by serial determinations the drop in pregnanediol excretion before miscarriage may be missed. The urinary pregnanediol level is usually low in preeclamptic toxemia, but not necessarily in diabetic pregnancy. The elevated "pregnanediol" excretion seen in adrenal hyperfunction is probably not due to pregnanediol, but to pregnane-3α, 17α, 20α-triol (cf. Chap. VIII, p. 127). However, the rise in "pregnanediol" observed after the administration of adrenocorticotropic hormone may be used as a test of adrenocortical function.

The effects of progesterone on the genital tract are intimately related to those of the estrogens. In some respects these hormones act synergistically, in others antagonistically. In the absence of estrogens large doses of progesterone are required to produce an effect on the rabbit endometrium. After it is "primed" with a small dose of estrogens—large doses may inhibit the action of progesterone—the endometrium undergoes secretory changes, becomes more vascularized, and glycogen is deposited in the epithelial cells. Together with other hormones progesterone stimulates mammary development. Progesterone produces vaginal mucification, increases the basal temperature and, in large doses, it has a sedative effect. Progesterone administration may inhibit ovulation in women and produce azoospermia in men by inhibiting the production of pituitary gonadotropins. The effect of progesterone on smooth muscles has been studied in various animals. In the rabbit progesterone diminishes the frequency and amplitude of contractions of the myometrium. If estrogens are given first, progesterone counteracts their effect, but if they are given afterward or simultaneously, they may potentiate the progesterone effect. Progesterone also decreases the motility of the fallopian tubes. At certain dose levels it acts as an estrogen antagonist in inhibiting the estrogen-induced growth of the chick oviduct.

Little is known concerning the mechanism of action of progesterone. It appears to increase the sodium content and decrease the potassium content of the myometrial cell. The decreased sodium and potassium gradient may be responsible for the decreased responsiveness of the progesterone-dominated myometrium to oxytocin. Progesterone has also been found to increase the carbonic anhydrase activity of the rabbit endometrium. Since Δ^4-3-keto steroids, including progesterone, are reduced by enzymes requiring TPNH, it has also been suggested that progesterone and other Δ^4-3-ketosteroids act by stimulating enzymatic reactions requiring TPN. The latter is a cofactor in the dehydrogenation of various substrates, but reduction of Δ^4-3-ketosteroids is not reversible. Moreover, there is no correlation between their endocrinological effect and their ability to stimulate dehydrogenation reactions requiring TPN.

4. Analysis

Progesterone was isolated from corpora lutea by solvent extraction, followed by solvent partition and adsorption chromatography. In the isolation from placenta the tissue was subjected to a preliminary alkali digestion, which does not appreciably attack progesterone. Ketone reagents are quite useful for further purification. In the separation of progesterone from other steroids by alumina chromatography the bis-2,4-dinitrophenylhydrazone has been employed. Girard's reagent, a quaternary ammonium salt, gives water-soluble hydrazones with ketosteroids (Figure 7.8). The derivatives can be used for the solvent separation of ketonic from nonketonic steroids, for the separation of ketosteroids by paper chromatography, and for the quantitative estimation of ketosteroids by polarography. Thiosemicarbazones of Δ^4-3-ketosteroids have a high extinction around 300 mμ and can be determined in the presence of saturated 3-ketosteroids, which have a low extinction at this wavelength. The ultraviolet absorption of α,β-unsaturated 3-ketones near 240 mμ is extensively used in structural determination, in quantitative assays, and in their detection in paper chromatograms. The reddish yellow fluorescence produced by heating alkali-treated paper chromatograms is a specific test for Δ^4-3-ketosteroids.

$$H_3C-\overset{\overset{\displaystyle CH_3}{|}}{\underset{\underset{\displaystyle CH_3}{|}}{N^+}}\!-CH_2CONHNH_2 + O{=}C\diagup^{\diagdown} \rightarrow H_3C-\overset{\overset{\displaystyle CH_3}{|}}{\underset{\underset{\displaystyle CH_3}{|}}{N^+}}\!-CH_2CONHN{=}C\diagup^{\diagdown}$$

Girard's Reagent T   Hydrazone

FIGURE 7.8. GIRARD'S DERIVATIVE.

While chemical methods will ultimately replace biological methods in the quantitative analysis of progesterone, at the present bioassays must be used for the minute amounts present in natural sources. Originally, Corner and Allen used ovariectomized pregnant rabbits as test animals, but infantile rabbits pretreated with estrogens are now preferred. In the Clauberg test the latter are subcutaneously injected with the test dose and later the uterine endometrium is examined for secretory changes. The Hooker-Forbes assay is more sensitive—as little as 0.0002 γ of progesterone can be detected—but less specific. After intrauterine injection of ovariectomized mice, the nuclei of the stromal cells in their endometrium undergo typical histological changes. More recently, the measurement of carbonic anhydrase activity in the rabbit endometrium has been proposed as a method for assaying progestational compounds.

For the determination of pregnanediol the urine may be extracted with butanol, which is then washed with alkali and evaporated. The residue is dissolved in a small amount of water, and the pregnanediol glucosiduronate precipitated with acetone. After recrystallization, the glucosiduronate may be determined gravimetrically. Alternatively, it may be hydrolyzed and either the pregnanediol or the glucuronic acid is determined colorimetrically, the latter with naphthoresorcinol. Free pregnanediol may be extracted from the urine with toluene after hydrolysis by acid or by the enzyme β-glucuronidase. The toluene extract is washed and evaporated, the residue dissolved in ethanol, and pregnanediol precipitated by the addition of sodium hydroxide. In every case the so-called pregnanediol represents a mixture of steroids. For the specific determination of pregnanediol it is necessary to oxidize contaminants with permanganate, chromatograph on alumina, acetylate a certain fraction, and to rechromatograph it. The specificity of the final colorimetric determination with concentrated sulfuric acid depends on the thoroughness of the isolation procedure. Another colorimetric method is based on the purple color produced on addition of an ethanolic potassium hydroxide solution to the 3,5-dinitrobenzoate of pregnanediol.

5. Analogs

Progesterone is used clinically in many ovarian and menstrual disorders. It has been recommended for the treatment of certain amenorrheas and functional uterine bleeding, and progesterone with or without estrogens is often routinely given in the prophylactic management of habitual and threatened abortion. Unfortunately, this hormone is relatively ineffective when given by mouth and the parenteral administration of aqueous or oil suspensions frequently produces painful local reactions. This difficulty is only partially circumvented by the use of sublingual preparations or vaginal suppositories, because they are less effective than parenteral injections.

Intensive research activity in the field of progesterone analogs has yielded not only a number of steroids with very promising biological properties, but also some interesting leads concerning the relationship between structure and hormonal activity. Reduction of the 4,5-double bond of progesterone abolishes its hormonal activity, but the progesterone metabolite pregnane-3,20-dione has pronounced anaesthetic properties. Reduction of the 20-keto group of progesterone to a 20α-hydroxyl group greatly diminishes the hormonal activity. The epimeric Δ^4-pregnen-20β-ol-3-one (Figure 7.5) is twice as active as progesterone in the Hooker-Forbes assay, although it has only one-tenth to one-fifth of the progesterone activity in the Clauberg test. Pregnanediol has no progestational effect, but it antagonizes progesterone in the decidual reaction in rats. The progesterone precursor pregnenolone (Figure 7.4) is also devoid of progestational activity, but more potent than progesterone in its antiestrogenic effect.

21-Hydroxyprogesterone, the adrenocortical hormone desoxycorticosterone (Figure 7.7), has about one-tenth of the activity of progesterone in the Clauberg test. While 11β-hydroxyprogesterone has almost no progestational activity, it inhibits the uterotropic action of estrogens, although less effectively than progesterone. 11-Dehydroprogesterone (Figure 7.9), on the other hand, has a progestational activity superior to that of progesterone in all tests. 17α-Hydroxyprogesterone was found to be 60 times more active than progesterone in the Hooker-Forbes assay, but inactive in the Clauberg test and ineffective in women. However, the 17-*n*-caproate, Delalutin (Figure 7.9), is an effective progestational hormone. This is the first instance in which a relatively inactive compound was shown to be converted to an active hormone by esterification. 17α-Hydroxyprogesterone caproate in sesame oil is used in the clinic as a parenteral preparation when a prolonged progestational effect is desired. The 17α-acetoxyprogesterone (Figure 7.9) also has some clinical value. It is much more effective than progesterone when given by mouth.

The first orally effective progesterone analog discovered was 17α-ethynyl testosterone (ethisterone, 17-isopregneninolone) (Fig-

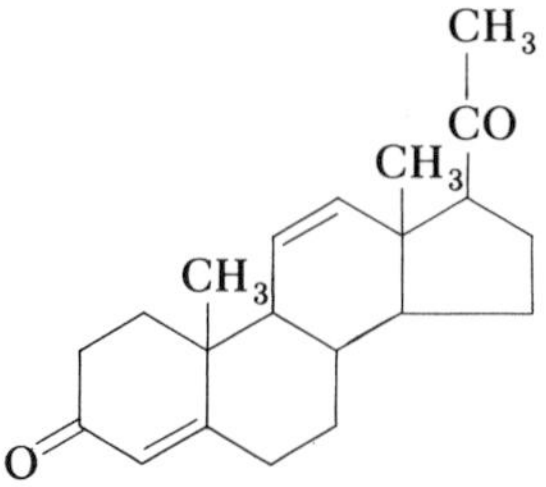

11-Dehydroprogesterone

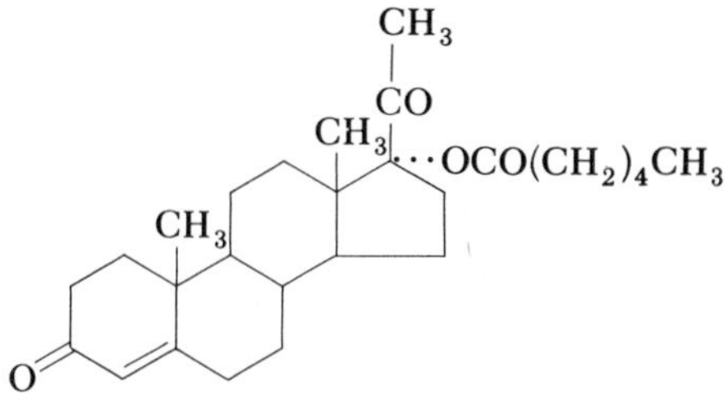

Delalutin

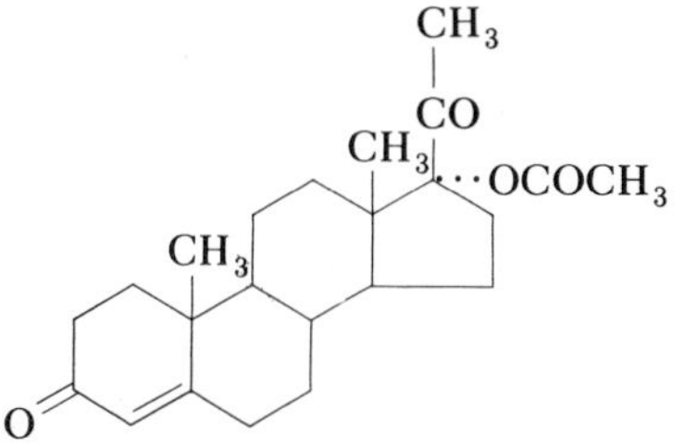

17α-Acetoxyprogesterone

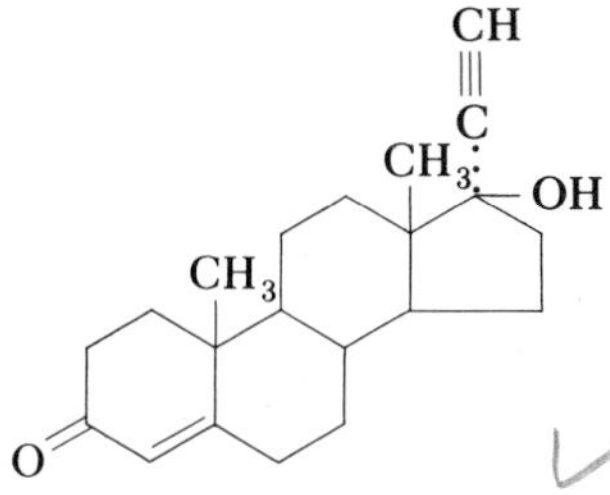

Ethisterone

FIGURE 7.9. PROGESTERONE ANALOGS I.

ure 7.9). The substance is structurally related to both progesterone and testosterone (Chap. IX, p. 138), and indeed shows some androgenic activity. Given by mouth it is about 15 times as active as an oral dose of progesterone, although when compared in subcutaneous administration it has only about one-third of the activity of progesterone in women and rabbits. Although parenterally administered progesterone has the same effect on monkeys as on women, ethisterone is inactive by mouth in the monkey.

Removal of a methyl group from steroid molecules may have a dramatic effect on their biological activity. The position from which the methyl group has been eliminated is indicated with the prefix nor. 21-Norprogesterone (Figure 7.10) is much less active than progesterone, but shows some androgenic activity. 19-Norprogesterone (Figure 7.10) has a higher activity than progesterone in the rabbit test, and the 19-norethisterone (17α-ethynyl-19-nortestosterone), which is used clinically under the name Norlutin

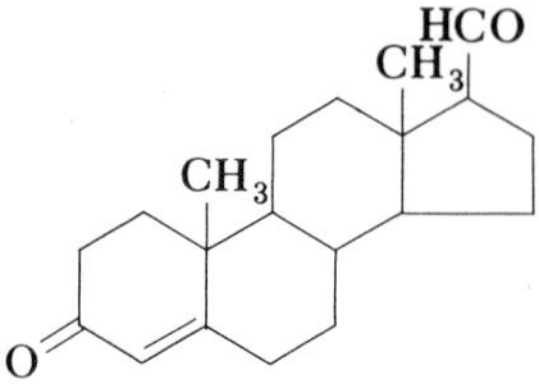

21-Norprogesterone

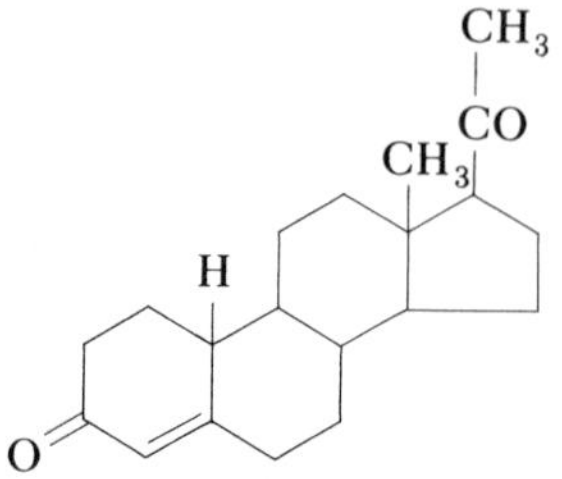

19-Norprogesterone

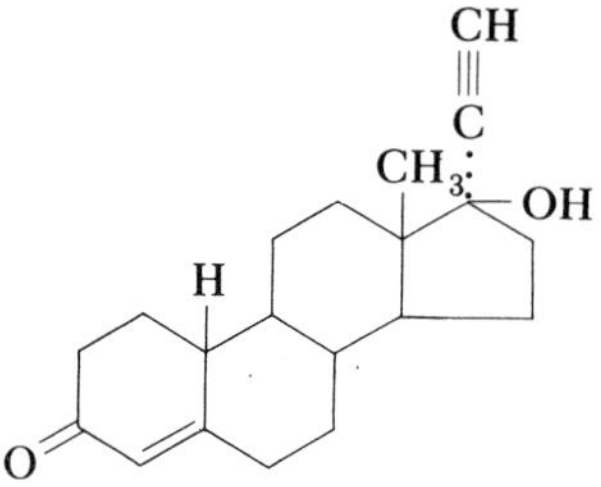

Norlutin

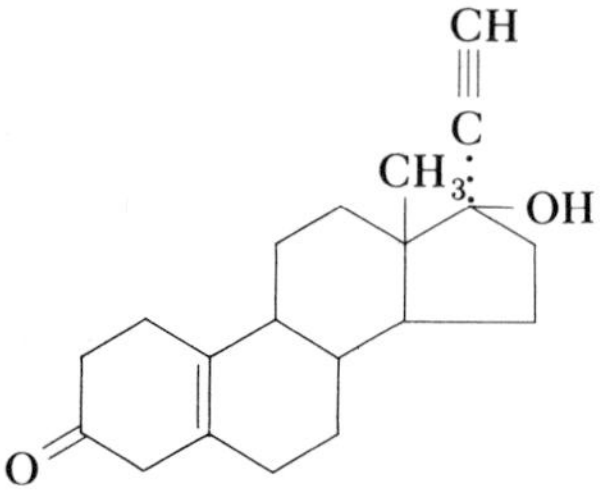

Norethynodrel

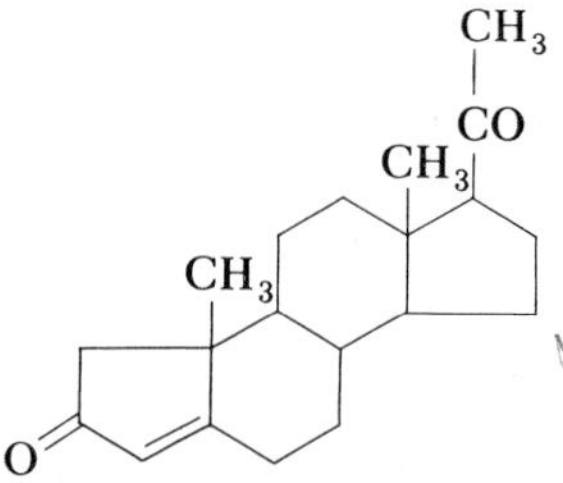

A-Norprogesterone

FIGURE 7.10. PROGESTERONE ANALOGS II.

(Figure 7.10), is more active than ethisterone in the rabbit. Nor-lutin is a potent orally effective progestational hormone, which also inhibits ovulation. 17α-Ethynyl-Δ⁵⁽¹⁰⁾-estrenolone (norethyno-drel) (Figure 7.10) is similar to Norlutin in its effects, but some-what less active progestationally. Norlutin produces temporary sterility in male and female rats. 17α-Methyl-19-nortestosterone is also progestationally active, but has more resemblance to testosterone in its androgenic and anabolic effects. The 17α-ethyl and 17α-vinyl analogs of 19-nortestosterone have about the same oral and parenteral progestational effect as 17α-ethynyl-19-nortesto-

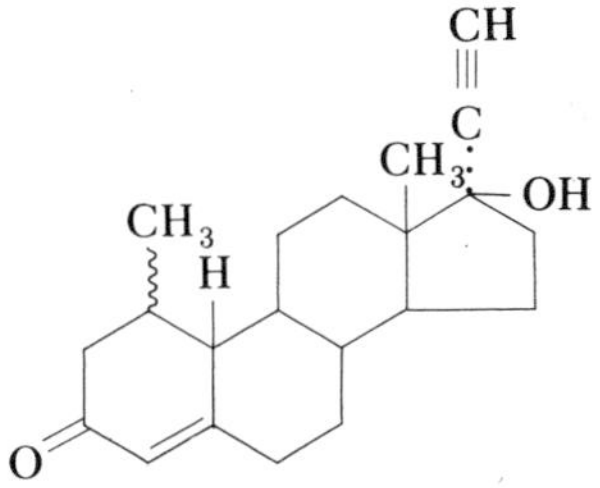

1-Methylnorlutin

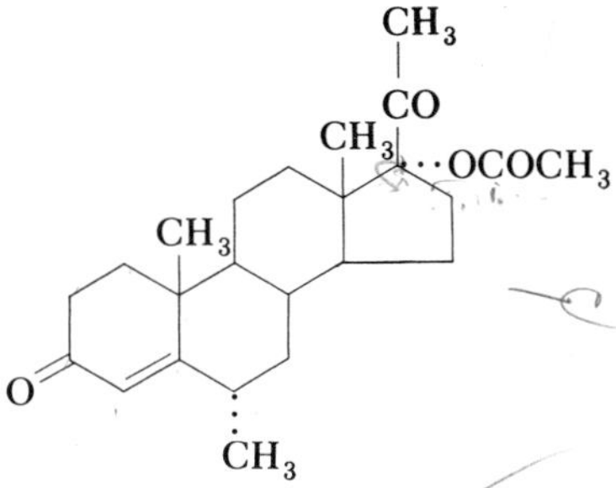

Provera

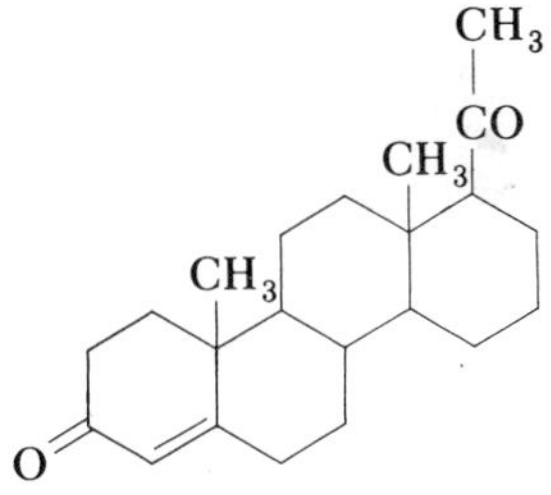

D-Homoprogesterone

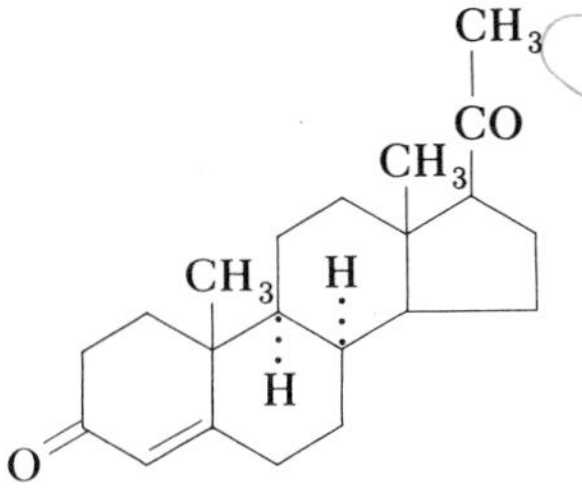

8-Isoprogesterone

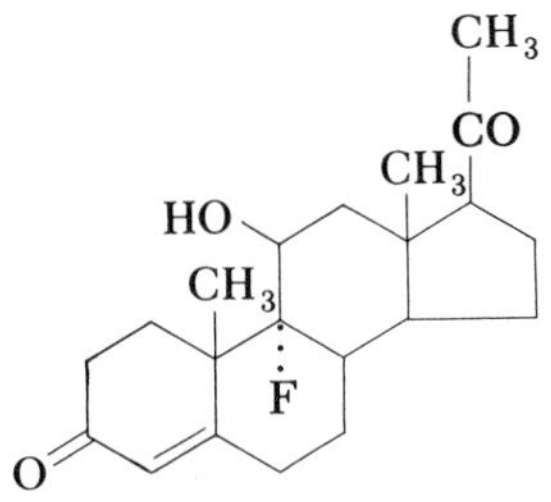

9α-Fluoro-11β-hydroxyprogesterone

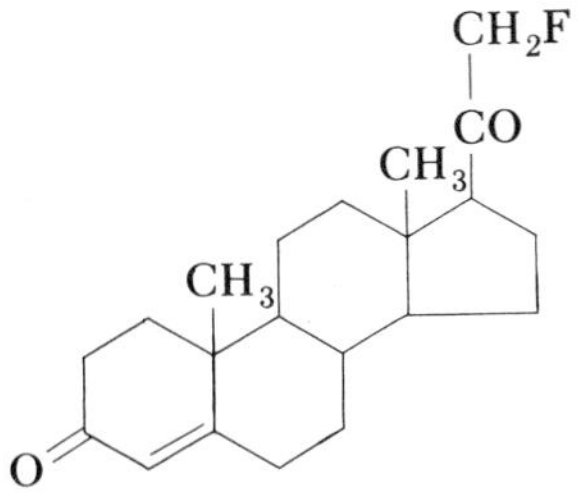

21-Fluoroprogesterone

FIGURE 7.11. PROGESTERONE ANALOGS III.

sterone. Contraction of ring A in progesterone produces A-nor-progesterone (Figure 7.10). This analog has no progestational effect, but antagonizes the effect of androgens in rats and chicks.

The addition of methyl groups to the steroid molecule may also have very drastic effects on their biological activity. The 1 ξ-methylnorlutin (Figure 7.11) is as active progestationally as Norlutin, and 6α-methyl-17α-acetoxyprogesterone (Provera) (Figure 7.11) is said to be the most potent oral progestin synthesized to date. Because of their powerful inhibitory effect on ovulation, steroids of this type are potentially valuable as orally effective contraceptives.

Other modifications of the progesterone structure have also yielded active hormones. Enlargement of the D ring of steroids leads to the so-called D-homosteroids. D-Homoprogesterone (Figure 7.11) was found to inhibit ovulation. The progesterone analog with B/C *cis*-junction, 8-isoprogesterone (Figure 7.11), is almost as active as progesterone. The introduction of halogens in the 9α-position potentiates the activity of adrenocortical hormones (cf. Chap. VIII, p. 132). A similar effect on progesterone analogs has been observed. While 11β-hydroxyprogesterone has only 1 per cent of the progestational effect of progesterone, its 9α-fluoro analog (Figure 7.11) has 10 per cent of the activity of progesterone. Cortisol (cf. Chap. VIII, p. 111), which is progestationally inactive, acquires an activity of about 5 per cent of progesterone by the conversion to 9α-fluorocortisol (Chap. VIII, p. 132). Both compounds are powerful inhibitors of estrogen-induced uterine growth. 21-Fluoroprogesterone (Figure 7.11) is more active than progesterone by the oral route and has an even greater antiestrogenic effect than the 9α-fluorocortisol. The progestational activity of amphenone and other nonsteroidal agents is due to their blocking effect on the adrenal hydroxylation reactions leading to the adrenocortical hormones and will be discussed in Chap. VIII, p. 114.

VIII

Corticosteroids

1. Biosynthesis

NO LESS THAN 46 steroids have been isolated from the adrenal cortex so far, chiefly by research groups led by Reichstein, Kendall, Wintersteiner, and more recently, by Wettstein. Most of these steroids probably represent precursors or catabolites of the adrenocortical hormones and have not been found in adrenal vein blood. In this chapter only the biologically active corticosteroids and their derivatives will be considered. The adrenocortical hormones are: 11-desoxycorticosterone, corticosterone, 11-dehydrocorticosterone, aldosterone, 11-desoxycortisol, cortisol, and cortisone. Their structures (cf. Figure 8.1) have two features in common: the Δ^4-3-keto group and the 20,21-ketol group. They differ from each other by the presence or absence of a 17α-hydroxyl group and by the presence or absence of an oxygen function at C-11 (11β-hydroxyl or 11-keto group). In aldosterone a —CHO group replaces the 18-methyl group. Trivial names are extensively used in the corticosteroid field. The names are derived from either corticosterone or cortexone (11-desoxycorticosterone). Some cumbersome names have been shortened, e.g. 11-dehydro-17-hydroxycorticosterone to cortisone and 11-desoxycorticosterone to DOC. In some cases the letter designations used by the original investigators have survived, e.g. Reichstein's Compound S (11-desoxycortisol, cortexolone, or 17-hydroxycortexone) and Kendall's Compounds A, B, E and F. Aldosterone was known as electrocortin prior to the recognition of its unique 18-aldehyde group. The systematic name of this compound is Δ^4-pregnen-18-al-11β,21-diol-3,20-dione.

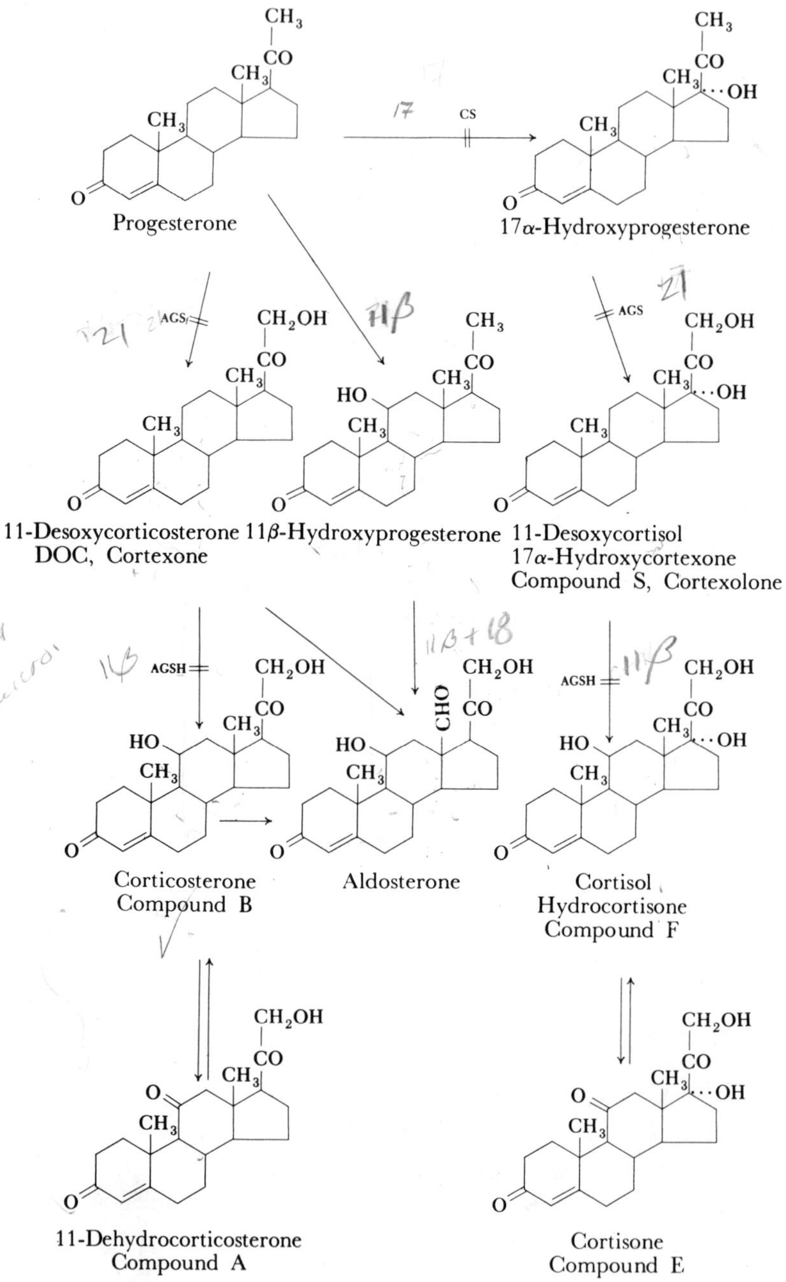

FIGURE 8.1. BIOSYNTHESIS OF CORTICOSTEROIDS.

The role of progesterone in the biogenesis of steroid hormones and the enzymatic reactions in adrenal tissues have been discussed in Chap. VII, p. 99. Figure 8.1 outlines the sequence of hydroxylation reactions in the adrenal cortex. Progesterone is hydroxylated in either the 21-, 11β-, or 17α-position to yield desoxycorticosterone, 11β-hydroxyprogesterone, and 17α-hydroxyprogesterone, respectively. Desoxycorticosterone may be further hydroxylated (oxidized) at C-11 to corticosterone or at both C-11 and C-18 to aldosterone. While the hydroxylations at C-11, C-21, and C-17 occur in the mitochondria (C-11) and microsomes of the cells in the zona reticularis and zona fasciculata of the adrenals, the enzyme system for the C-18 oxidation is localized in the outer layer of the gland, the zona glomerulosa. The conversion of corticosterone and of 11β-hydroxyprogesterone to aldosterone has been demonstrated *in vitro* by use of preparations from the zona glomerulosa. 21-Hydroxylation of 17-hydroxyprogesterone produces 11-desoxycortisol, which can be enzymatically hydroxylated at C-11 to yield cortisol. The 11β-hydroxyl group in both corticosterone and cortisol can be reversibly oxidized to a keto group, giving 11-dehydrocorticosterone and cortisone, respectively.

The true nature of the adrenocortical secretion is best evaluated by a comparison of adrenal vein blood and peripheral blood, but greater insight into the mechanism of the biosynthetic process can be gained by *in vitro* studies. However, as one proceeds from the perfusion of the whole gland to incubation with adrenal tissue slices, thence to tissue homogenates and subcellular fractions, and finally to isolated enzyme systems there is an increasing chance of obtaining results which bear but little resemblance to those obtained *in vivo*. In the perfusion of isolated beef adrenals and in incubation experiments with adrenal slices the adrenocorticotropic hormone of the anterior pituitary (ACTH) increases the conversion of labeled cholesterol into corticosteroids. However, this effect cannot be demonstrated with adrenal homogenates or cell-free preparations. It is quite possible that ACTH acts on cell membranes by expediting the entry of rate-limiting substrates or cofactors into the cells. It has also been shown that ACTH activates adrenocortical phosphorylase by increasing the AMP concentration in that tissue. In the intact animal the adrenal cholesterol concentration falls following the administration of ACTH. This fall is preceded by a drop in the adrenal ascorbic acid content, which can be accounted for by the increase in adrenal vein ascorbic acid concentration. The role of vitamin C in the biogenesis of adrenal steroids is still a matter of dispute. It is held by some that ascorbic acid inhibits steroid hydroxylation and that its disappearance signals the release of this inhibition. Another opinion is that ascorbic acid stimulates the hydroxylation of steroids by activating a DPNH oxidase in the adrenals. While no definite information on the mode of action of ACTH is available, it is certain that it exerts its effect in the events leading to the degradation of the cholesterol side chain, which yields pregnenolone (cf. Chap. VII, p. 95).

The regular sequence of enzymatic hydroxylation reactions is apparently blocked in certain endocrine diseases with the result that certain products fail to be elaborated while their precursors accumulate (cf. Sec. 3, p. 127). Blockade has also been produced by the administration of certain nonsteroidal agents. Thus, amphenone B, 3,3-bis-(*p*-aminophenyl)-2-butanone dihydrochloride (Figure 8.2), inhibits the biosynthesis of Compounds B, E, and F and produces its progestational effect by allowing some progestationally active precursors to accumulate. 2-Methyl-1,2-bis-(3-pyridyl)1-propanone, also known as SU 4885 (Figure 8.2), appears to inhibit 11β-hydroxylation specifically, causing the adrenals to

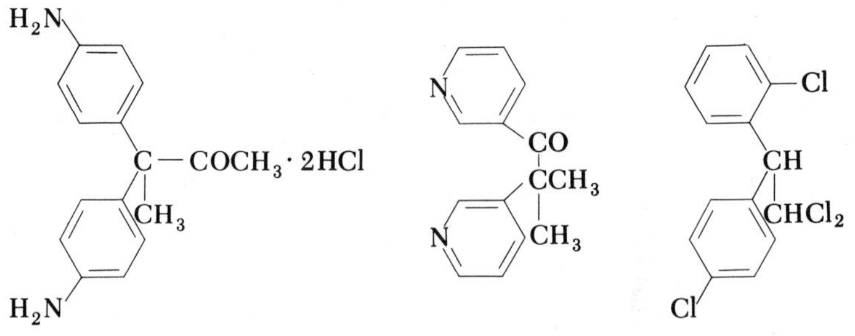

Amphenone B   SU 4885   *o,p*-DDD

FIGURE 8.2. ADRENAL INHIBITORS.

secrete 11-desoxycortisol instead of cortisol. Cortisol production returns after the administration of SU 4885 is discontinued, provided pituitary function is normal. This suggests the use of this drug in testing pituitary ACTH reserve. Insecticides of the DDT type produce a selective necrosis of the adrenal cortex in the dog. The 2 - (*o* - chlorophenyl) - 2 - (*p* - chlorophenyl) 1,1 - dichloroethane, *o,p*-DDD (Figure 8.2), is especially active in this respect and has been suggested for the treatment of adrenal carcinoma.

There is some evidence that the synthesis of corticosteroids may also proceed from acetate without going through the cholesterol pathway. In the perfusion of adrenals with C^{14}-acetate the ratio of specific activities of corticosteroids to cholesterol was found to be 6.5; whereas perfusion with C^{14}-cholesterol gave a ratio of 0.35. Furthermore, the addition of ACTH to the perfusion fluid increased the corticosteroid production from C^{14}-cholesterol 1800 per cent, but the conversion of radioactive acetate to corticosteroids was increased only 40 per cent. These and other experiments indicate the existence of a cholesterol-independent pathway of corticosteroidogenesis which is not under ACTH control. However, *in vivo* the biosynthesis from cholesterol is more important, because it is much more efficient. It has also been claimed that corticosteroids may be formed from C_{19} steroids. No evidence for placental neogenesis of corticosteroids is available at present.

The biosynthesis of corticosteroids from progesterone by microorganisms (cf. Chap. VII, p. 101) is of considerable commercial importance. Thus, 21-hydroxylation by *Ophiobolus herpotrichus* can be used for the preparation of cortexone from progesterone, of 17-hydroxycortexone from 17-hydroxyprogesterone, and of dehydrocorticosterone from 11-ketoprogesterone. The 11β-hydroxylation by *Cunninghamella blakesleeana* or *Curvularia lunata* can be used to convert cortexone to corticosterone or to convert 11-desoxycortisol to cortisol. *Cephalothecium roseum* hydroxylates corticosteroids in the 17α-position and converts corticosterone to cortisol and dehydrocorticosterone to cortisone. It simultaneously introduces an 11α-hydroxyl group into desoxycorticosterone to give 11-epicortisol. Cortisone is generally prepared by the oxidation of 11-epicortisol. In the total synthesis of aldosterone advantage was taken of the stereospecificity of microorganisms. When the synthetically

prepared racemic lactone in Figure 8.3 was incubated with *Ophiobolus herpotrichus*, only the D-form was hydroxylated at C-21.
Separation and reduction of this lactone then produced the D-aldo-
sterone hemiacetal.

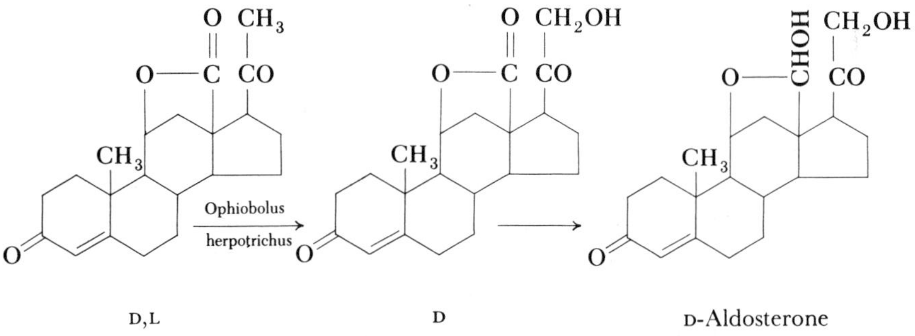

FIGURE 8.3. STEREOSPECIFIC MICROBIOLOGICAL HYDROXYLATION.

Not only the natural hormones, but also some of their phar-
macologically important analogs (Sec. 5, p. 130) have been prepared microbiologically. *Corynebacterium simplex*, *Didymella lycoper-
sici*, *Bacillus sphaericus*, and other microorganisms dehydrogenate
corticosteroids in the 1,2-position. *Didymella vodakii*, *Pestalotia
funera*, and *Streptomyces rosechromogenus* hydroxylate them in the 16α-
position. The synthesis of triamcinolone (cf. Sec. 5, p. 135) illustrates the usefulness of microorganisms in this area (Figure 8.4).

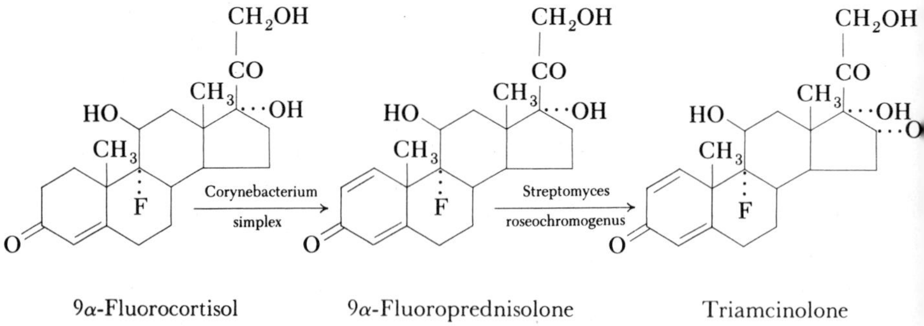

9α-Fluorocortisol   9α-Fluoroprednisolone   Triamcinolone

FIGURE 8.4. MICROBIOLOGICAL SYNTHESIS OF TRIAMCINOLONE.

9α-Fluorocortisol is dehydrogenated to 9α-fluoroprednisolone, and the subsequent 16α-hydroxylation yields triamcinolone.

2. Metabolism

The main secretory products of the adrenal gland are corticosterone and cortisol. The relative amounts of these two hormones depend on the species. In man, dog, and monkey the cortisol secretion predominates, but rats, mice, and rabbits secrete mainly corticosterone. In cattle the cortisol:corticosterone ratio is about 1. The adrenals of the bull frog produce some corticosterone, but the main hormone secreted is aldosterone. In the blood stream the corticosteroids (as well as other steroid hormones) circulate in combination with serum proteins. The blood level of corticosteroids in normal persons is below 20 γ per 100 ml, that of aldosterone below 0.1 γ per 100 ml.

The corticosteroids are metabolized, primarily in the liver, and excreted in man almost exclusively through the kidneys. Very small amounts of adrenocortical hormones are normally found in the urine. They are largely reduced and conjugated with glucuronic acid in the liver. Conjugation is effected by the enzyme glucuronosyl transferase, which couples the 3α-hydroxyl group of the metabolites with uridine diphosphate glucuronic acid to yield 3α-(β-D-glucosiduronates) (cf. Figure 7.6).

Much of our information about the metabolism of corticosteroids is derived from *in vivo* studies, in which labeled or unlabeled hormones are administered to animals or human subjects and their urine is examined for metabolites. A comparison between the results of *in vivo* and *in vitro* experiments shows certain differences. *In vivo*, the Δ^4-3-keto group of the adrenocortical hormones is largely reduced to give 3α-hydroxypregnanes; whereas *in vitro* reduction to 3β-hydroxyallopregnanes predominates. All of the ring A-reduced corticosteroids isolated from adrenal glands are allopregnanes, and almost all of them have a 3β-hydroxyl group. Some of these differences may be due to species differences, since most of the *in vitro* work has been carried out with bovine or rodent tissues, and some may also be due to technical problems in the identification of the metabolites. It is also conceivable that the kidneys hinder the excretion of allopregnanes more than that of pregnanes or that the enzymes responsible for the reduction to the 5β-series are more labile and suffer destruction in the course of the preparation of tissues for *in vitro* studies.

For the purpose of presenting a large number of metabolic studies on corticosteroids in concise form, four figures (8.5, 8.6, 8.7 and 8.8) are presented, which show the main reactions observed *in vitro* as well as *in vivo* in a variety of species. Metabolites which have been isolated from urine are shown below the horizontal line.

After the administration of desoxycorticosterone (Figure 8.5), pregnanediol has been isolated from the urine of men, but not of women. The Δ^4-3-keto group is reduced to pregnane as well as allopregnane derivatives, and the 20-keto group to 20α- as well as 20β-hydroxyl groups. One could speculate that the progestational effect of desoxycorticosterone may be due to a metabolic reduction of this hormone to progesterone.

The metabolism of corticosterone and of dehydrocorticosterone may be presented together (Figure 8.6), since the 11-keto and 11β-hydroxyl groups are interchangeable in the organism. Stepwise reduction in ring A produces, first, the 3-ketopregnane or dihydro derivatives (DHA and DHB), and then the 3α-hydroxypregnane or tetrahydro derivates (THA and THB). Further reduction in the side chain gives rise to the minor metabolites pregnane-3α,20α-diol-3-one and pregnane-3α,11β,20α-triol. Allopregnane-3α,11β, 21-triol-20-one (not shown) has also been found in the urine of persons treated with corticosterone. Since normal gonadal and placental tissues are apparently incapable of 11-hydroxylation, it may be taken for granted that 11-oxygenated urinary metabolites are of adrenal origin.

The metabolism of desoxycortisol (Figure 8.7) involves not only the now familiar reductions in ring A and in the side chain, but also cleavage of the side chain to 17-ketosteroids. The reaction is mediated by an enzyme, 17-ketodesmolase, which converts 17α-hydroxy C_{21} steroids to the 17-ketosteroids of the C_{19} series. It is an important metabolic reaction, leading from the corticosteroid series to the androgen series, to be discussed in Chap. IX, p. 140.

(Text continues on p. 124.)

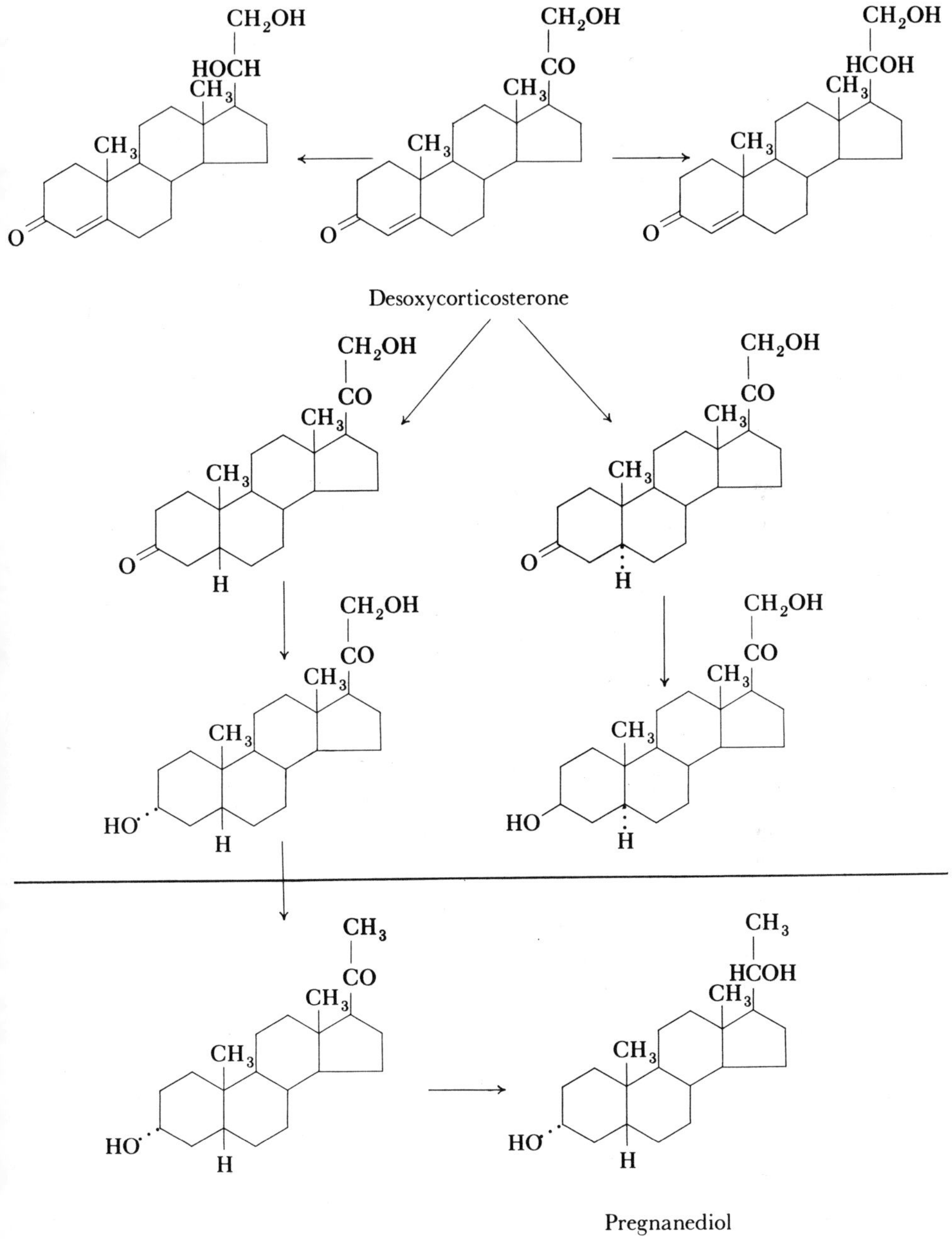

FIGURE 8.5. METABOLISM OF DESOXYCORTICOSTERONE.

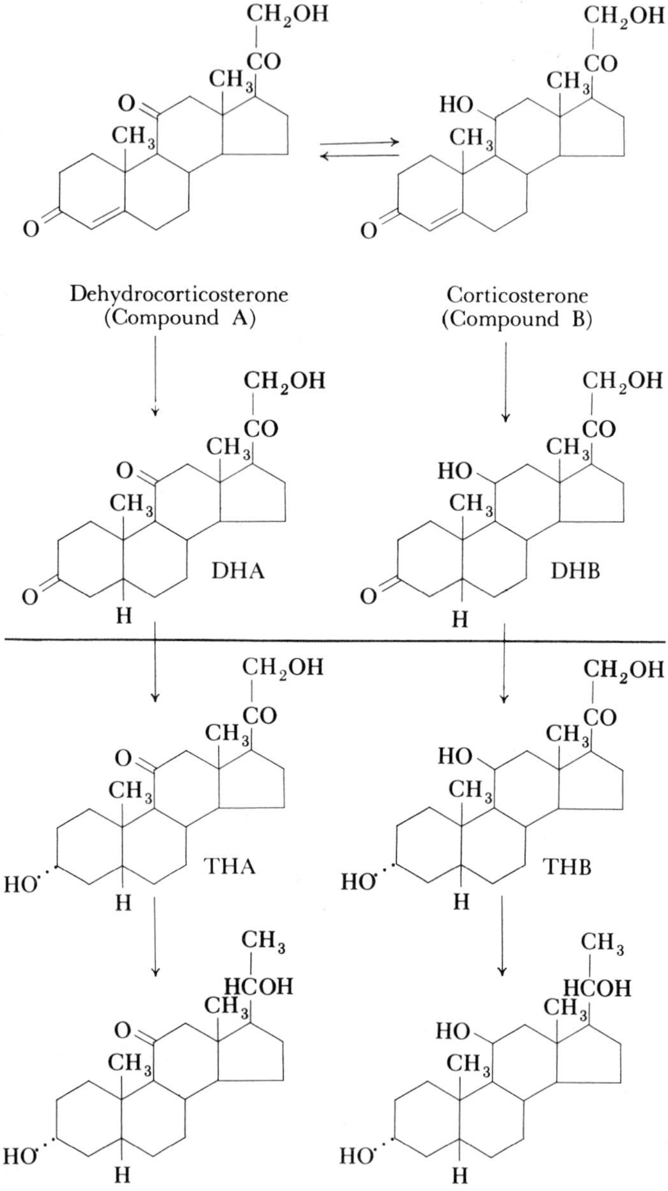

FIGURE 8.6. METABOLISM OF CORTICOSTERONE
AND DEHYDROCORTICOSTERONE.

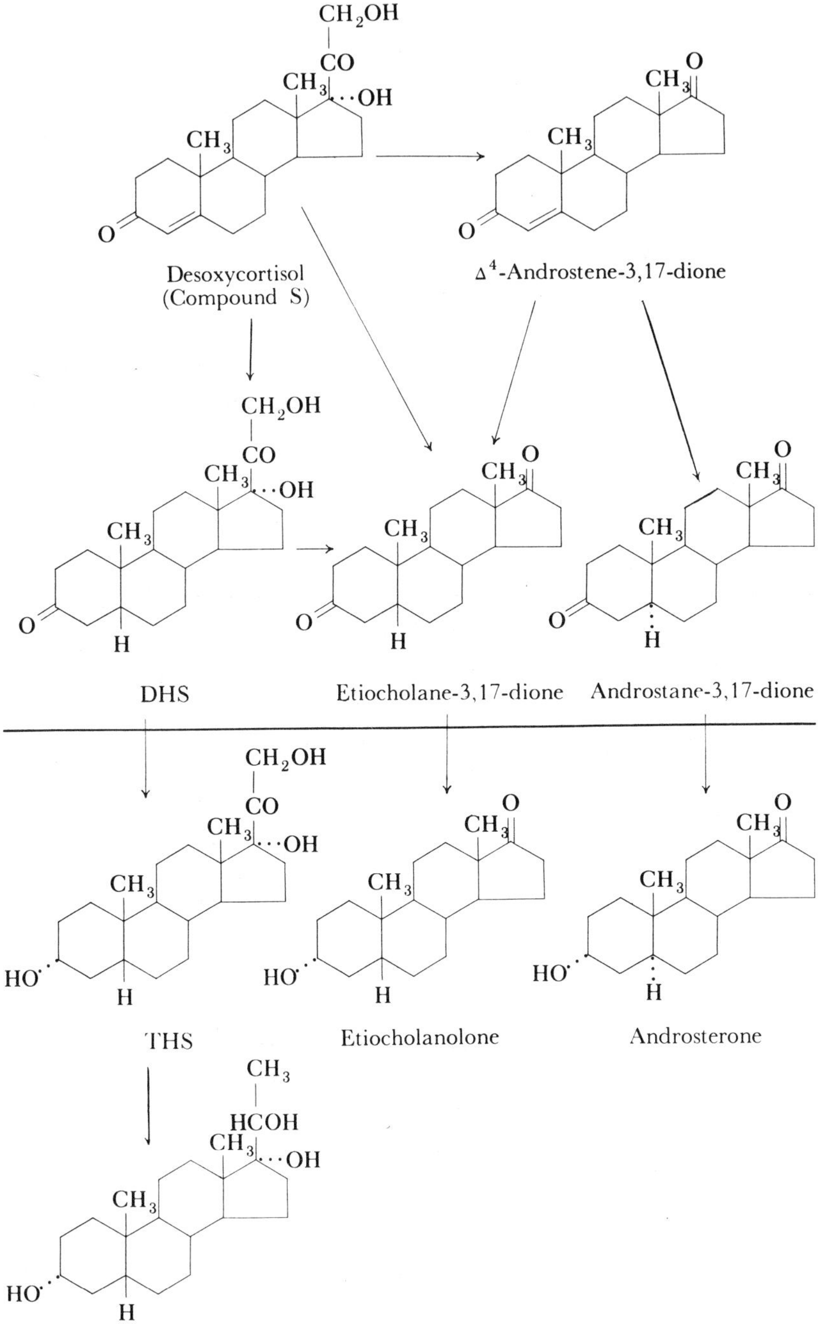

FIGURE 8.7. METABOLISM OF DESOXYCORTISOL.

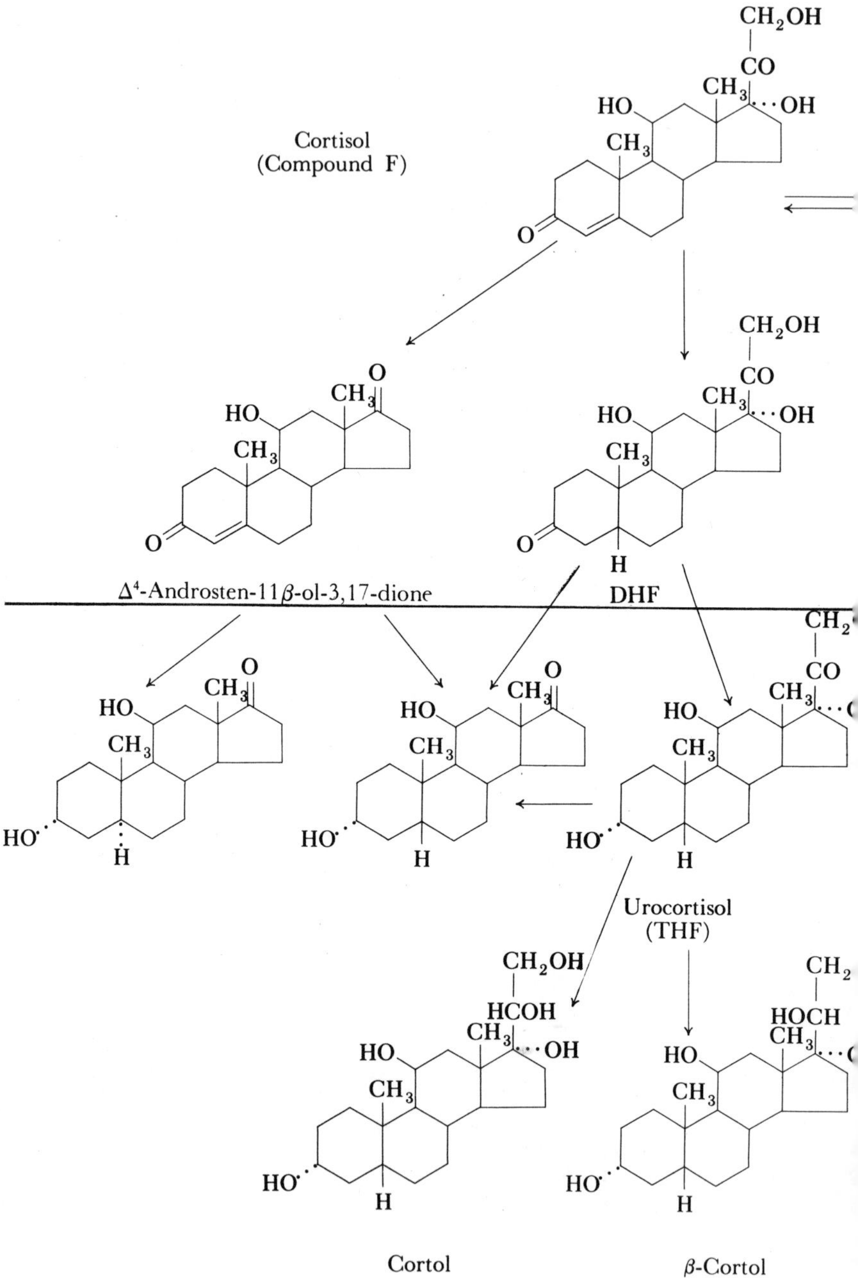

Cortisol
(Compound F)

Δ⁴-Androsten-11β-ol-3,17-dione

DHF

Urocortisol
(THF)

Cortol

β-Cortol

FIGURE 8.8. METABOLISM

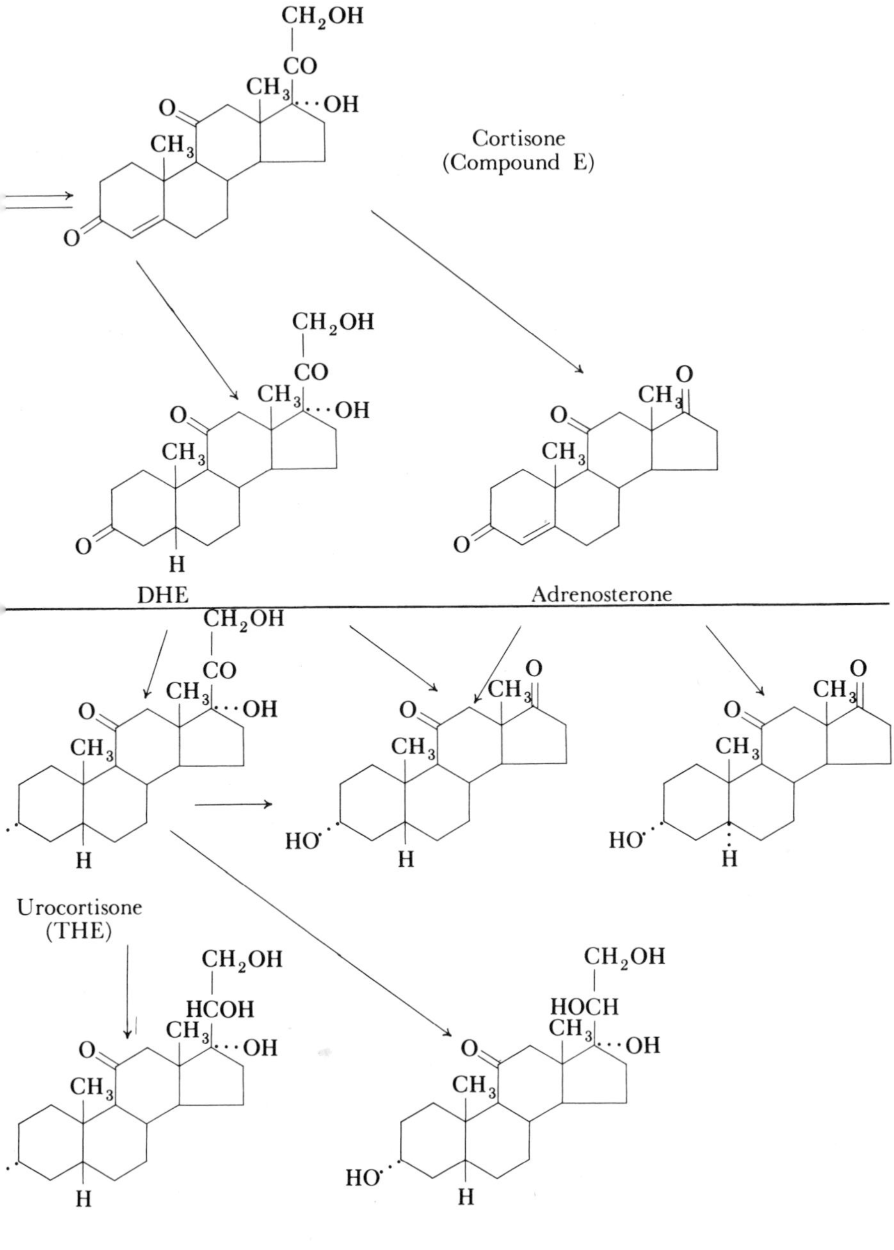

Cortisone
(Compound E)

DHE

Adrenosterone

Urocortisone
(THE)

Cortolone

β-Cortolone

RTISOL AND CORTISONE.

Figure 8.8, presenting the metabolism of cortisol and cortisone, combines all the metabolic reactions discussed above. Cortisol and cortisone are interchangeable in the organism. In fact, it has been stated that 11-ketosteroids are only biologically active to the extent that they are reduced to 11β-hydroxysteroids. Removal of the side chain yields the two adrenal 17-ketosteroids Δ^4-androsten-11β-ol-3,17-dione and Δ^4-androstene-3,11,17-trione (adrenosterone). Reduction of the Δ^4-3-keto group leads *via* DHE and DHF to the main urinary metabolites THE (urocortisone) and THF (urocortisol). The 20-keto group of THE and THF may be reduced to the 20α- or 20β-hydroxy derivatives, the cortols and cortolones. Allopregnane derivatives (not shown) have also been identified as metabolites of Compounds E and F. Normal adults excrete about 5 mg of urocortisone, 3 mg of urocortisol, and 3 mg of cortol and cortolone per day. Aldosterone is also reduced and conjugated, but free aldosterone (up to 20 γ per day) is likewise excreted in the urine.

3. Endocrinology

The adrenocortical hormones have profound effects on many metabolic processes in animals. Extirpation of the adrenal cortex leads to a continual loss of sodium and water from the body with a concomitant rise in the potassium levels in the tissue fluids, and finally to death in a shock-like state. The ability of corticosteroids to decrease the reabsorption of potassium and to increase the reabsorption of sodium by the renal tubular epithelium (mineralocorticoid activity) varies among the hormones. Aldosterone is about 100 times as active as desoxycorticosterone, while corticosterone has about one-tenth, and cortisone and cortisol only one-hundredth to one-fiftieth of the mineralocorticoid activity of desoxycorticosterone. When administered in excessive amounts, the mineralocorticoids increase the retention of salt and water. Adrenocortical hormones have also a profound effect on gluconeogenesis. After adrenalectomy the liver glycogen and blood sugar levels are low, while the administration of corticosteroids increases the catabolism of proteins and the deposition of glycogen in the liver. In excessive administration the blood sugar may be elevated (diabetogenic action). The effect on carbohydrate metabolism (glucocorticoid activity) also varies among adrenocortical hormones. Cortisol is most active in this respect and cortisone is somewhat less active. Corticosterone has about half and aldosterone about one-fourth of the glucocorticoid activity of cortisol. Other biological effects of administered corticosteroids include the increase in blood lipides, the suppression of lymphatic tissue growth (thymus, spleen, lymph nodes) and of the proliferation of fibroblasts in tissue culture and in wound healing, the drop in circulating lymphocytes and eosinophiles, the inhibition of the inflammatory reaction to bacterial and chemical agents (antiphlogistic activity), the inhibition of the effect of hyaluronidase on membrane permeability, the ulcerogenic activity, and the increase in the electroshock threshold of nervous tissues.

The secretion of adrenocortical hormones is continuous, but subject to diurnal variations. The adrenals of a normal adult secrete about 20-30 mg of cortisol and 20-200 γ of aldosterone per day. The control of corticosteroidogenesis by ACTH is a perfect example of the operation of negative feed-back systems in biochemical regulation. Low blood levels of adrenocortical hormones stimulate the hypophysis to secrete ACTH, while high blood levels depress the pituitary secretion. The aldosterone secretion is only to a minor, if any, extent under the control of the pituitary. It responds to changes in the electrolyte concentration and fluid volume in the body. A fall in the sodium or a rise in the potassium level of the blood and a decrease in extracellular fluid activates the diencephalon to secrete a humoral factor which stimulates aldosterone secretion. Selye has argued that a number of nonspecific stimuli which place the organism under a stress, e.g. muscular exercise, cold, trauma, burns, drugs, poisons, infections, X-rays, and psychological tension, are capable of eliciting a pituitary-adrenal response. The alarm reaction is a generalized response of the organism to the damaging influence and consists in an increase of adrenaline output followed by a recovery phase in which the secretion of adrenocortical hormones is increased.

Using the 17-ketosteroid (cf. Chap. IX, p. 149) and corticosteroid excretion, as determined by a variety of assay methods (cf. Sec. 4, p. 128), as an index of adrenal activity, it is found that the rate of secretion of adrenocortical steroids in man is low in child-hood and rises with age. It reaches a maximum at about the age of thirty and then gradually declines. The excretion of corticosteroids tends to be higher in men than in women and apparently rises twice in the course of pregnancy, once in the first and then again in the third trimester.

The effects of hypoadrenalism can be studied in man in Addison's disease, which may be due to primary atrophy or destruction of the adrenals by actinomycosis or tuberculosis. Persons afflicted with this disease show a peculiar pigmentation of the skin, muscular weakness, drowsiness, gastro-intestinal disturbances (anorexia, vomiting, diarrhea), and weight loss. The loss of salt and water leads to dehydration, and the impairment of gluconeogenesis is responsible for the hypoglycemia occasionally observed in this disease. The urinary excretion of corticosteroid metabolites, including the 17-ketosteroids, is low, and the patient does not respond to the administration of ACTH. Addison's disease is treated with salt-retaining corticosteroids, and in the case of adrenal crisis, by the administration of glucose and saline. In Simmonds' disease similar symptoms may be observed, but since the defect is in the anterior pituitary rather than in the adrenals, the patient's adrenals respond to the administration of ACTH with an increased corticosteroid production.

The symptoms of Cushing's disease illustrate the effects of hyper-adrenalism in man. The disease may be associated with a tumor of the anterior pituitary, but adrenal hyperplasia and tumors have been found in many cases. The patients, usually adult women, show fat deposits on the neck, hips, and trunk, the face is rounded and florid, and purplish striae appear on the abdomen. In some instances the patients may experience hypertension, amenorrhea, loss of libido, and depression. The overproduction of adrenocortical hormones, reflected in a high urinary excretion of corticosteroids and 17-ketosteroids, leads to sodium retention, loss of potassium, alkalosis, hyperglycemia, and even diabetes. The androgens resulting from the catabolism of corticosteroids are responsible for acne, hirsutism, and enlargement of the clitoris. However, in some cases the androgen production may be normal. The nitrogen balance as well as the calcium balance is negative and demineralization of the bones and even kyphosis may be observed.

In the adrenogenital syndrome, masculinization is due to excessive androgen production by the adrenal cortex. In the female fetus this condition produces pseudohermaphroditism, in the male fetus macrogenitosomia praecox. In children it leads to precocious pseudopuberty and in adult women to hirsutism and virilization of the external genitalia. Analysis of the urine of these patients for individual metabolites of the adrenocortical hormones has revealed that their adrenals are unable to carry out the 21-hydroxylation. Reference to Figure 8.1 shows that the block in 21-hydroxylation (AGS in Figure 8.1) causes an accumulation of 17α-hydroxy-progesterone, which is excreted in the form of pregnane-3α,17α, 20α-triol or degraded to androgens. At the same time the adrenal cortex is stimulated by the release of ACTH, unchecked by cortisol, whose production is diminished. The administration of ACTH to such patients further increases their pregnanediol, pregnanetriol, and 17-ketosteroid excretion, but cortisol suppresses the secretion of ACTH and of androgens. In the adrenogenital syndrome with hypertension (AGSH in Figure 8.1) the blockade seems to occur in the 11β-hydroxylation. As a result, desoxycortisol and its tetrahydro derivative are excreted in the urine. The disease responds favorably to the administration of cortisol or cortisone, which inhibit the pituitary ACTH secretion. Another variant of the disease entails a loss of sodium chloride from the body. In the salt-losing syndrome there may be an overproduction of an aldosterone antagonist by the adrenals. The disease is treated with desoxycorticosterone. A so-called sodium excretion factor (S.E.F.) in the adrenals has recently been identified as allopregnane-3β,16α-diol-20-one (Figure 8.9).

In Conn's syndrome, a disease characterized by hypernatremia, polyuria, alkalosis, hypertension, and a high excretory level of aldosterone, the adrenal glands generally reveal an adenoma, rarely hyperplasia. The metabolic defect resulting in hyperaldosteronism is said to be due to an inability of the adrenals to perform the 17α-hydroxylation (CS in Figure 8.1). Primary aldosteronism may also be involved in the pathogenesis of edemata (e.g. Mach's syndrome) and periodic hypokalemic paralysis. Sec-

3β,16α-dihydroxy-5α-pregnan-20-one

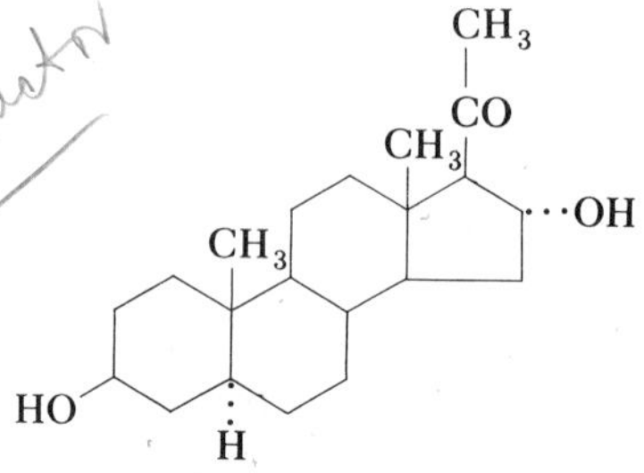

FIGURE 8.9. SODIUM EXCRETION FACTOR.

ondary aldosteronism may be the result of sodium or water loss and potassium excess, but is most commonly seen in diseases characterized by edema, such as congestive heart failure, hepatic cirrhosis, and nephrosis.

4. Analysis

Bioassays of corticosteroids have largely been replaced by the less laborious, cheaper, and more accurate chemical methods of analysis. However, bioassays have played an important part as a guide to the isolation of the active hormones and continue to find application in the testing of new analogs (cf. Sec. 5, p. 130). Adrenalectomized rats and mice are commonly used for this purpose, and in the simplest form of the test the survival time, especially at low temperatures (cold test), and the effect of administered materials on life maintenance may be determined. Corticosteroids sustain the muscular responsiveness of the gastrocnemius muscle of adrenalectomized rats to short electrical stimulation. This property forms the basis of the muscle work test. The liver glycogen test measures the ability of the test dose to promote the deposition of glycogen in fasting adrenalectomized animals. Mice are more sensitive test animals than rats. The effect of corticosteroids on the electrolyte metabolism of adrenalectomized rats forms the basis of another assay procedure. The decrease in the urinary Na/K ratio is proportional to the logarithm of the injected dose. The analysis of Na^{24} and K^{42} after injection of the radioisotopes was used in the work leading to the isolation of aldosterone. Other bioassay methods are based on the drop in circulating eosinophiles, on the thymus involution, and on other biological properties of adrenocortical hormones.

The isolation of corticosteroids from adrenal glands involves homogenization of the tissues with acetone, dilution of the acetone extract with water and defatting it with petroleum ether, followed by extraction of the steroids with 1,2-dichloroethane or other organic solvents. The residue from this extraction is purified by solvent partition, countercurrent distribution, or partition chromatography. For the isolation from blood a procedure has been used in which a mixture of blood, methanol, and water inside a dialysis bag is extracted with dichloromethane. The analysis of free corticosteroids in urine requires adjustment of the pH to 1.0 and solvent extraction. A number of continuous extractors for urine have been described. The glucuronic acid conjugates must be hydrolyzed with β-glucuronidase prior to extraction. The urine extracts are subsequently washed with dilute alkali.

While the separation of corticosteroids, especially in the form of their acetates, can be accomplished by adsorption chromatography, partition chromatography has several decided advantages. Minute quantities of very closely related members of this relatively polar group of steroids can be separated conveniently by partition chromatography; whereas adsorption chromatography frequently produces artifacts and incomplete separations due to "tailing." Two types of solvent systems are widely used for paper chromatography of corticosteroids: two-phase organic solvent systems and alcohol-containing aqueous systems. In the former, the paper is impregnated with propylene glycol, formamide, or other relatively polar organic solvents, and less polar solvents such as toluene, benzene, and chloroform are used as eluents. The aqueous solvent systems contain an alcohol, which promotes the solubility of the steroids in the stationary phase. Paper chromatography, especially in conjunction with radioactive steroids, has played a major role in metabolic studies of corticosteroids. The composition of the so-called amorphous fraction of adrenal extracts had eluded biochemical investigation until the advent of these techniques. They are of great value for the analysis of minute amounts of hormones such as aldosterone in body fluids.

After suitable purification, the corticosteroids may be quantitatively determined by a variety of methods. Analytical procedures based on the presence of a Δ^4-3-keto group have already been discussed in Chap. VII, p. 104. Figure 8.10 gives a survey of procedures based on the presence of various side chains in corticosteroid metabolites. The α-ketols reduce alkaline solutions containing either silver diammine, cupric, ferricyanide, or phosphomolybdate ions, or various tetrazolium salts. Periodic acid oxidation gives one mole of formaldehyde with the steroids having a hydroxyl group at C-21 and either a carbonyl or a hydroxyl group at C-20. Depending on the nature of the side chain, various oxidation products are formed, which may be used for the diagnosis of the side chain. Periodate oxidation of a 17,20-diol produces acetaldehyde and the corresponding 17-ketosteroid. The glycerol type of side chain also yields a 17-ketosteroid under these conditions, but formaldehyde is liberated instead of acetaldehyde. Not only the steroids yielding 17-ketosteroids by periodate treatment, but also the steroids containing a dihydroxyacetone side chain are ketogenic when bismuthate is used as the oxidizing agent. All 17-hydroxypregnanes are converted to 17-ketosteroids by chromic acid oxidation. Reduction with sodium borohydride may be used for the selective determination of 17-hydroxypregnan-20-ones, since they become ketogenic only after reduction to 17,20-dihydroxypregnanes. Phenylhydrazine and sulfuric acid (Porter-Silber method) give a specific color test for 17,21-dihydroxypregnan-20-ones. Dinitrophenylhydrazine in alkali reacts not only with the side chain types indicated, but also with all α,β-unsaturated ketones. The latter also interfere with the phosphomolybdate reduction.

5. Analogs

Adrenocortical hormones are used clinically not only in replacement therapy, but also in the so-called collagen diseases (e.g. rheumatoid arthritis and lupus erythematosus). While the discovery of the beneficial effects of cortisone on patients with rheumatoid arthritis by Hench, Kendall, *et al.* in 1949 was responsible for the renaissance of steroid research, it is an ironic fact that no derange-

Side Chain	CH$_2$OH CHOH COH<	CH$_2$OH CO COH<	CH$_3$ CO COH<	CH$_3$ CHOH COH<	CH$_2$OH CO CH<	CH$_2$OH CHOH CH<
Reducing	−	+	−	−	+	−
Formaldehydogenic	+	+	−	−	+	+
Acetaldehydogenic	−	−	−	+	−	−
Ketogenic ⎧ IO$_4$	+	−	−	+	−	−
⎪ BiO$_3$	+	+	−	+	−	−
⎨ CrO$_3$	+	+	+	+	−	−
⎩ BH$_4^-$, BiO$_3^-$	+	+	+	+	−	−
Phenylhydrazine	−	+	−	−	−	−
Dinitrophenylhydrazine	−	+	+	−	+	−

FIGURE 8.10. ANALYTICAL PROPERTIES OF CORTICOSTEROIDS.

ment of corticosteroid metabolism has been demonstrated so far in rheumatoid arthritis. The anti-inflammatory effect of adrenocortical hormones is also exhibited by nonsteroidal drugs such as by aspirin, phenylbutazone (sodium 4-butyl-1,2-diphenyl-3,5-pyrazolidinedione) and various antimalarials. These agents alleviate the symptoms (pain, swelling, and stiffness of joints), but do not alter the course of the disease. The inhibition of the inflammatory reaction and fibroblastic activity makes corticosteroids useful therapeutic agents in a variety of conditions (allergic diseases, burns, etc.), but it may also endanger patients with infectious diseases (e.g. tuberculosis) by abetting their dissemination. Other untoward effects of corticosteroid therapy are edema and hypertension due to salt retention, mental disturbances (euphoria, restlessness, depression), vertebral fractures, peptic ulcers, and diabetes in predisposed individuals.

The clinical importance of cortisone and cortisol prompted a number of laboratories to attempt the synthesis of these hormones. As a consequence of the original concept of high structural specificity of corticosteroid activity the prospects of producing analogs with biological activity were at first viewed with skepticism. However, the break-through came with the discovery that certain 9α-halogenated intermediates in the synthesis of 11-oxygenated adrenocortical hormones were even more effective than cortisone and cortisol in the survival, liver glycogen, and thymus involution tests. This discovery stimulated a great many attempts to synthesize corticosteroid analogs with greater anti-inflammatory activity than that of natural hormones in the hope of dissociating the therapeutic properties from the side effects of these drugs. A comparison of various 9α-halo derivatives of cortisol showed that the glucocorticoid activity increases with increasing electronegativity of the halogen substituent. The derivative most active in this respect, 9α-fluorocortisol (Figure 8.11) has about 10 times the glucocorticoid and anti-inflammatory activity, but approximately 125 times the mineralocorticoid activity of cortisol in the rat. The fluoro derivative causes less sodium retention than the other 9α-halo derivatives in the rat, but greater sodium retention than 9α-chlorocortisol in dog and man. At high levels of administration 9α-fluorocortisol produces renal lesions and causes a net loss of sodium from the body.

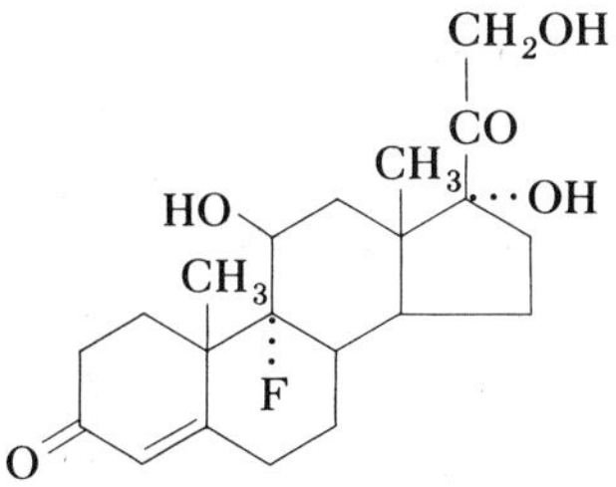

9α-Fluorocortisol

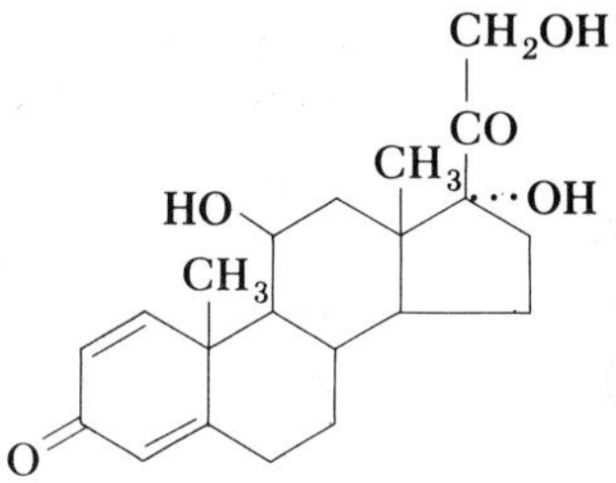

Prednisolone

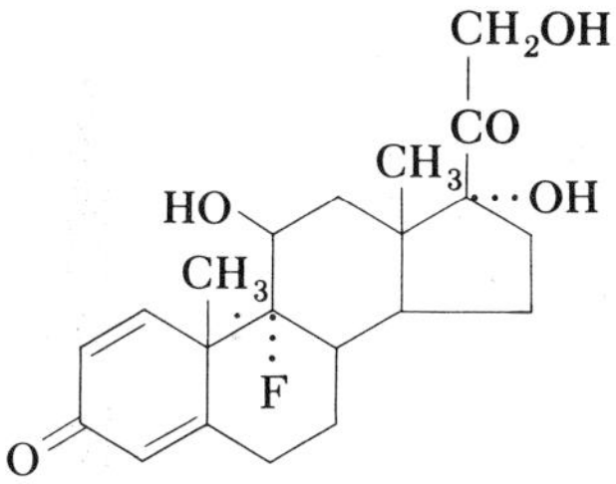

Δ[1]-9α-Fluorocortisol

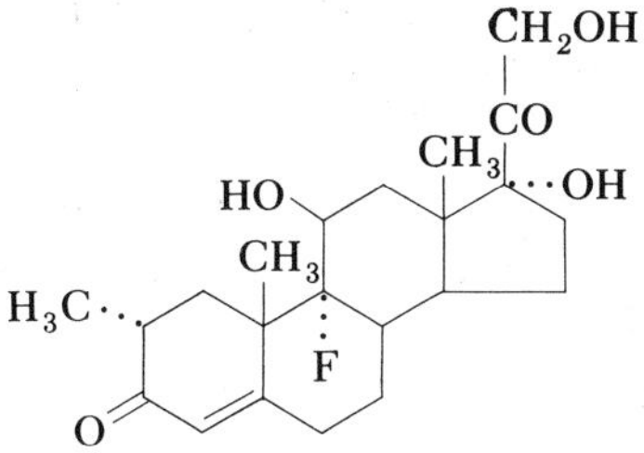

2α-Methyl-9α-fluorocortisol

FIGURE 8.11. CORTICOSTEROID ANALOGS I.

The drug is not useful for systemic treatment, but has found some application in dermatology.

The Δ^1-derivatives of cortisone and cortisol, prednisone and prednisolone (Figure 8.11) respectively, have the advantage over the parent compounds that their glucocorticoid and anti-inflammatory activity is increased 3–5 times; whereas the mineralocorticoid activity is lower than that of the parent hormones. This makes prednisone and prednisolone useful therapeutic agents for rheumatic diseases. It was natural now to test the effect of incorporating both structural changes in the hormone molecule. The resulting Δ^1-9α-fluorocortisol (Figure 8.11), however, showed no dissociation of the glucocorticoid and mineralocorticoid activity. Both activities are about 50 times as great as that of cortisol, and the antirheumatic activity in patients is 15 times that of cortisol. This drug is not used in rheumatic and allergic diseases but has some value in Addison's disease.

The 2α-methyl derivatives of cortisol and cortisone have greater glucocorticoid activity than the parent hormones in the rat, but not in man and dog. However, in all species they exhibit a higher mineralocorticoid activity than desoxycorticosterone. The 2α-methyl-9α-fluorocortisol (Figure 8.11) has 3 times the mineralocorticoid activity of aldosterone, and is the most potent electrolyte regulator known at present. The introduction of a 6α-methyl group into the cortisol molecule increases the glucocorticoid and to some extent also the anti-inflammatory activity of the hormone in the rat. At the same time 6α-methylcortisol is less sodium-retaining than cortisol. 6α-Methylprednisolone (Medrol) and especially 6α-methyl 9α-fluoroprednisolone (Figure 8.12) are highly active anti-inflammatory substances, which actually promote sodium and water excretion. Dexamethasone (Hexadecadrol) (Figure 8.12) is the 16α-methyl-9α-fluoroprednisolone. It was shown to have in

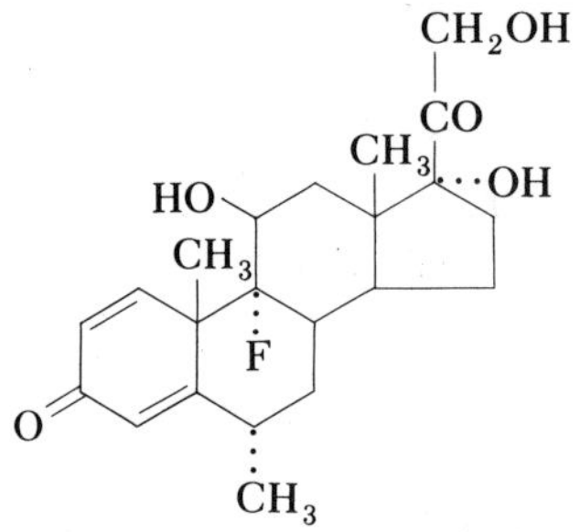

6α-Methyl-9α-fluoroprednisolone

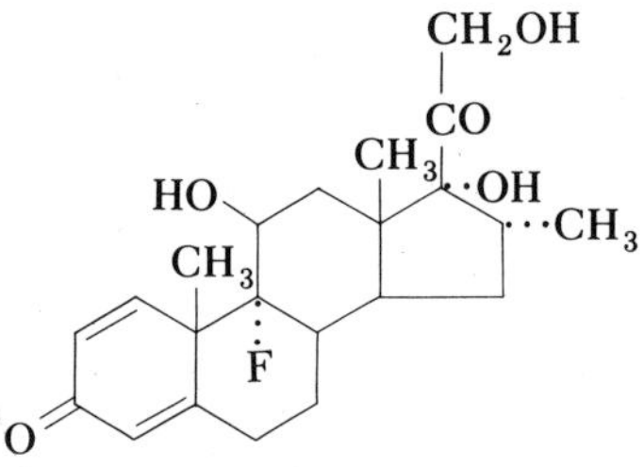

Dexamethasone

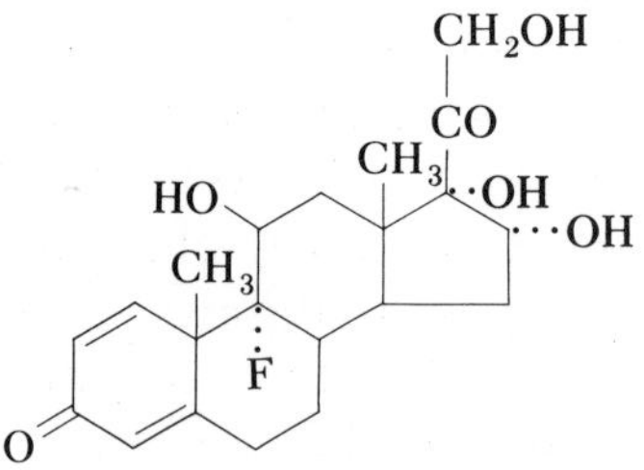

Triamcinolone

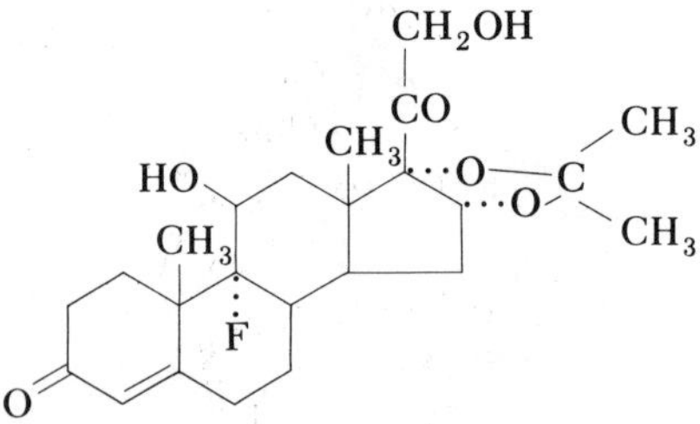

Acetonide of 9α-Fluoro-16α-hydroxycortisol

FIGURE 8.12. CORTICOSTEROID ANALOGS II.

rats 700 times the effect of cortisol in producing adrenal atrophy, 400 times the effect in producing thymus involution, and 190 times the granuloma inhibiting effect of cortisol. In man the anti-inflammatory activity is 30 to 40 times as great as that of cortisol, and it is thus the most potent antiarthritic steroid known today. The mineralocorticoid activity, on the other hand, is very low. However, it has been shown to have an adverse effect on the carbohydrate tolerance of patients. A 6α-fluoro derivative of dexamethasone is said to have similar potency in rats, but has not been tested in patients at the time of this writing.

Introduction of a 16α-hydroxyl group into cortisol analogs suppresses and eliminates their sodium-retaining properties without greatly affecting their glucocorticoid activity. Triamcinolone (Aristocort, 16α-hydroxy-9α-fluoroprednisolone) (Figure 8.12) has 36 times the glucocorticoid activity of cortisol, but no mineralocorticoid activity in the rat. It is 4 times as effective as cortisol in collagen and allergic diseases and shows no evidence of promoting sodium retention in man. This drug is more active by oral administration than by parenteral route. It is of interest to note that the introduction of a 16α-hydroxyl group abolishes sodium retention even in 2α-methyl-9α-fluorocortisol (cf. above). The glucocorticoid activity of the latter is thereby depressed by a factor of 20. Ketals and acetals of 16α-hydroxy derivatives have also been prepared and tested. The acetonide shown in Figure 8.12 has 120 times the activity of cortisone acetate in the glycogen deposition test and a higher ratio of anti-inflammatory:glucocorticoid activity than the parent compound. It also causes some sodium retention.

The effect of introducing various groups into the hormone molecule is to some extent additive and predictable ("enhancement factors"). The generalizations, however, do not always hold. The opinion has been expressed that the glucocorticoid activity of hormone analogs is related to the ability of the liver to inactivate the compounds. Those which cannot be readily reduced in ring A are said to have a higher activity, but undoubtedly other factors must be involved since the correlation is not very good. While steroids must contain a Δ^4-3-keto group for glucocorticoid activity, the α-ketol group is not required.

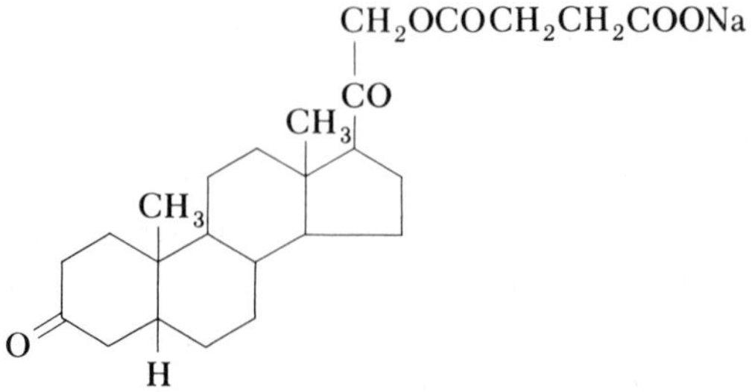

$$\text{CH}_2\text{OCOCH}_2\text{CH}_2\text{COONa}$$

FIGURE 8.13. VIADRIL.

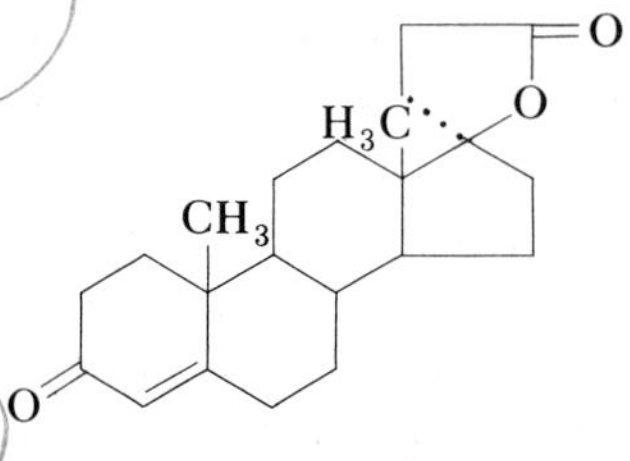

SC-5233 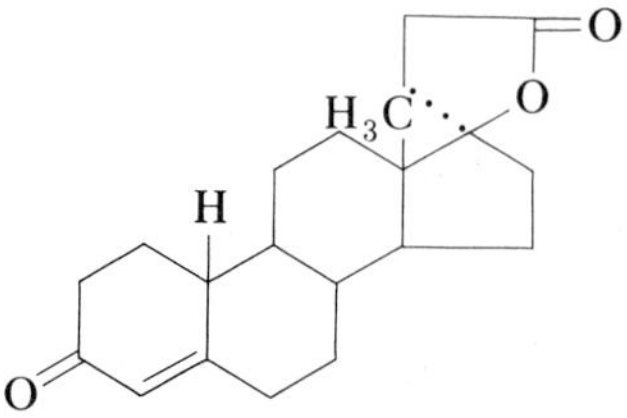   SC-8109

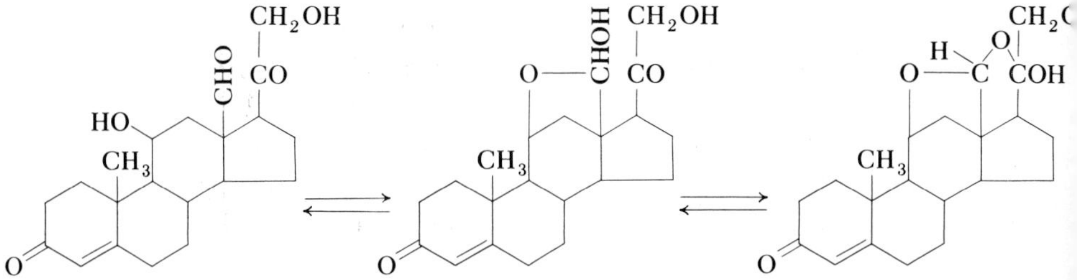

Aldosterone

FIGURE 8.14. ALDOSTERONE AND ANTAGONISTS.

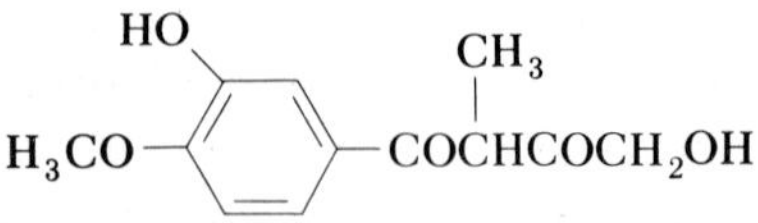

FIGURE 8.15. COMPOUND Y.

There are several isolated pieces of information on the biological activity of corticosteroids which are worth mentioning. The 21-succinate of pregnan-21-ol-3,20-dione (Figure 8.13), related to desoxycorticosterone, is devoid of mineralocorticoid activity, but has valuable anaesthetic properties. Sold under the name of Viadril or Hydroxydione, the compound exhibits almost no toxicity and no cardiac or respiratory depression. It will be recalled that pregnane-3,20-dione (Chap. VIII, p. 106) also has anaesthetic properties.

Several 17-spirolactones have been prepared and tested. The Δ^4-androsten-3-one-17-spirolactone, known as SC-5233 (Figure 8.14), has no effect on the mineral balance of animals but counteracts the effect of administered desoxycorticosterone or aldosterone. The 19-nor analog of this compound, known as SC-8109 (Figure 8.14), is 5 times more active in this respect and increases the aldosterone excretion. The compounds bear a resemblance to aldosterone, which is shown in the hemiacetal and full acetal form in Figure 8.14. It is interesting to note that SC-8109 has about the same progestational activity as 19-norethisterone and that progesterone itself exhibits a slight antialdosterone activity.

Recently, a compound has been isolated from the adrenal cortex, which has weak glucocorticoid and mineralocorticoid activity, but is not a steroid. The probable structure of Compound Y is shown in Figure 8.15.

IX

Androgens

1. Biosynthesis

COMPLETE OXIDATIVE REMOVAL OF the side chain in cholesterol, progesterone, etc. leads to the C_{19} steroids. These are often referred to as androgens (Greek *andros*, man, and *gennao*, produce), although not all of them have androgenic activity. Their systematic names are derived from those of the hydrocarbons etiocholane (Greek *aitio-*, fundamental), in which the A/B ring juncture is *cis*, and androstane (A/B *trans*) (cf. Figure 9.1). Thus, the testicular hormone, testosterone (Figure 9.1), is named Δ^4-androsten-17β-ol-3-one. Chromic acid oxidation of dibromocholesteryl acetate yields, after several steps and among other products, Δ^5-androsten-3β-ol-17-one (dehydroepiandrosterone, androstenolone) (Figure 9.2). This reaction has been an important avenue of approach to the partial synthesis of steroid hormones, but the yields are so poor that it is no longer used.

Certain microorganisms can also effect the removal of steroid side chains. The degradation of cholestenone to 3-keto-Δ^4-

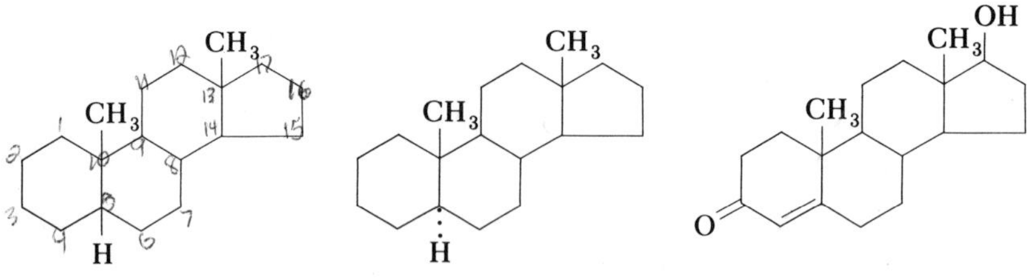

Etiocholane   Androstane   Testosterone

FIGURE 9.1. C_{19} STEROIDS.

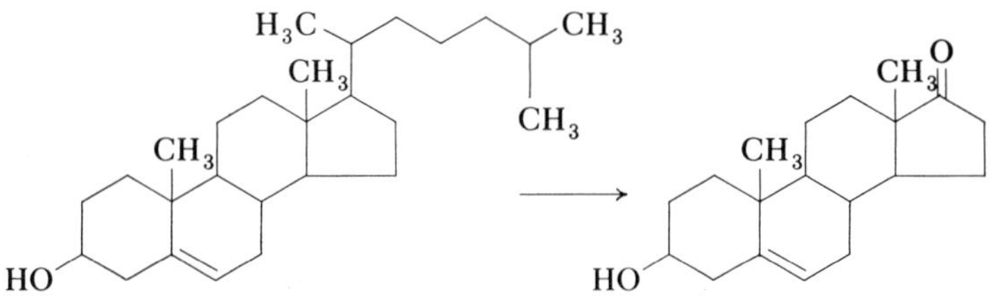

Cholesterol   Dehydroepiandrosterone
(as acetate dibromide)

FIGURE 9.2. LABORATORY PREPARATION OF
DEHYDROEPIANDROSTERONE.

etiocholenic acid by *Proactinomyces erythropolis* is shown in Figure 9.3. The microbiological oxidation of progesterone and of various 17-hydroxysteroids by *Penicillium* and *Aspergillus* species to Δ^4-androstene-3,17-dione (cf. Figure 9.4) may be used for the preparation of androgens. Testosterone and testololactone are also formed in the process.

A testosterone-adapted strain of *Pseudomonas* has been found to contain two dehydrogenases: a 3α-dehydrogenase, which activates oxygen at C-3 specifically and a β-dehydrogenase, which acts on oxygens at either C-3 or C-17. Both enzymes require DPN and catalyze the dehydrogenation of alcohol to keto groups as well as the reduction of ketones to the corresponding alcohols. The reversible reduction of androstenedione to testosterone and its reduction to dehydroepiandrosterone by *Pseudomonas testosteroni*

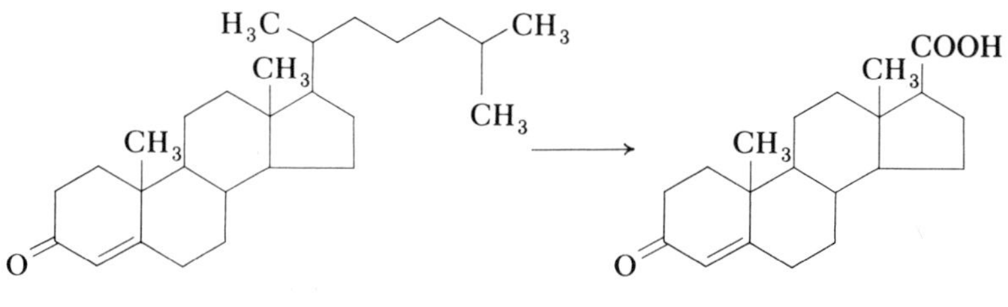

Cholestenone   3-Keto-Δ^4-etiocholenic Acid

FIGURE 9.3. MICROBIOLOGICAL DEGRADATION OF THE
SIDE CHAIN.

as well as the reduction of androstenedione to etiocholan-17β-ol-3-one by *Bacillus putrificus* are shown in Figure 9.5.

In the mammalian organism androgens are produced mainly by the adrenal cortex, testes, and ovaries. One biosynthetic pathway leads from 17-hydroxyprogesterone (cf. Chap. VII, p. 100) to androstenedione (Figure 9.6). Desmolase activity has been found not only in adrenal and gonadal tissues, but also in the liver.

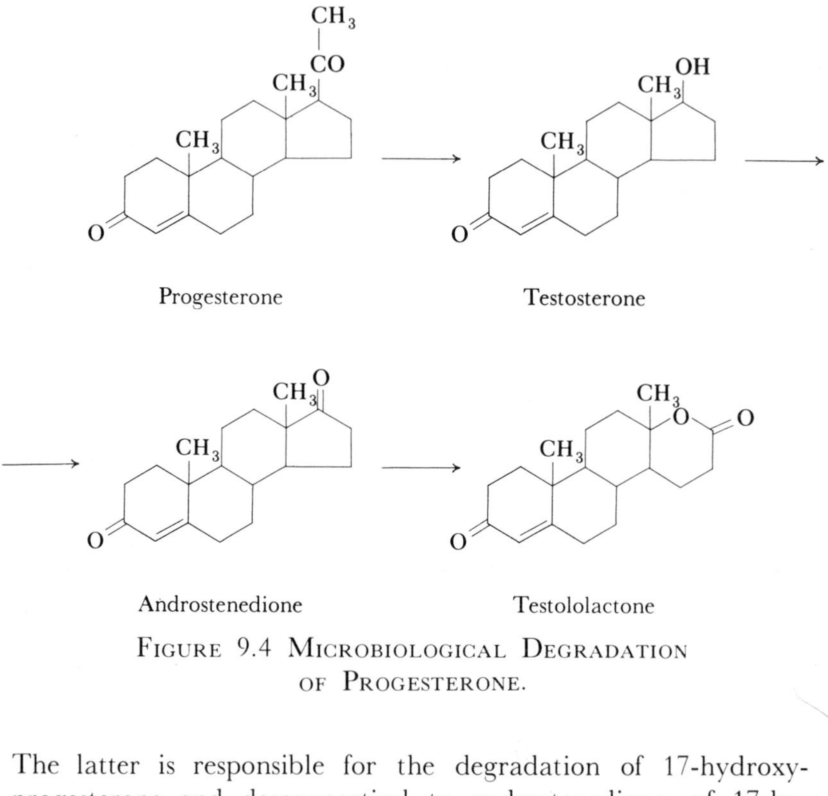

Progesterone   Testosterone

Androstenedione   Testololactone

FIGURE 9.4 MICROBIOLOGICAL DEGRADATION
OF PROGESTERONE.

The latter is responsible for the degradation of 17-hydroxy-progesterone and desoxycortisol to androstenedione, of 17-hydroxypregnenolone to dehydroepiandrosterone, and of cortisol or cortisone to 11β-hydroxyandrostenedione or adrenosterone (not shown). 11β-Hydroxylation of androstenedione is analogous to the reaction discussed in Chap. VII, p. 99. The gonads, liver, kidneys, and other tissues carry out the reversible reduction of the 17-keto group in androstenedione to testosterone, and rabbit

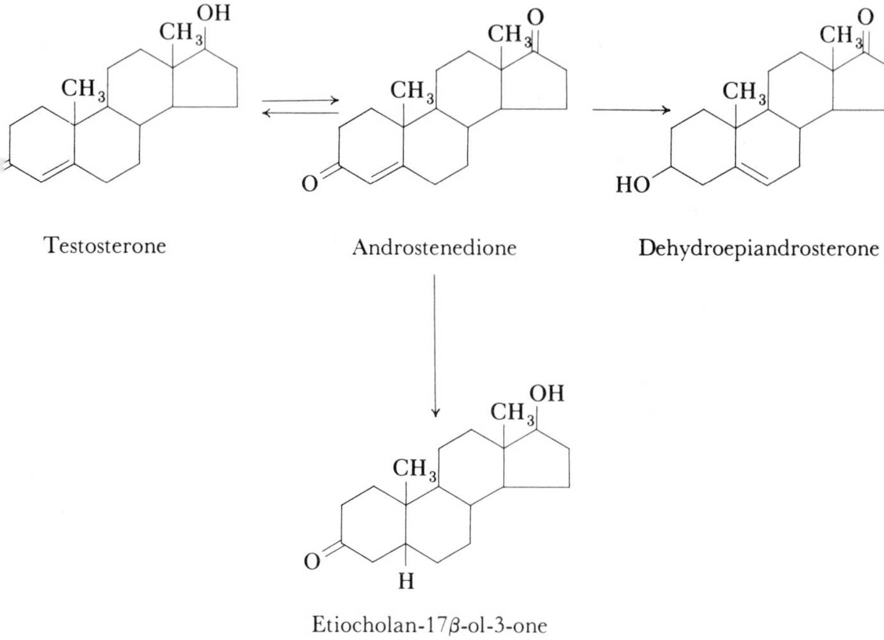

Testosterone   Androstenedione   Dehydroepiandrosterone

Etiocholan-17β-ol-3-one

FIGURE 9.5. MICROBIOLOGICAL REDUCTION OF
ANDROSTENEDIONE.

tissues also to the 17α-epimer of testosterone (not shown). The
second pathway, via dehydroepiandrosterone, is not so well established. It is believed that pregnenolone (cf. also Figure 7.4)
may be first hydroxylated to 17-hydroxypregnenolone and later
degraded to dehydroepiandrosterone. It has been calculated that
the human adrenals produce 15 to 30 mg of dehydroepiandrosterone per day, and this steroid has been demonstrated in adrenal
glands and in adrenal vein blood. It does not appear to originate
from the gonads. The adrenals convert dehydroepiandrosterone
to androstenedione.

While the production of androgens by the adrenals is controlled by the pituitary corticotropin (ACTH), the gonadal biosynthesis of androgens is regulated by the gonadotropic hormones
of the pituitary and placenta. The sex hormones in turn control to some extent the secretion of gonadotropins. The possibility exists that, as in the case of the adrenocortical hor-

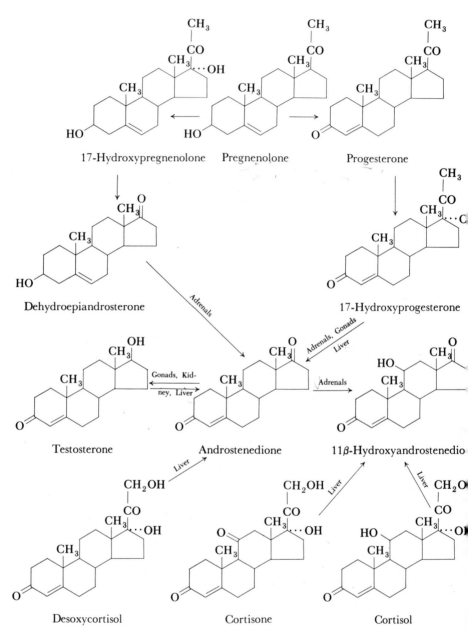

FIGURE 9.6. BIOGENESIS OF ANDROGENS.

mones, cholesterol may not be an obligatory precursor of testicular androgens. Amphenone and DDD (cf. Chap. VIII, p. 114) also block the adrenal synthesis of androgens.

2. Metabolism

The C_{19} steroids are chiefly metabolized by the liver and excreted in the urine. Figure 9.7 summarizes some of the more important metabolic pathways of the androgens (cf. also Figures 8.7, 8.8, 9.6, and 10.3). Reduction of the 17-keto group converts dehydroepiandrosterone to Δ^5-androstene-$3\beta,17\beta$-diol and 16-hydroxylation produces Δ^5-androstene-$3\beta,16\alpha,17\beta$-triol. The 4,5-double bond of testosterone is reduced to give androstan-17β-ol-3-one. In the case of androstenedione, reduction to androstanedione or etiocholanedione may occur. While the reduction to androstanedione may be effected by liver tissue from both male and female rats, only male rat liver can produce etiocholanedione. In man, there appears to be no sex difference in this respect. After the administration of testosterone, approximately equal amounts of androstan-3α-ol-17-one (androsterone) and etiocholan-3α-ol-17-one (etiocholanolone,5β-androsterone) are excreted in the urine. However, patients with myxedema, given testosterone, excrete up to 8 times as much 5β-androsterone as androsterone. After treatment with triiodothyronine the ratio of these two substances in the urine becomes normal. There is another interesting aspect of the ratio of $5\beta:5\alpha$ reduction. While this ratio is between 1.5 and 2.0 for C_{19} steroids without an oxygen function at C-11, a larger proportion of 5α (androstane) metabolites is formed in the presence of an oxygen function at C-11. C_{21} steroids are predominantly excreted as 5β (pregnane and etiocholane) metabolites, regardless of the presence or absence of an oxygen function at C-11 (cf. Chap. VIII, p. 117). It can therefore be assumed that the side chain of the corticosteroids remains intact until the 4,5-double bond has been reduced.

Reduction of the 3-keto group in androstanedione and etiocholanedione gives rise to both the 3α-hydroxysteroids (androsterone and etiocholanolone, respectively) and the 3β-hydroxysteroids (epiandrosterone and etiocholan-3β-ol-17-one, re-

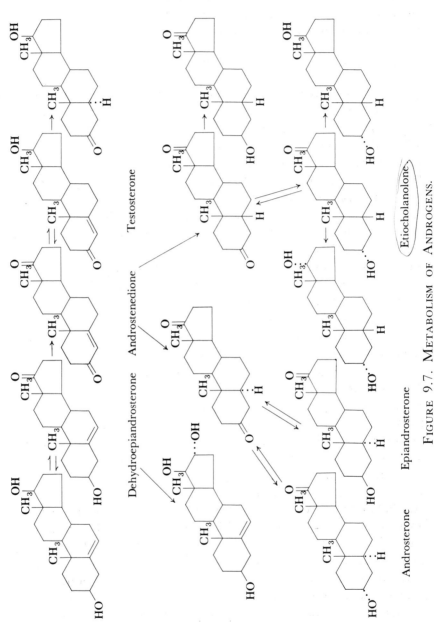

Figure 9.7. Metabolism of Androgens.

spectively). While both rabbit and guinea pig tissues can carry out the reduction to 3α-hydroxysteroids, rabbit liver and kidney are incapable of 3β-reduction. In man the 3-keto group is predominantly reduced to a 3α-hydroxyl group. The 17-keto group is exclusively reduced to a 17β-hydroxyl group in human and guinea pig tissues. In rats the relative proportion of 3α- and 3β-reduction is sex dependent. Incubation of androstanedione or androstenedione with liver tissue from male rats yields 3β- and 3α-hydroxyandrostan-17-one in a ratio of 2.3-3.5. In contrast, female rat liver produces the two compounds in a ratio of 0.12-0.16. In the case of male rats the ratio decreases after castration and rises again on treatment with androgens, but in the case of female rats castration has no effect on this ratio, although androgen treatment increases it.

The hydroxylation of androgens at C-16 is indicated in Figure 9.7, but other hydroxylation reactions have also been observed. The 11β-hydroxylation, previously believed to be confined to adrenal tissues, has been demonstrated in tissue slices from an interstitial cell tumor. Hydroxylation at C-19 leads to the estrogen series (Chap. X, p. 156).

The concentration of dehydroepiandrosterone sulfate in the blood has been estimated by chemical methods (cf. Sec. 4, p. 149) to range from 40 to 130 γ per 100 ml in normal men and from 25 to 100 γ per 100 ml in normal women. The chief excretory route of androgens in man is the urine, but considerable quantities have been isolated from the feces of cattle, especially after progesterone administration. The urinary steroids are conjugated with either glucuronic or sulfuric acid. The 3α-hydroxysteroids are largely conjugated with glucuronic acid, whereas the conjugates of 3β-hydroxysteroids are exclusively sulfates. Chemical estimation of urinary androgens as 17-ketosteroids indicates an average excretion of 15 mg per day in normal men. For women this figure is around 10 mg, which indicates that in men the adrenals contribute approximately two-thirds of the 17-ketosteroids to the mixture. Androsterone and etiocholanolone account for about two-thirds of the urinary 17-ketosteroids, and 3β-hydroxysteroids (largely dehydroepiandrosterone) normally do not exceed one-fifth of the total 17-ketosteroids.

3. Endocrinology

Androgens stimulate the development of the male reproductive organs and secondary sex characteristics. The extent of their influence and the nature of the response depend on the species. Although sex is genetically determined, the differentiation of developing sex organs and somatic structures is influenced by the sex hormones. In lower animals, e.g. in frogs in the larval or tadpole stage, sex reversal may be effected by androgens. In the cow, the androgens of the male embryo can affect the sex organs of a female twin in such a way as to produce a sterile intersex, known as freemartin. The general effects of androgens may be observed in the growth stimulation of sexual and nonsexual tissues. The effects on the male sex organs include growth responses of the seminal vesicles, prostate, vasa deferentia, epididymis, and penis. Androgens also stimulate spermatogenesis, and in male rodents they stimulate the growth of the coagulating glands, which furnish the enzyme responsible for the coagulation of a protein to form the vaginal plug. The effects on the female sex organs may be mediated by the pituitary. While the prolonged administration of androgens blocks the gonadoptropin secretion, single doses increase, particularly, the output of the follicle-stimulating hormone. Androgens induce ovulation in amphibians and stimulate the growth of the oviduct in birds and of the ovary in rodents. In spayed rodents progestational changes may be obtained in the estrogen-primed uterus by large doses of androgens. Androgens stimulate the growth of the clitoris and of the female prostate, and the development of the mammary glands.

The effects of androgens on nonsexual tissues are accompanied by an increased vascularity of the tissues. Like the corticosteroids, the androgens cause a flushing of the skin in the human subject. Androgens increase both the red blood cell count and the hemoglobin content of the blood. They also stimulate the sebaceous secretion and may produce acne. Androgens also promote tanning of the skin in man and characteristic pigmentation in fish as well as the pigmentation of the plumage and beak in birds. The effect on the growth of comb and wattles in the chicken forms the basis of a bioassay method for androgens. The characteristic distribution of facial and body hair in man is also influenced by androgens. Castration demonstrates the effects of androgens on various glands and organs: The anterior pituitary increases in size and its gonado- trophin content increases. The adrenals also usually hypertrophy after gonadectomy in the male rat, while the administration of androgens decreases adrenal activity. Castration leads to a de- crease in the size of the kidneys and of the heart. There is a general decrease in skeletal muscle mass and an accumulation of sub- cutaneous fat. Castration also prevents the involution of the thymus gland, which may be produced by the administration of androgens.

Castration or androgen administration produce certain char- acteristic changes in animal behavior. Androgens have a stimu- lating effect on the mating behavior of males and females and may be involved in the agressiveness of males. Aside from their purely physical effects on the development of the vocal apparatus in man, frog, etc. and the foreclaw in reptiles, which is used in courtship, they have undoubtedly some effect on sexual behavior. Castration of the male is known to abolish the male call in certain amphibians and birds, change the copulatory activity of rodents, the courtship behavior of birds, and the characteristic posture of dogs during micturition. Administration of androgens to the female of certain species may induce male type of courtship behavior and copulatory patterns.

On a more fundamental level, the androgens have profound effects on enzyme activity and metabolism. The succinic dehydro- genase and cytochrome oxidase activity in the seminal vesicles and prostate decrease after castration and are restored to normal by the administration of androgens. The renotropic activity of androgens also involves an increase in the arginase activity and a decrease in the alkaline phosphatase activity in the kidneys. Castration increases the kidney alkaline phosphatase concentration without affecting the acid phosphatase concentration. In patients with bone metastases due to a cancer of the prostate, castration or estrogen treatment decrease the serum acid phosphatase; whereas androgen treatment increases it. The androgens promote nitrogen retention by increasing protein synthesis and by decreas- ing the rate of amino acid catabolism. They are particularly active in decreasing urea excretion. The anabolic effect of androgens on muscular development is referred to as myotropic action. It is not necessarily correlated with their virilizing effect (cf. Sec. 5, p. 151). The androgens also promote bone growth and maturation of the epiphyseal centers.

There are a number of human abnormalities which illustrate the general effects of androgen lack and androgen excess. Leydig cell tumors in prepuberal boys produce excessive amounts of androgens and give these children the appearance of an "Infant Hercules." Premature epiphyseal closure leads to short stature, there is excessive muscular development, and the androgenic effect manifests itself in macrogenitosomia. While androgen excess in prepuberal girls is always due to adrenal disorders (cf. Chap. VIII, p. 126), postpuberal women may also be afflicted with masculinizing ovarian diseases (arrhenoblastoma, masculinovoblastoma, hilus cell tumor, Stein-Leventhal syndrome). These patients may show acne and hirsutism, baldness, enlargement of the clitoris, and atrophy of the uterus. Ovulation may cease and they may show a typical male body habitus. The lack of androgens in the male castrate or in eunuchoidism may produce a female body type. If androgen deficiency occurs in the prepuberal boy, his genitalia remain undeveloped. As an adult, he may be tall, but weak and obese, with a pale, beardless face showing a characteristic wrinkling. Eunuchiodism may be due to sclerosing tubular degeneration (Klinefelter's syndrome) and other primary disorders, or it may be secondary to a pituitary deficiency.

As measured by the urinary 17-ketosteroid excretion, the androgen production in children is very low and rises after the age of about seven. It reaches a peak in the third decade of life and falls off in old age, perhaps due to a decrease in adrenal function. The 17-ketosteroid excretion may show a rise in response to physical or emotional stress (cf. Chap. VIII, p. 125) and a decrease in starvation. Abnormally low excretion values have been observed in eunuchoidism and usually, but not always, as a result of castration, Addison's disease, panhypopituitarism, myxedema, and advanced liver disease. Abnormally high excretion values are often found in patients with interstitial cell tumors, masculinizing ovarian tumors, and adrenal hyperfunction. In adrenocortical tumors often, but not always, the proportion of dehydroepiandrosterone may be increased in relation to the other 17-ketosteroids, while a normal proportion is found in adrenal hyperplasia. Although much effort has been expended in finding a diagnostic application for the excretion values of individual 17-ketosteroids in patients with other types of tumors, no useful generalizations can be drawn from that work.

4. Analysis

Two types of biological assay methods for androgens, based on their ability to stimulate male sex characteristics, are presently in use. In the comb growth test, chicks or capons are injected with the test material. The test is more sensitive when the material is directly applied to the comb. The length, height, or lateral area of the comb are used as a measure of androgenic activity. The second type of test depends on the weight increase and histological changes in the seminal vesicles and prostate of immature or castrated male rodents, which have been repeatedly injected with the test material. The international unit of androgenic activity is the activity of 0.1 mg of androsterone. The anabolic effect of steroids seems to correlate well with the weight increase of the levator ani muscle in castrated rats.

The most popular chemical assay method is based on the Zimmermann test, which is not specific for androgens. In the Zimmermann reaction all 17-ketosteroids, whether androgenic or not, give a purple color with *m*-dinitrobenzene and potassium hydroxide, while some other ketones, including testosterone, give only a fleeting color, which soon changes to brown. In the Pincus reaction, androsterone and many other 17-ketosteroids give a blue color with antimony trichloride in acetic acid, while dehydroepiandrosterone does not react. The latter gives a blue color on treatment with concentrated sulfuric acid, followed by dilution with water. The Pettenkofer reaction with sulfuric acid and furfural in acetic acid (cf. Chap. VI, p. 92) has also been applied to the determination of dehydroepiandrosterone. The specificity of these tests can be increased by the fractionation of the steroid-containing extracts (cf. below) or by measuring the absorption of the colored products at more than one wavelength and correcting for the absorption due to interfering chromogens. C_{19} steroids with a hydroxyl group at C-17 can be determined as 17-ketosteroids after chromic acid oxidation.

For the isolation of 17-ketosteroids from urine the conjugates must first be hydrolyzed by enzymes or, more commonly, by heating the urine with acid. Although the latter produces a number of artifacts, this treatment does not affect the 17-keto group on which the final estimation is based. The free steroids are then extracted with organic solvents in separatory funnels or continuous extractors. The extract must be washed with alkali to remove estrone, which is also a 17-ketosteroid (cf. Chap. X, p. 156). The neutral 17-ketosteroid fraction may be subjected to a Girard separation prior to the colorimetric determination. If further fractionation is desired, the alcoholic steroids may be separated from the non-alcoholic steroids by converting the former into the alkali-soluble hemiphthalates or hemisuccinates. The alcohol fraction may be further subdivided into 3α- and 3β-hydroxy steroids by digitonin precipitation. 17-Ketosteroids can be separated by adsorption chromatography on alumina, preferably by the application of gradient elution. Paper chromatography of 17-ketosteroids is best accomplished by use of two-phase organic solvent systems. The Zimmermann reaction is applicable to both column and paper chromatography.

Isolated 17-ketosteroids can be readily identified on the basis of their characteristic infrared spectra. Many of the technical advances in infrared spectroscopy have been made in connection with problems in steroid analysis, e.g. micromethods have been devised in which steroids are mulled in nujol, plated out as thin films, or dispersed in potassium bromide. With certain refinements in instrumentation, infrared spectra of microgram quantities of steroids can now be obtained.

5. Analogs

In the capon comb test the order of biological activity is testosterone > androsterone > dehydroepiandrosterone > epiandrosterone. However, a mixture of androsterone and dehydroepiandrosterone in the proportion of 95:5 is less potent than androsterone, whereas a 25:75 mixture is more potent than androsterone. Etiocholanolone has no androgenic, but a pyrogenic effect. Δ^5-Androstene-3β,17β-diol is not androgenic, but stimulates spermatogenesis. Pregnenolone, which is not androgenic either, is effective in spermatogenesis and maintenance of testis weight in hypophysectomized rats.

Androgens are valuable clinically not only for substitution therapy in hypogonadal men, but also as anabolic agents in debilitating conditions. They have also been useful in the palliation of metastatic breast cancer. Their most serious side effect in women is virilization, but they may also cause salt and water retention. The synthesis of androgen analogs has two objectives. One is to produce more potent androgens, and the other is to dissociate their androgenic activity from the anabolic effect. Unfortunately, the ratio of myotropic/androgenic activity determined in rats is not always applicable to man.

When administered by injection, some of the esters of testosterone are more potent androgens than testosterone itself. This may be due to a decrease in the rate of absorption and consequent improvement in utilization. Figure 9.8 shows the structures of testosterone propionate and testosterone cyclopentylpropionate, which are used as long-acting androgens in oily vehicles. Further increases in the chain length of the fatty acid decrease the androgenic potency of testosterone esters. 17-Methyltestosterone (Figure 9.8) is considerably more active than testosterone when given by mouth. It is even more effective by sublingual or buccal route. Methyltestosterone and 17-methyl-Δ^5-androstene-3β,17β-diol (Figure 9.8) have the same myotropic/androgenic ratio as testosterone in the rat, but the methylandrostenediol causes less salt retention than testosterone. Although androstan-17β-ol-3-one (Figure 9.8) has a lower myotropic/androgenic ratio than testosterone in the rat, it has a higher ratio than testosterone in the guinea pig; also it has less salt-retaining effect than testosterone. The 17-methylandrostanolone (not shown) and androstane-3α,17β-diol (Figure 9.8) are also potent androgens.

The introduction of an 11β-hydroxyl group into methyltestosterone increases its myotropic activity more than the androgenic

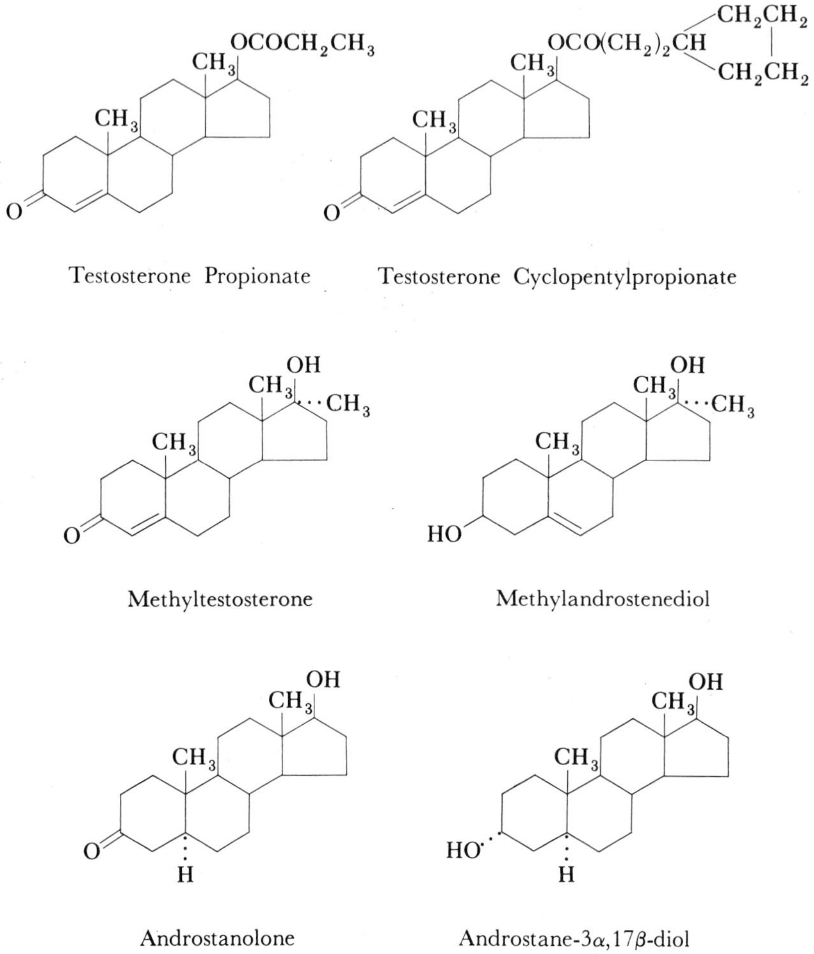

Testosterone Propionate

Testosterone Cyclopentylpropionate

Methyltestosterone

Methylandrostenediol

Androstanolone

Androstane-3α,17β-diol

FIGURE 9.8. ANDROGEN ANALOGS I.

potency. Thus, 11β-hydroxy-17-methyltestosterone (Figure 9.9) has 3 times the myotropic potency of methyltestosterone, but the same androgenic activity. The 11β-hydroxy and 11-keto derivatives of 9α-fluoro-17-methyltestosterone show about 20-fold enhancement in the anabolic and about 10-fold enhancement in the androgenic activity of methyltestosterone. The former is sold under the name Halotestin (Figure 9.9) and is one of the most potent anabolic agents obtained so far. In rat assays, 19-nortestosterone

(Figure 9.9) has a myotropic effect equivalent to that of testosterone propionate, but only 6 per cent of its androgenic potency. The same is true for the 17α-methyl and 17α-ethyl derivatives of 19-nortestosterone, which also have some progestational activity. 17-Ethyl-19-nortestosterone, which is marketed under the name Nilevar (Figure 9.9), is five times as active as 19-nortestosterone by the oral route. Nilevar and SC-6584 (17-propyl-19-nordihydrotestosterone, cf. Figure 9.9) have been found to have hypotensive action in rats. The 17α-ethynyl derivatives of testosterone and

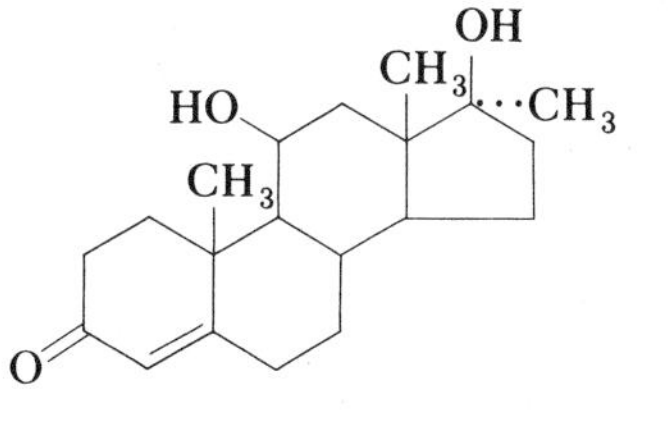

11β-Hydroxy-17-methyltestosterone

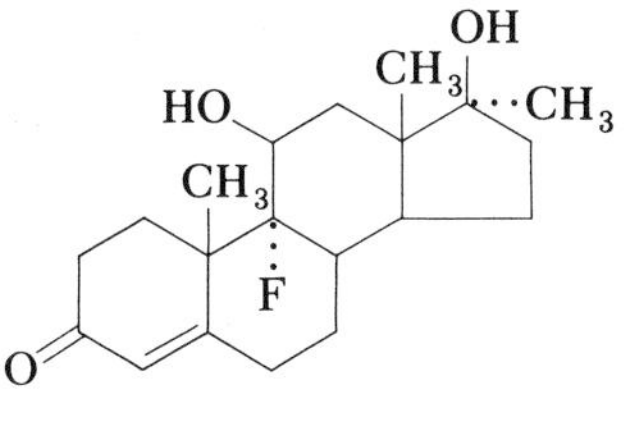

Halotestin

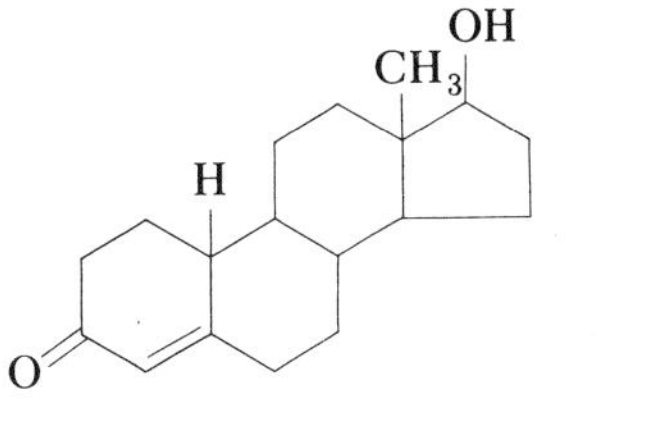

19-Nortestosterone

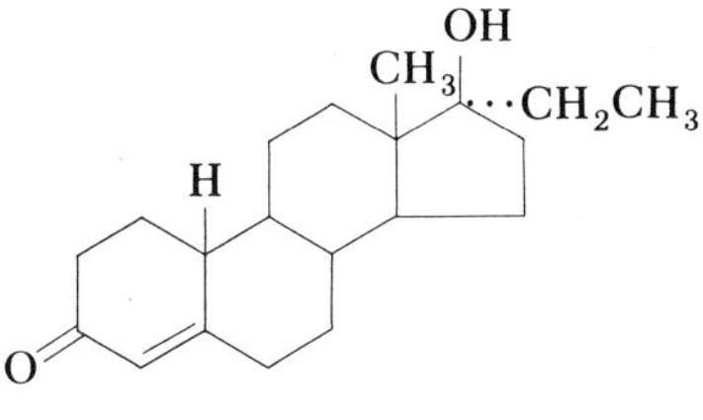

Nilevar

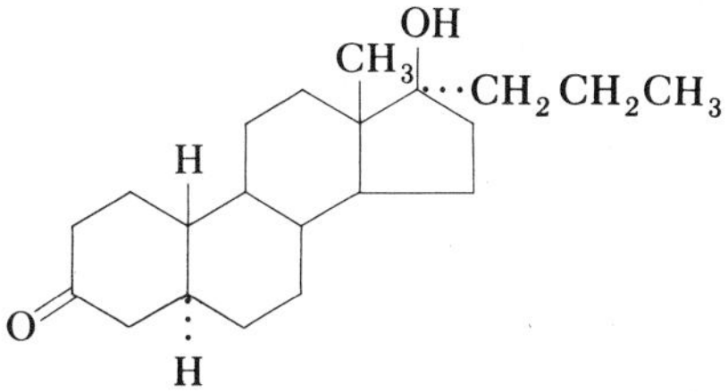

SC-6584

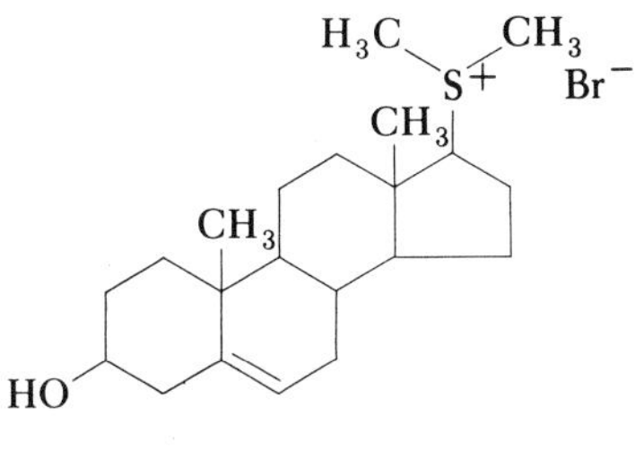

Sulfonium Analog of Dehydroepiandrosterone

FIGURE 9.9. ANDROGEN ANALOGS II.

nortestosterone have been discussed in Chap. VII, p. 107. Their myotropic and androgenic activities are very low. Sulfonium analogs of the type shown in Figure 9.9 have shown promise as ganglionic blocking agents in animal experiments. It has also been announced that the propionate of 2α-methylandrostan-17β-ol-3-one (not shown) is a potent inhibitor of mammary tumors.

X

Estrogens

1. Metabolism

A GROUP OF SEX hormones, characterized by their ability to produce heat (estrus) in females of various mammalian species, is
called estrogens. Many plants contain estrogenic substances. For
instance, the tubers of *Butea superba*, which have been used as an
aphrodisiac, contain an estrogenic substance of unknown constitution. Estrogenic activity has also been detected in *Asclepias
tuberosa*, in sprouting oat seeds, in garlic, alder catkins, sage
leaves, tulip bulbs, licorice roots, and beet seeds. Manifestations
of estrogen stimulation in Australian ewes have been traced to
their diet. The isoflavone genistein (Figure 10.1) occurs in red
and subterranean clover, and the flavone coumestrol (Figure 10.1)
was recently isolated from ladino clover and from alfalfa.

Steroids with estrogenic activity belong to the C_{18} series and
contain an aromatic A ring. Figure 10.2 shows the structures of
two representatives of the estrogen series, which also occur in
plants. Estrone has been isolated from palm kernel residues and
estriol from willow catkins and flowers. As the trivial names indicate, estrone (formerly also known as estrin, folliculin, or

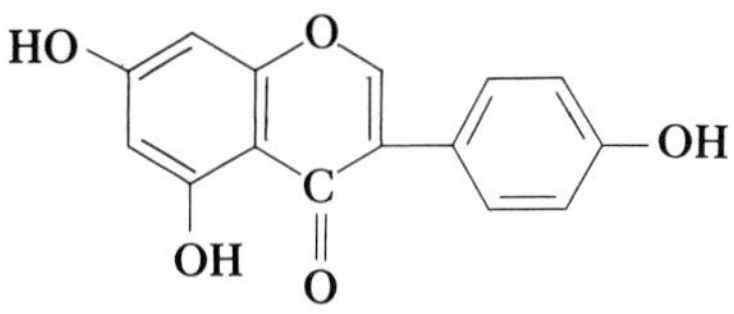

Genistein 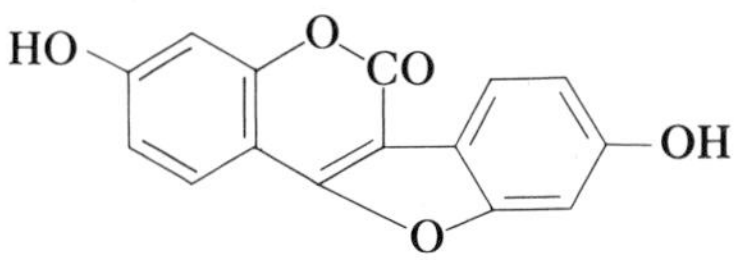   Coumestrol

FIGURE 10.1. FLAVONOID ESTROGENS.

theelin) is a ketosteroid, while estriol (formerly called theelol) contains 3 hydroxyl groups. The systematic names are based on the structure of the C_{18} hydrocarbon estrane, also shown in Figure 10.2. Thus, estrone is named $\Delta^{1,3,5(10)}$-estratrien-3-ol-17-one and estriol $\Delta^{1,3,5(10)}$-estratriene-3,16α,17β-triol.

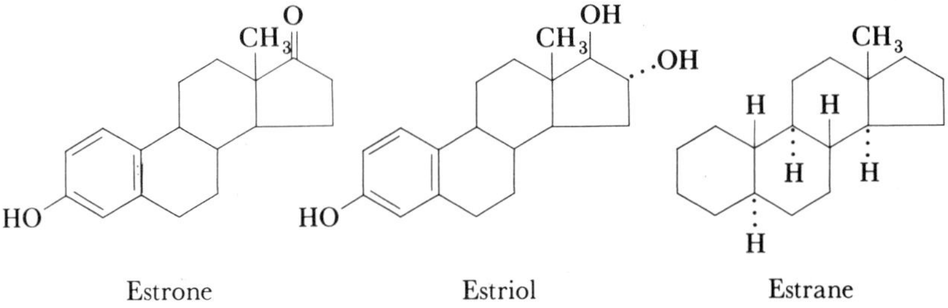

Estrone   Estriol   Estrane

FIGURE 10.2. STRUCTURE OF ESTROGENS.

In the animal body estrogens are formed by the ovaries, testes, placenta, and adrenal cortex. The biosynthesis of estrogens from acetate has been established by incubation and perfusion experiments. Evidence for the transformation of cholesterol to estrogens is based on the isolation of tritiated estrone from the urine of a pregnant woman fed tritiated cholesterol. Incubation of radioactive progesterone with bovine ovaries has yielded labeled 17-hydroxyprogesterone and androstenedione. Both *in vivo* and *in vitro* experiments have clearly shown that testosterone can be converted to estrogens by animal tissues, and it is quite possible that androgens are the major source of estrogens in animals. It has been found that adrenal tissue hydroxylates androstenedione in the 19-position, and that 19-hydroxyandrostenedione is an efficient precursor of estrone in adrenal, placental and ovarian tissue. The sequence of reactions leading to the aromatization of ring A is shown in Figure 10.3. An enzyme system which aromatizes C_{19} steroids in the presence of TPNH and oxygen has been found in the microsome fraction of placental tissue. The biogenesis of steroidal estrogens in plants may also involve oxidation at C_{19} (cf. Chap. V, p. 77). The microorganisms *Pseudomonas testosteroni* and *Septomyxa affinis* have been shown to convert 19-nortestosterone to estrone. This reaction (Figure 10.4) is a dehy-

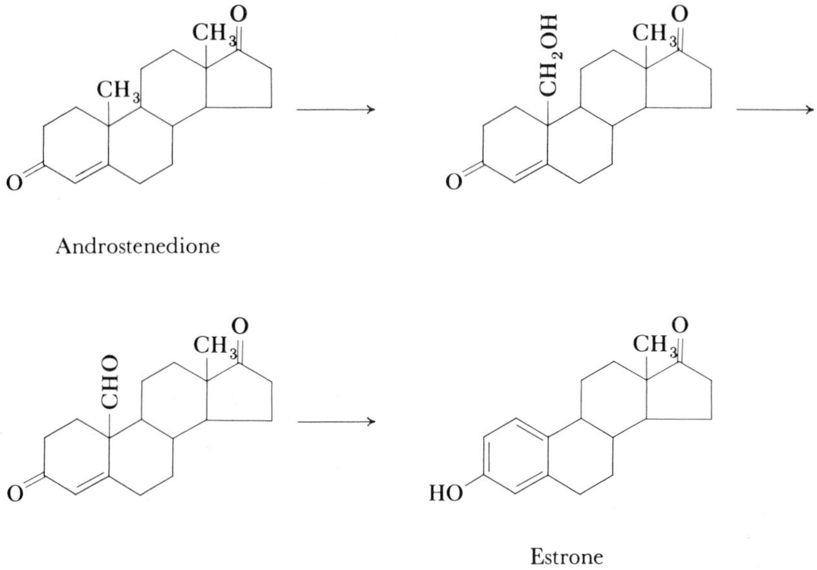

Androstenedione

Estrone

FIGURE 10.3. BIOSYNTHESIS OF ESTROGENS.

drogenation leading to the introduction of a 1,2-double bond, followed by enolization.

Of all the animal tissues from which estrogens have been isolated stallion testes have been found to be the richest source. The urine of stallions has an even greater estrogen content than that of pregnant mares. Two of the estrogens isolated from equine urine are shown in Figure 10.5. They differ from estrone in having additional double bonds in ring B. The presence of equilenin has

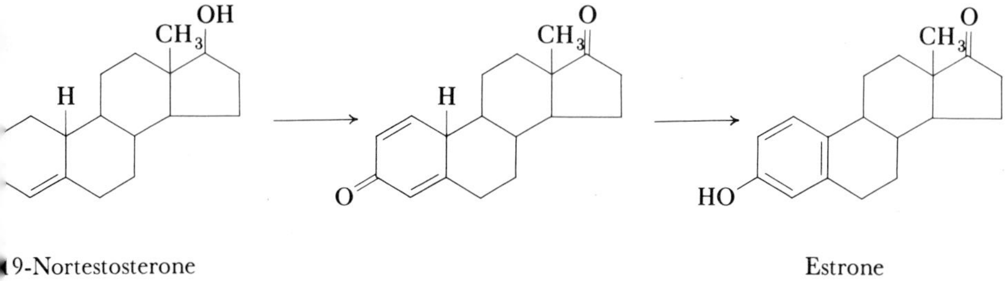

19-Nortestosterone   Estrone

FIGURE 10.4. MICROBIAL SYNTHESIS OF ESTRONE.

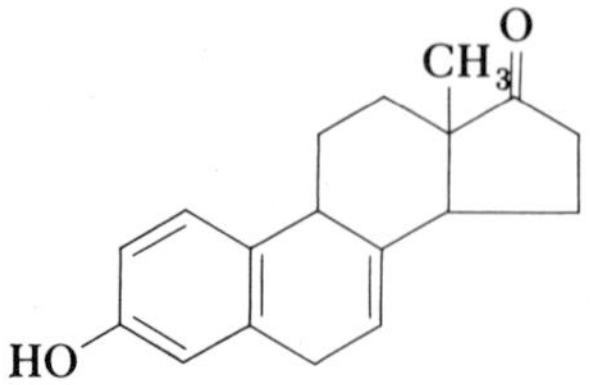

Equilin 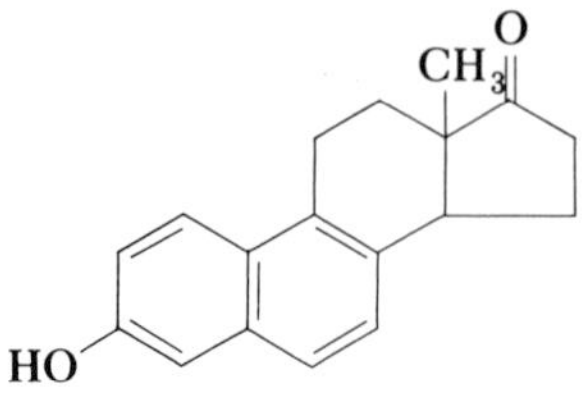   Equilenin

FIGURE 10.5. ESTROGENS UNSATURATED IN RING B.

also been demonstrated in a feminizing adrenal tumor in man. The metabolic role of estrogens unsaturated in ring B is still unknown.

Figure 10.6 summarizes some of the metabolic reactions of estrogens, most of which have been established by *in vivo* experiments. Estradiol (cf. Figure 10.6), which was known as α-estradiol before the β-configuration at C-17 was demonstrated, is interconvertible with estrone in most animal species. The reversible reaction is mediated by the enzyme estradiol-17β dehydrogenase in the presence of DPN. Both compounds are irreversibly oxidized to estriol. In rabbits the administration of estrone is not followed by an excretion of estriol, but of estradiol-17α. Many of the earlier ideas about the species differences in estrogen excretion had to be revised in the face of more recent evidence. Estriol, which had been considered as typical primate estrogen is also produced by the dog and rat. Estradiol-17α has been identified in the urine of both the pregnant mare and the pregnant goat. The incubation of estrone with beef adrenals produces 18-hydroxyestrone, a compound also found in human pregnancy urine. The most unusual metabolic reaction of estrone involves the introduction of a methyl ether group at C-2. 2-Methoxyestrone (Figure 10.6), 2-methoxyestradiol, and 2-methoxyestriol (not shown) have been isolated from human urine. Marrian, who had a leading part in this field, postulated the pathways indicated in Figure 10.7 for the metabolism of estrogens. As in previous figures, the demonstrated conversions are shown by solid arrows. The 16-hydroxylation of estrone may perhaps yield both the α- and the β-epimer. The dehydrogenation of estriol to 16α-hydroxyestrone is known not to occur. 16-Ketoestradiol is apparently reversibly reduced to both the α- and the β-epimer (estriol and 16-epiestriol).

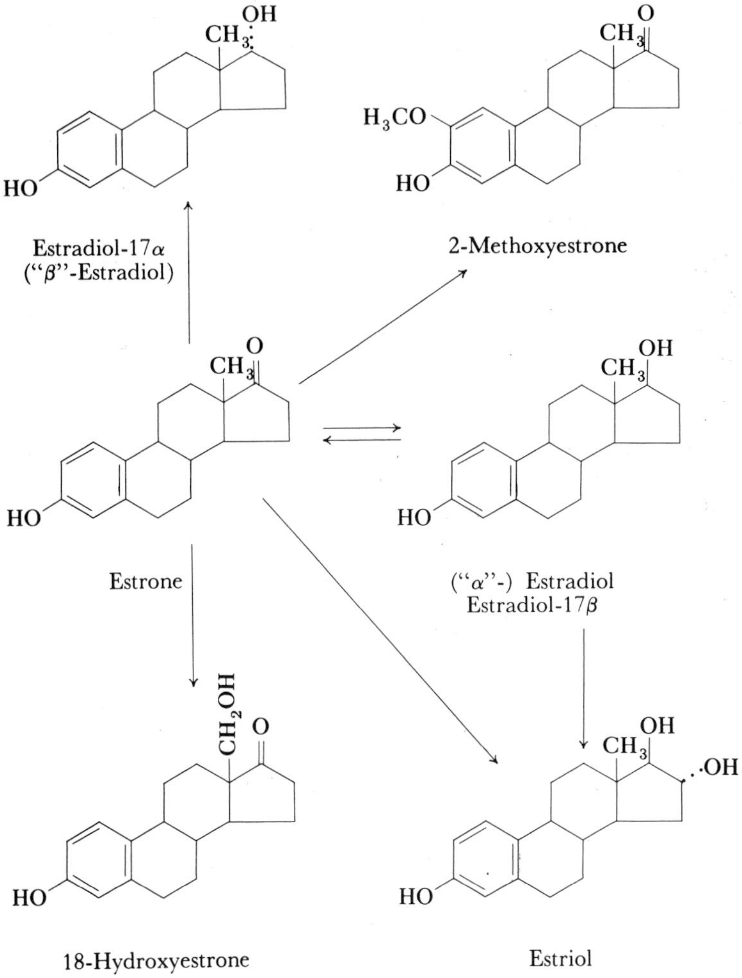

FIGURE 10.6. METABOLISM OF ESTROGENS I.

The nature of the primary product of the gonads is still in doubt, but only estrone and estradiol have been isolated from ovaries and testes. The placenta, on the other hand, contains mostly estriol. One-half to two-thirds of the estrogens circulating in the blood stream are bound to serum proteins. They are metabolized to less active substances mainly in the liver and—at least in rats—in the spleen. The liver not only inactivates estrogens, but presumably also converts certain synthetic "proestro-

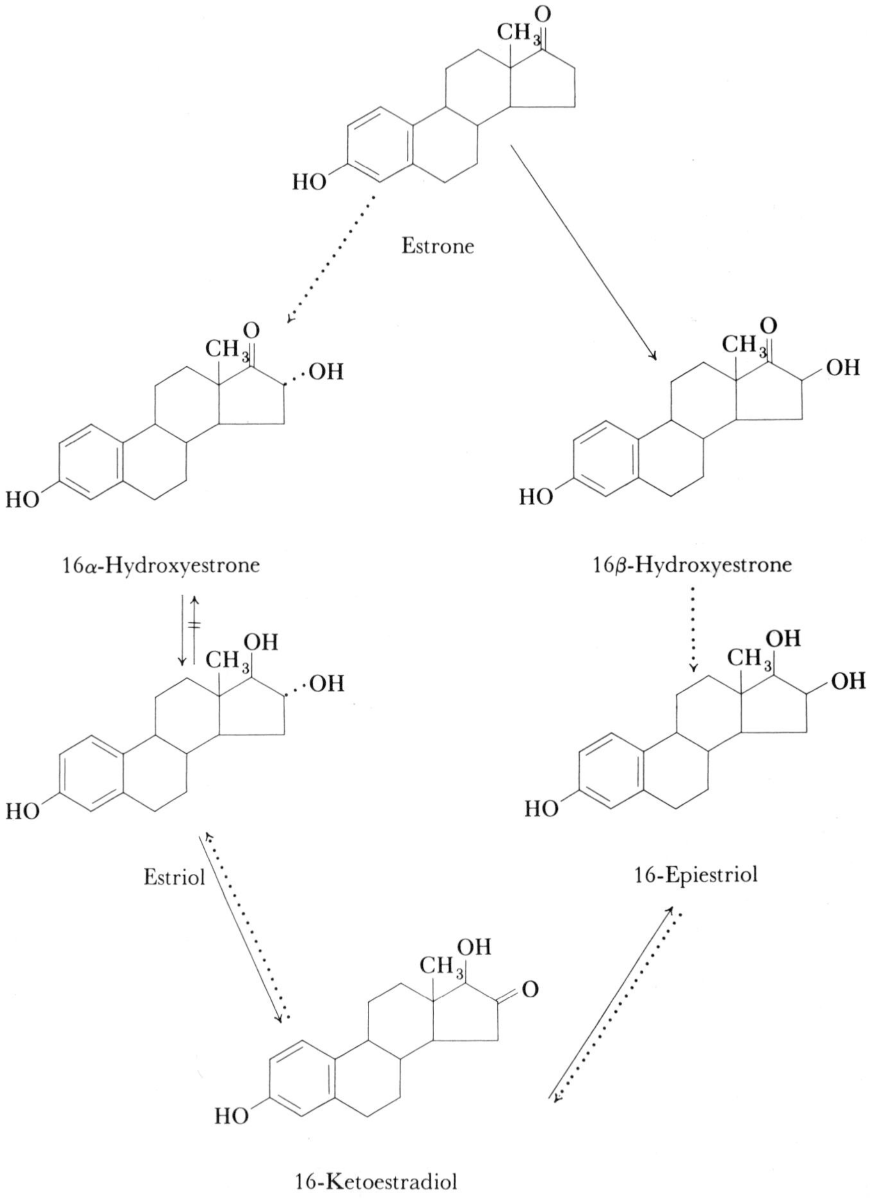

FIGURE 10.7. METABOLISM OF ESTROGENS II.

gens" to more active estrogenic hormones. The liver secretes the estrogens into the biliary tract, where they may be recirculated and—again, in rats, but to some extent also in man—excreted by way of the feces. The liver also conjugates the estrogens with glucuronic and sulfuric acid prior to their elimination by the kidneys. While the fecal estrogens probably occur in the free form, in the urine the estrogens are excreted as conjugates. After the administration of estrone or estradiol to a person, only 20-25 per cent of the dose can be recovered from the urine in the form of estrone, estradiol, and estriol. Of the administered estriol 80 per cent is recovered unchanged from the urine.

The urinary estrogen excretion in children is below 7 γ per day and begins to rise between the ages of 8 and 11. Normal men excrete from 6 to 18 γ of estrogens in 24 hours. In normally menstruating women the estrogen excretion shows two maxima during their menstrual cycle, one around the thirteenth day and one around the twenty-first day after the onset of menstruation. The maxima thus coincide with the time of ovulation and maximum luteal activity. The total estrogen excretion ranges from a minimum of about 10 γ to a maximum of about 50 γ per day. Estriol is always present in largest quantity, and estrone and estradiol in a ratio of about 2:1. During pregnancy the estrogen excretion gradually rises. Prior to delivery a woman excretes an average of 30 mg of estriol and 2 mg of each estrone and 16α-hydroxyestrone per day. The high estriol excretion is undoubtedly due to the placental synthesis of this hormone. The newborn infant also excretes large amounts of estriol in the meconium and urine. The urinary estriol occurs always in the form of the glucuronide. The urinary estrogens in men are largely of testicular origin, and in castrated or menopausal women the adrenals secrete small amounts of estrogens. The blood levels of estrogens are very low, in the neighborhood of 0.5 γ per 100 ml, and have not been sufficiently studied.

2. Endocrinology

The estrogens stimulate the growth and development of the female reproductive organs and secondary sex characteristics. They induce proliferation in the epithelium of the fallopian tubes, endometrium, cervix, and vagina. Especially in the preovulatory phase, estrogens produce changes in the tubular mucosa and stimulate the contraction and motility of the fallopian tubes, which promote the transport of the ovum. The growth of the endometrial mucosa is accompanied by an increased blood supply to this tissue produced by increased coiling of the spiral arterioles. At the same time the alkaline phosphatase, DPNH oxidase, lactic dehydrogenase, and β-glucuronidase activity of the uterus are increased. The myometrium hypertrophies and in some species undergoes rhythmic contractions, In rats, rabbits, and guinea pigs the water content of the uterus shows an increase. In the preovulatory phase the cervical mucus increases in amount, while its viscosity decreases. After estrogen stimulation the mucus shows a typical fern or palm leaf pattern on drying. The proliferation of the vaginal epithelium and corn fication of the superficial layers in rodents form the basis for a bioassay of estrogens. In primates there is an increased glycogen and mucopolysaccharide deposition in the vagina. Conversion of the glycogen to lactic acid produces an acid pH in the vagina and promotes the growth of *Lactobacillus vaginalis*. The proliferation of the uterus and vagina may be due to a stimulation of nucleotide synthesis. The mitotic activity in these tissues is greatly increased by estrogens.

Estrogens, together with pituitary factors and progesterone, stimulate mammary growth. While the proliferation of the lobular-alveolar system in primates is under progesterone control, estrogens are responsible for the growth of the stroma and duct system. The growth and pigmentation of the nipples as well as of the labia of the vagina are stimulated by estrogens. The distribution of subcutaneous fat and of body hair and the smooth character of the skin in women are likewise controlled by estrogens. Estrogens induce the opening of the vaginal introitus in rodents, and estriol has been shown to increase the size of the vagina in rabbits. It is possible that this hormone increases the lumen of the birth canal in preparation for delivery.

The estrogen secretion is under the control of pituitary gonadotropins. Conversely, large doses of estrogens inhibit the release of the follicle-stimulating and luteinizing hormones and may inhibit ovulation and eventually lead to involution of accessory sex organs. During pregnancy the estrogens block the production of lactogenic hormone. Excessive doses of estrogen may also depress growth hormone production and lead to stunted growth and premature closure of the epiphyses. The rise in body temperature at ovulation may be due to an effect of estrogens on the basal metabolic rate. Estrogens also have some effect on salt and water retention and may raise the blood pressure. They decrease clotting time and have some clinical usefulness in the control of bleeding. Estrogens favor a positive calcium balance, especially in birds, and induce the absorption of the pubic bones in the mouse. While estrogens tend to decrease the serum cholesterol in man, they produce lipemia and hypercholesterolemia in birds. The effect on lipide metabolism, together with an increase in protein anabolism and food efficiency make estrogen treatment of poultry and livestock commercially attractive. In the cat, dog, and monkey, estrogens induce mating reactions and sexual receptivity of the female, but in guinea pigs progesterone must be given simultaneously to produce this effect.

Folic acid is required for the response of the genital tract to estrogens. The androgens, adrenocortical and progestational hormones antagonize some of the effects of estrogens. Estrone and estradiol inhibit the effect of testosterone on comb growth in the capon. Many questions about the role of estrogens in the genesis of mammary and uterine cancer have been raised by the demonstration that estrogens may induce tumors in certain animals. On the other hand, estrogen treatment has benefited some patients with cancer of the breast or prostate. Estrogen treatment is also used for menopausal symptoms, especially hot flashes, in cases of delayed puberty, and for the suppression of lactation. The toxic side effects such as nausea and vomiting are similar to those sometimes observed in pregnancy. In primates withdrawal of estrogen treatment produces bleeding similar to menstruation.

The effects of estrogen deficiency in man may be observed in Turner's syndrome. In women with this disease the gonads are vestigial as a result of events in early embryonic life. Consequently the uterus remains infantile, the vagina is atrophic, there are no labia minora and infantile labia majora, the breasts are underdeveloped, and pubic and axillary hair is scanty. On the other hand, hyperestrogenism may result from acute damage to the liver. This condition may produce menstrual dysfunction in women and gynecomastia in men. Feminizing adrenocortical tumors in men may also produce gynecomastia and atrophy of penis and testes. The assay of urinary estrogens may be helpful in diagnosing functioning ovarian tumors. In pregnancy, a drop in estriol excretion may indicate placental dysfunction and death of the fetus.

The function of estrogens in plants is still unknown, but it has been observed that the administration of estrogens and androgens to higher plants may influence their sexual expression.

The mechanism of action of estrogens has been the subject of much speculation. Their effect on mitotic activity and cellular differentiation has been interpreted as an effect on barriers in the cell which prevent nucleotide-containing templates from participating in protein synthesis. According to another view, the pair estrone-estradiol is believed to have a coenzyme-like action in a pyridine nucleotide transhydrogenating system.

3. Analysis

One of the most popular bioassay methods for estrogens is the Allen-Doisy method. The test substance is injected into ovariectomized rats or mice, and vaginal smears are examined at intervals for the appearance of cornified epithelial cells. Intravaginal application of the test material allows the detection of a few thousandths of a γ of estrogen. Owing to the low precision of the method, a minimum of 20 animals must be used at each dose level. Another widely used bioassay method depends on the growth response of the uterus of immature rats or mice or of the chick oviduct to estrogen treatment. A convenient version of this method takes advantage of the fact that the uterine weight increases appreciably in 6 hours due to the accumulation of water in the endometrial stroma. The potency of estrogen preparations can also be estimated from the time elapsed between their injection into immature rodents and the estrogen-induced vaginal opening. Results may be expressed in rat units or mouse units, but it is preferable to use the international unit, which is defined as the activity of 0.1 γ of the monobenzoate of estradiol-17β.

The results of bioassays depend not only on the method used, but also on the manner in which the test material is administered. In the vaginal smear and uterine weight methods the biological activity of the natural estrogens decreases in the order estradiol > estrone > estriol. The potency of a mixture of these estrogens is difficult to assess, since the potencies of the components are additive in the vaginal smear method, but estriol and estrone antagonize the effect of estradiol, and estriol inhibits the response to estrone in the uterine growth method. In addition, urine extracts contain substances which augment the potency of estrogens. If bioassays are still used in spite of their shortcomings, it is because they are very sensitive and specific and because chemical methods are likewise not free of defects.

The hydrolysis of urinary estrogen conjugates prior to extraction is still an unsolved problem. Enzymatic hydrolysis fails to liberate all of the estrogenic substances in urine, and acid hydrolysis entails considerable losses. The addition of zinc dust to the urine prior to boiling it with hydrochloric acid increases the estrogen yield, presumably owing to conversion of some estrogens of low potency to estrogens of higher potency. Extraction of the hydrolyzate is carried out with benzene, toluene, or other organic solvents. The phenolic nature of estrogens permits their separation as a group from the extract by a strong alkali solution. Estriol, being more polar than estrone and estradiol, can be separated from the latter by extraction with weaker alkali solutions. Estrone, equilin, and equilenin may be isolated in the form of their Girard hydrazones. The estrogens are recovered from the alkali solution after neutralization by reextracting them with an organic solvent. Much pigment and chromogenic material is likewise extracted, especially if the pH of the aqueous solution is too low. The extract may be further purified by partition between solvents or by countercurrent distribution. The separation into individual estrogens may be accomplished either by partition chromatography on columns with aqueous, preferably alkaline, stationary phase and gradient elution, by adsorption chromatography on alumina after conversion of the estrogens to their methyl ethers, or by countercurrent distribution.

The chemical determination of the purified fractions may be based on the Kober reaction, but corrections must be made for interfering chromogens. In the Kober reaction estrogens are heated with 60 per cent sulfuric acid containing phenol, hydroquinone, or β-naphthol. On dilution with water and reheating a pink color is produced. The absorption due to interfering substances may be estimated by measuring the absorption at different wavelengths or after destruction of the pink color by peroxide treatment. The fluorescence produced by treatment of estrogens with sulfuric or phosphoric acid forms the basis of very sensitive, but rather nonspecific assay methods.

There are a number of specific color tests for estrogens. The 17-ketosteroids, including estrone, give the Zimmermann test (cf. Chap. IX, p. 149). Equilenin may be differentiated from equilin and estrone by the blue dye formed when it is coupled with the diazonium salt Fast Black K. Estriol gives a blue color when treated with arsenic acid in sulfuric acid and a violet color with *p*-toluenesulfonic acid in phosphoric acid. Several methods for the identification of estrogens by paper chromatography are also available.

4. Analogs

As mentioned at the beginning of this chapter, estrogenic activity is not restricted to members of the steroid group. This was first discovered in 1933, at a time when the structure of natural estrogens was not yet established. Work on aromatic compounds with estrogenic activity led Dodds to the speculation that anol (*p*-propenylphenol) should be a potent estrogen. Crude preparations of this substance actually showed estrogenic activity, but it was found later that this was due to the presence of minute amounts of diethylstilbestrol. The *trans* form of diethylstilbestrol (stilbestrol) is more active than the *cis* form and, as written in Figure 10.8, the structure of the compound bears a superficial resemblance to that of estradiol. The *meso* form of the saturated analog, hexestrol (Figure 10.8), has only about 10 per cent of the activity of stilbestrol, which is more active than estrone. Several compounds of the stilbestrol series are orally effective. Dienestrol and benzestrol (Figure 10.8) have about equal potency. The order of activity depends on the route of administration. It is diethyl-

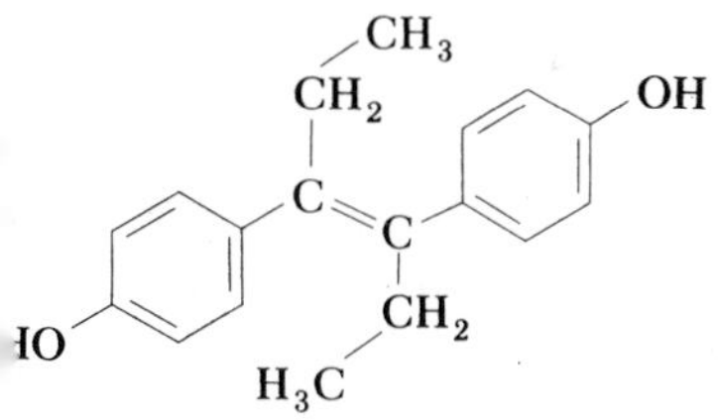

Diethylstilbestrol

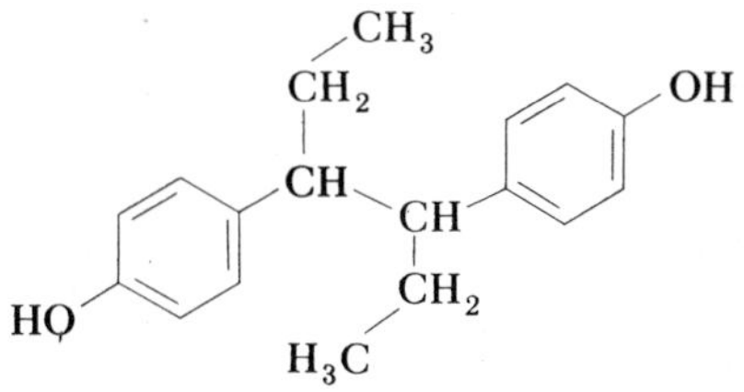

Hexestrol

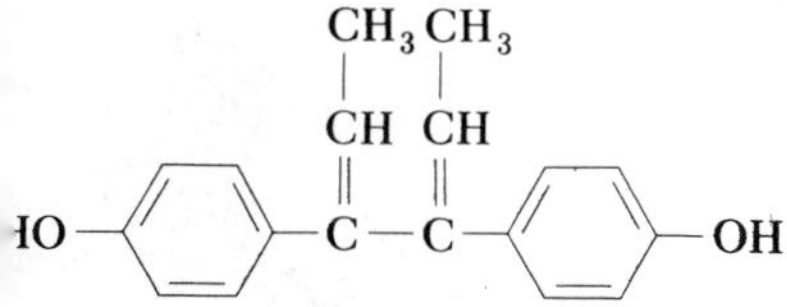

Dienestrol

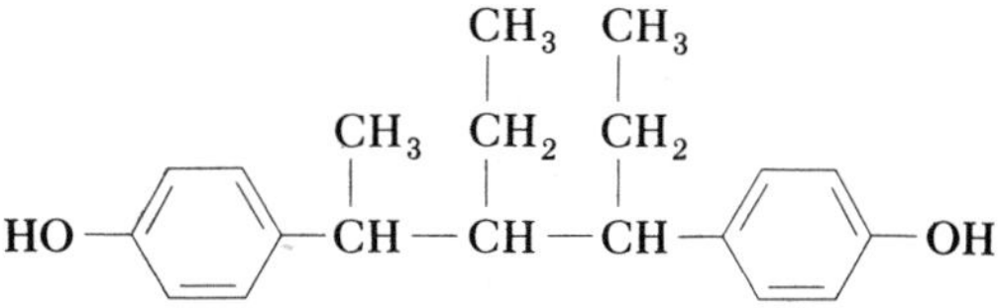

Benzestrol

FIGURE 10.8. STILBENE DERIVATIVES.

stilbestrol > dienestrol > hexestrol when the compounds are administered by mouth, but diethylstilbestrol > hexestrol > dienestrol when they are given parenterally.

The estrogenic activity of triphenylethylene derivatives is not so high, but they are very useful on account of their prolonged action. When administered subcutaneously, 1,1-bis(*p*-ethoxyphenyl)-2-bromo-2-phenylethylene (bromotriphenylethylene) and trianisylchloroethylene (TACE) (cf. Figure 10.9) are stored in the body fat and slowly released. The triphenylethane derivative known as MER-25 (Figure 10.9) has the interesting property of blocking the response of the uterus, chick oviduct, vagina, and pituitary to estrogen stimulation.

Figure 10.10 illustrates the fact that the biological activity of the steroidal estrogens does not necessarily depend on the integrity of the ring system. Doisynolic acid (named after Prof. E. A. Doisy), bisdehydrodoisynolic acid, and Horeau's acid lack ring D or both rings C and D, yet they have high estrogenic activity, at least in the rat. The enlargement of the D ring greatly reduces, but does not abolish the biological activity of estrone and estra-

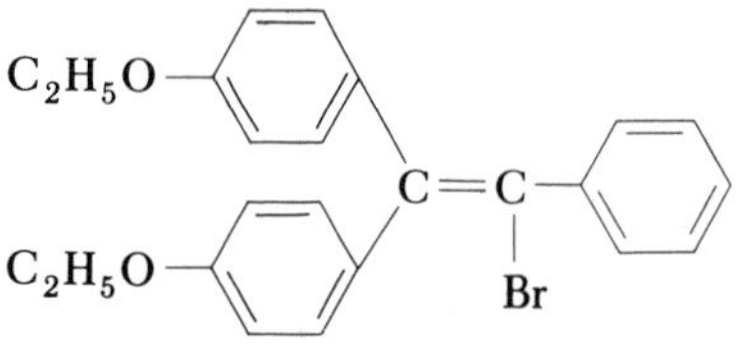

Bromotriphenylethylene

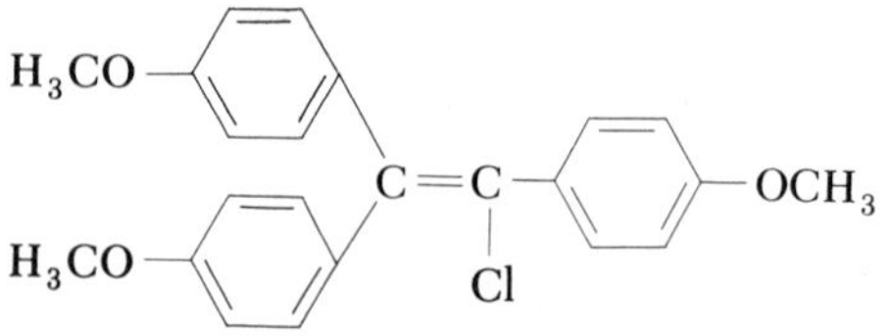

TACE

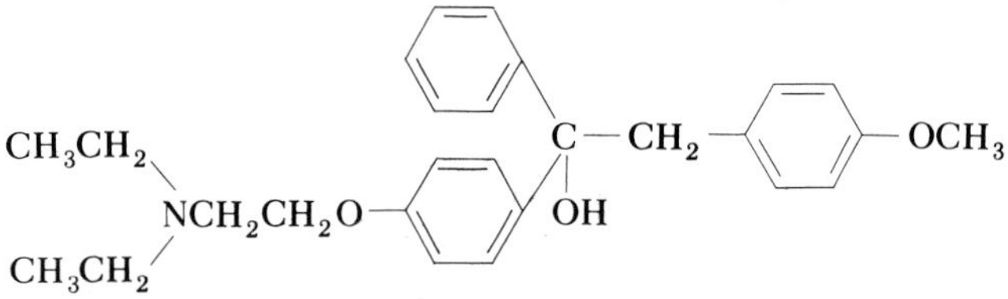

MER-25

FIGURE 10.9. TRIPHENYLETHANE DERIVATIVES.

diol. The structure of D-homoestradiol is shown in Figure 10.11. The introduction of an ethynyl group at C-17 increases the oral effectiveness of estradiol. 17α-Ethynylestradiol (Figure 10.11) is one of the most active oral estrogen preparations. The decreasing order of effectiveness of steroidal estrogens by the oral route is ethynylestradiol > estriol > estradiol > estrone. By subcutaneous route, however, estriol is the least active of these estrogens.

Estrogens find increasing application in the meat and poultry industry. Because of its low price diethylstilbestrol is used almost exclusively. The implantation of diethylstilbestrol pellets under

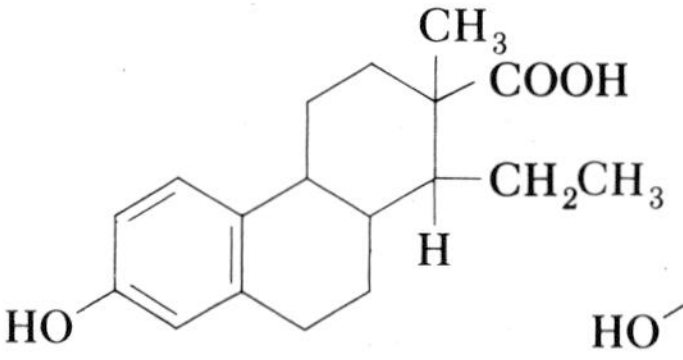

dl-cis-Doisynolic Acid 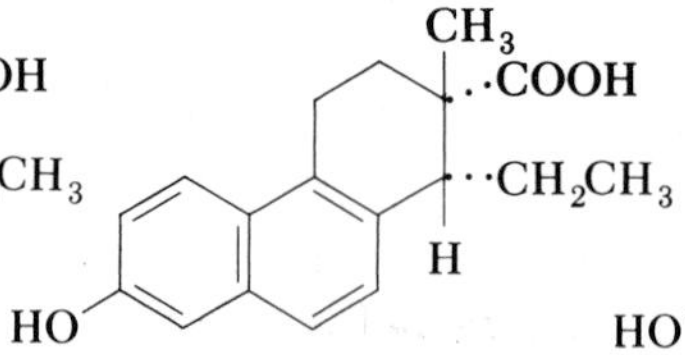   *l-cis*-Bisdehydrodoisynolic Acid 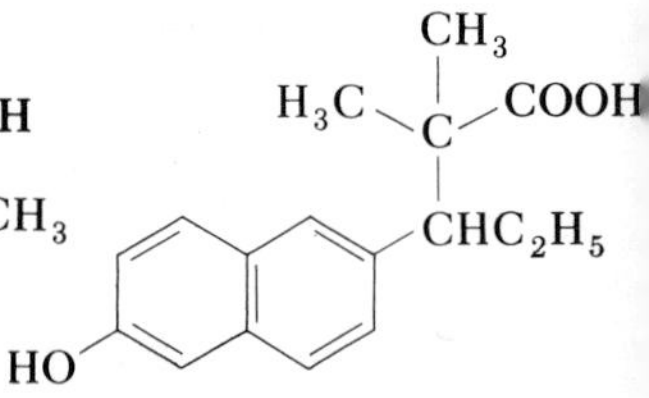   Horeau's Acid

FIGURE 10.10. ESTROGENOLIC ACIDS.

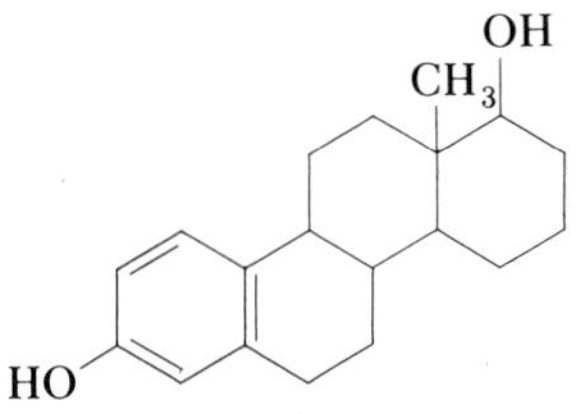

D-Homoestradiol 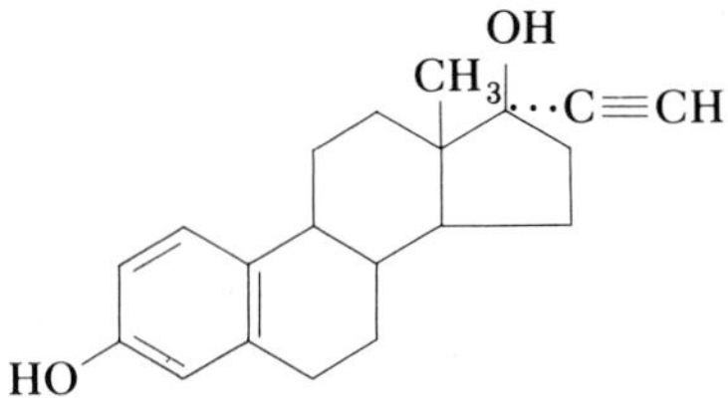   17α-Ethynylestradiol

FIGURE 10.11. ESTRADIOL ANALOGS.

the skin near the head of the chicken produces more tender and juicier meat. A comparison of the lipide-increasing/estrogenic ratio among various estrogen analogs has shown that the 3-methyl ether of 16-methylestriol, Manvene (Figure 10.12), gives a very

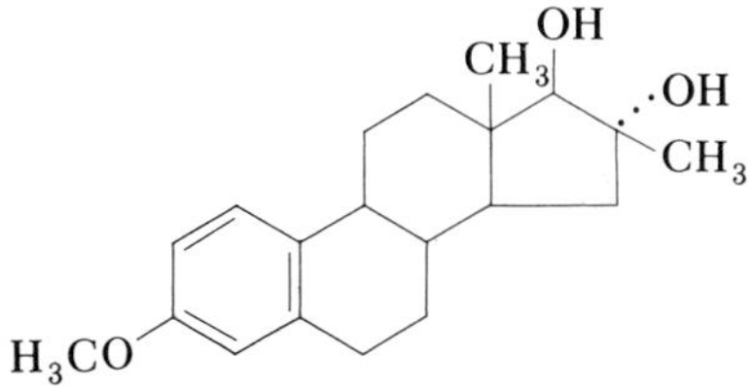

FIGURE 10.12. MANVENE.

favorable ratio. This is also true of the 3-methyl ether of 16-ketoestradiol. For human therapy both synthetic and natural estrogens are used. Premarin is an extract of pregnant mares' urine, containing a mixture of conjugated estrogens, which can be given by mouth or parenterally. Various esters of estradiol, when given intramuscularly, show a prolonged effect.

LITERATURE

Literature

As an introduction to the literature on the biochemistry of steroids, a classified list of selected review articles and monographs published since 1950 is presented. Within each section the references are listed in reverse chronological order. Since each item is cited only once, the subject index (p. 219) should be consulted for cross reference. The journal abbreviations follow the form used by *Chemical Abstracts*. For journals not abstracted in that publication the abbreviations in the *Current List of Medical Literature* are given.

1. ORGANIC CHEMISTRY
a. Steroids

1. Fieser, L. F., and Fieser, M., "Steroids," Reinhold Pub. Corp., New York, 1959.
2. Shoppee, C. W., "Chemistry of the Steroids," Butterworths Scientific Publications, London, 1958.
3. Klyne, W., "The Chemistry of the Steroids," Methuen and Co., London, 1957.
4. Rosenberg, A. P., and Greenblatt, R. B., A Simplified Introduction to Steroid Chemistry for the Clinician, *J. Am. Geriat. Soc.* **5,** 486–96 (1957).
5. Bloch, K., Synthesis and Degradation of Labeled Steroids, in S. P. Colowick and N. O. Kaplan, eds., "Methods in Enzymology," Vol. IV, p. 732–51, Academic Press, New York, 1957.
6. Fieser, L. F., Steroids, *Sci. American* **192,** 52–60 (1955).
7. Nazarov, I. N., and Bergel'son, L. D., "Khimiya Steroidnykh Gormonov," [Chemistry of Steroid Hormones], Akad. Nauk S. S. R., Moscow, 1955.
8. Hirschmann, H., Chemistry of Steroid Hormones, in G. Pincus and K. V. Thimann, eds., "The Hormones," Vol. III, p. 521–88, Academic Press, New York, 1955.

9. Lettré, H., Inhoffen, H. H., and Tschesche, R., "Über Sterine, Gallensäuren und verwandte Naturstoffe," 2nd. ed., Bd. I, F. Enke, Stuttgart, 1954; Bd. II, *ibid.*, 1959.

10. Shoppee, C. W., and Shoppee, E., Steroids: Sterols and Bile Acids, in E. H. Rodd, ed., "Chemistry of Carbon Compounds," Vol. II, Part B, p. 765–875, Elsevier Pub. Co., New York, 1953.

11. Shoppee, C. W., and Shoppee, E., Sex Hormones; Adrenocortical Hormones, in E. H. Rodd, ed., "Chemistry of Carbon Compounds," Vol. II, Part B, p. 876–982, Elsevier Pub. Co., New York, 1953.

12. Shoppee, C. W., and Shoppee, E., Steroids: Cardiotonic Glycosides and Aglycones, Toad Poisons; Steroid Saponins and Sapogenins, in E. H. Rodd, ed., "Chemistry of Carbon Compounds," Vol. II, Part B, p. 983–1050, Elsevier Pub. Co., New York, 1953.

b. Stereochemistry

13. Barton, D. H. R., and Cookson, R. C., Principles of Conformational Analysis, *Quart. Revs. (London)* **10**, 44–82 (1956).

14. Dauben, W. G., and Pitzer, K. S., Conformational Analysis, in M. S. Newman, ed., "Steric Effects in Organic Chemistry," p. 1ff., Wiley, New York, 1956.

15. Klyne, W., The Conformations of Six-Membered Ring Systems, *Progr. in Stereochem.* **1**, 36–89 (1954).

16. Mills, J. A., and Klyne, W., The Correlation of Configurations, *Progr. in Stereochem.* **1**, 177–222 (1954).

17. Nazarov, I. N., and Bergel'son, L. D., Stereokhimiia steroidnykh soedinenii, [Stereochemistry of Steroids], *Uspekhi Khim.* **21**, 566–614 (1952).

18. Barton, D. H. R., The Conformation of the Steroid Nucleus, ·*Experientia* **6**, 316–29 (1950).

c. Nomenclature

19. International Union of Pure and Applied Chemistry, "Nomenclature of Organic Chemistry" p. 73–82, Steroids. Butterworths Scientific Publications, London, 1958.

20. Courtois, J. E., "La nomenclature des vitamines et des stéroïdes, *Bull. soc. chim. biol.* **38**, 295–319 (1956).

21. Horeau, A., Jacques, J., Mathieu, J.-P., and Petit, A., A propos de la nomenclature des antipodes optiques dans les composés stéroïdes, *Bull. soc. chim. France*, **1955**, 1304–5.

22. International Union of Pure and Applied Chemistry, Tentative Rules for Steroid Nomenclature, Comptes rendus XVIIIe Conference, Zurich, p. 190–8, 1955.

23. Nazarov, I. N., O nomenklature sinteticheskikh steroidnykh soedinenii i rodstvennykh im veshchestv, [Nomenclature of Synthetic Steroids and Related Substances], *Izvest. Akad. Nauk*

S.S.R., Otdel. Khim. Nauk **4**, 726–9 (1953); *Bull. Acad. Sci. U.S.S.R., Div. Chem. Sci.* **1953**, 651–4.

24. Cahn, R. S., Editorial Report on Nomenclature, *J. Chem. Soc.* **1951**, 3515–37.

25. Ciba Conference on Steroid Nomenclature, *Chem. and Ind.* **1951**, June 23, S.N. 1–11.

26. Cahn, R. S., and others, Vorschläge zur Nomenklatur der Steroide, *Helv. Chim. Acta* **34**, 1680–95 (1951.

d. Terpenes

27. Simmonsen, I., and Ross, W. C. J., "The Terpenes," Cambridge Univ. Press, Cambridge, 1957.

28. White, D. E., Pentacyclic Triterpenoids, *Revs. Pure and Appl. Chem.* (*Australia*) **6**, 191–248 (1956).

29. Jones, E. R. H., and Halsall, T. G., Tetracyclic Triterpenes, *Fortschr. Chem. org. Naturstoffe* **12**, 44–130 (1955).

30. Gascoine, R. M., and Simes, J. J. H., The Tetracyclic Triterpenes, *Quart. Revs.* (*London*) **9**, 328–61 (1955).

31. Bouché, R., La chimie des triterpènes, *J. pharm. Belg.* **10**, 1–39 (1955).

32. Barton, D. H. R., Triterpenoids, in E. H. Rodd, ed., "Chemistry of Carbon Compounds," Vol. II, Part B, p. 726–64, Elsevier Pub. Co., New York, 1953.

2. ANALYTICAL CHEMISTRY
a. Miscellaneous

33. Parsons, J., Baher, W. T., and Baker, G., X-ray Diffraction Powder Data and Index for Steroids, *Henry Ford Hosp. Med. Bull.* **6**, No. 4, Part II (1958).

34. Mathieu, J.-P., and Petit, A., "Constantes sélectionnées. Pouvoir rotatoire naturel. I. Stéroïdes," Masson et Cie, Paris, 1956.

35. Reuber, R., Tschesche, R., Schmidt-Thomé, J., Oertel, G., and Offe, H. A., Steroide, in Hoppe-Seyler/Thierfelder "Handbuch der physiologisch- und pathologisch-chemischen Analyse," 10th ed., Vol. III, Part 2, p. 1373–1647, Springer Verlag, Berlin, 1955.

36. Stoll, A., and Jucker, E., Phytosterine, Steroidsaponine und Herzglykoside, in K. Paech and M. V. Tracy, eds., "Moderne Methoden der Pflanzenanalyse," Vol. III, p. 141–271, Springer Verlag, Berlin, 1955.

b. Spectroscopy

37. Dobriner, K., Katzenellenbogen, E. R., and Jones, R. N., "Infrared Absorption Spectra of Steroids. An Atlas," Vol. I, Interscience, New York, 1953. (See Ref. 38 for Vol. II.)

38. Roberts, G., Gallagher, B. S., and Jones, R. N., "Infrared Absorption Spectra of Steroids. An Atlas," Vol. II, Interscience, New York, 1958.

39. Rosenkrantz, H., Infrared Analysis of Vitamins, Hormones and Coenzymes, *Methods of Biochem. Anal.* **5**, 407–53 (1957); Analysis of Steroids by Infrared Spectrometry, *Ibid.* **2**, 1–55 (1955).

40. Dorfman, L., Ultraviolet Absorption of Steroids, *Chem. Revs.* **53**, 47–144 (1953).

c. Chromatography

41. Neher, R., Chromatographie von Sterinen, Steroiden und verwandten Verbindungen, *J. Chromatography* **1**, 122–65; 205–58 (1958).

42. Heftmann, E., Partition Chromatography of Steroids, *Chem. Revs.* **55**, 679–711 (1955).

43. Bush, I. E., Chromatography of Steroids and Sterols, *Brit. Med. Bull.* **10**, 229–36 (1954).

44. Bush, I. E., The Possibilities and Limitations of Paper Chromatography as a Method of Steroid Analysis, *Recent Progr. in Hormone Research* **9**, 321–30 (1954).

3. BIOCHEMISTRY
a. Lipides

45. Deuel, H. J., "The Lipids. Their Chemistry and Biochemistry," Interscience, New York, 1951–7. 3 Vols.

46. Popják, G. and Le Breton, E., eds., "Biochemical Problems of Lipids. Proceedings of the Second International Conference, Ghent, 27–30 July 1955," Butterworths Scientific Publications, London, 1956.

47. Bergström, S., and Borgström, B., Metabolism of Lipides, *Ann. Rev. Biochem.* **25**, 177–95 (1956).

48. Lovern, J. A., "The Chemistry of Lipids of Biochemical Significance," Methuen, London, 1955.

49. Cook, R. P., Comparative Aspects of Lipid Absorption and Excretion, *Biochem. Soc. Symposia (Cambridge, Engl.)* **9**, 14–29 (1952).

b. Steroids

50. Bar, D., Stérols et stéroïdes, in P. Boulanger and J. Polonovski, eds., "Traité de biochimie générale," Vol. I, Part 1, p. 343–457, Masson et Cie, Paris, 1959.

51. Mosettig, E., Biochemistry of Steroids. A Report on Symposium IV, *Proc. Intern. Congr. Biochem., 4th Congr., Vienna,* **1958**, Transact. Plenary Sessions, p. 156–69.

52. Abraham, E. P., "Biochemistry of Some Peptide and Steroid Antibiotics," Wiley, New York, 1957. (Ciba Lectures in Microbial Biochemistry, 1957).

53. Butenandt, A., and Schramm, G., Die Steroide, in B. Flaschenträger and E. Lehnartz, eds., "Physiologische Chemie," Vol. I, p. 391–483, Springer Verlag, Berlin, 1954.

54. Samuels, L. T., and Reich, H., The Chemistry and Metabolism of the Steroids, *Ann. Rev. Biochem.* **21**, 129–78 (1952).

55. Lieberman, S., and Dobriner, K., Biochemistry of Steroids, *Ann. Rev. Biochem.* **20**, 227–64 (1951).

56. Meister, P., "Über den Zusammenhang zwischen Geruch und Konstitution bei Steroiden," Zürich, 1951.

c. Biogenesis

57. Ciba Foundation, "Symposium on the Biosynthesis of Terpenes and Sterols," Little, Brown and Co., Boston, 1959.

58. Bloch, K., Biosynthesis of Branched-Chain Compounds, in S. Graff, ed., "Essays in Biochemistry," p. 22–34, Wiley, New York, 1956.

59. Bloch, K., Chemical Structure as a Guide to the Study of Biochemical Syntheses, in D. E. Green, ed., "Currents in Biochemical Research," p. 474–92, Interscience, New York, 1956.

60. Heard, R. D. H., Bligh, E. G., Cann, M. C., Jellinck, P. H., O'Donnell, V. J., Rao, B. G., and Webb, J. L., Biogenesis of the Sterols and Steroid Hormones, *Recent Progr. in Hormone Research* **12**, 45–77 (1956).

61. Pincus, G., Mécanismes enzymatiques dans la biogenèse des stéroïdes, *Exposés ann. biochim. méd.* **18**, 1–16 (1956).

62. Tschesche, R., Neuere Vorstellungen auf dem Gebiete der Biosynthese der Steroide und verwandter Naturstoffe, *Fortschr. Chem. org. Naturstoffe* **12**, 131–68 (1955).

63. Ruzicka, L., Isoprene Rule and the Biogenesis of Terpenic Compounds, *Experientia* **9**, 357–67 (1953).

d. Metabolism

64. Cameron, C. B., The Liver and Steroid Metabolism, *Brit. Med. Bull.* **13**, 119–25 (1957).

65. Talalay, P., Enzymatic Mechanisms in Steroid Metabolism. *Physiol. Revs.* **37**, 362–89 (1957).

66. Grant, J. K., Enzymic Hydroxylation of Steroids, *Ann. Repts. on Progr. Chem. (Chem. Soc. London)* **52**, 316–33 (1955).

67. Heard, R. D. H., Jacobs, R., O'Donnell, U., Péron, F. G., Saffran, J. C., Solomon, S. S., Thompson, L. M., Willoughby, H., and Yates, C. H., The Application of C^{14} to the Study of the Me-

tabolism of the Sterols and Steroid Hormones, *Recent Progr. in Hormone Research* **9**, 383-410 (1954).

68. Staudinger, Hj., and Stoeck, G., Stoffwechsel des Cholesterins und der Steroidhormone, in B. Flaschenträger and E. Lehnartz, eds., "Physiologische Chemie," Vol. II/1b, p. 870–908, Springer Verlag, Berlin, 1954.

69. Fukushima, D. K., and Rosenfeld, R. S., Sterol and Steroid Metabolism, in D. M. Greenberg, ed., "Chemical Pathways of Metabolism," Vol. I, p. 349–411, Academic Press, New York, 1954.

e. Microbiological Transformations

70. Peterson, D. H., Microbiological Transformation of Steroids and their Application to the Synthesis of Hormones, *Proc. Intern. Congr. Biochem., 4th Congr., Vienna,* **1958,** Symposium IV, p. 83–119.

71. Stadtman, T. C., The Microbial Metabolism of Steroids, in R. P. Cook, ed., "Cholesterol," p. 457–63, Academic Press, New York, 1958.

72. Vischer, E., and Wettstein, A., Enzymic Transformations of Steroids by Microorganisms, *Advances in Enzymol.* **20,** 237–82 (1958).

73. Vischer, E., and Wettstein, A., Mikrobiologische Umwandlungen von Steroiden für technische Zwecke, *Angew. Chem.* **69,** 456–63 (1957).

74. Eppstein, S. H., Meister, P. D., Murray, H. C., and Peterson, D. H., Microbiological Transformations of Steroids and Their Applications to the Synthesis of Hormones, *Vitamins and Hormones* **14,** 359–432 (1956).

75. Peterson, D. H., Microbiological Conversions of Steroids, *Record Chem. Progr. (Kresge-Hooker Sci. Lib.)* **17,** 211–40 (1956).

76. Shull, G. M., Transformations of Steroids by Molds, *Trans. N. Y. Acad. Sci.* **19,** 147–72 (1956).

77. Fried, J., Thoma, R. W., Perlman, D., Herz, J. E., and Borman, A., The Use of Microorganisms in the Synthesis of Steroid Hormones and Hormone Analogues, *Recent Progr. in Hormone Research* **11,** 149–81 (1955).

78. Wettstein, A., Conversion of Steroids by Microorganisms, *Experientia* **11,** 465–79 (1955).

79. Peterson, D. H., Microorganisms and Steroid Transformations, in S. A. Waksman, ed., "Perspectives and Horizons in Microbiology," p. 121–37, Rutgers Univ. Press, New Brunswick, N. J., 1955.

80. Hanč, O., and Riedl-Tumová, E., Die mikrobielle Umwandlung von Steroiden, *Pharmazie* **9,** 877–90 (1954).

81. Florey, K., Hydroxylierungen von Steroiden durch biologische Methoden, *Chimia (Switz.)* **8,** 81–7 (1954).

82. Finch, C. A., Synthesis of Adrenocortical Hormones. III. Microbiological Methods, *Mfg. Chemist* **25,** 247–51 (1954).

4. STEROLS
a. General

83. Kritchevsky, D., "Cholesterol," Wiley, New York, 1958.

84. Djerassi, C., Plant Steroids and Related Substances, *Proc. Intern. Congr. Biochem., 4th Congr., Vienna*, **1958**, Symposium IV, p. 1–20.

85. Glover, J., and Morton, R. A., The Absorption and Metabolism of Sterols, *Brit. Med. Bull.* **14,** 226–33 (1958).

86. Cook, R. P., and Rattray, J. B. M., Methods of Isolation and Estimation of Sterols, in R. P. Cook, ed., "Cholesterol," p. 117–43, (cf. also Appendix, p. 481–98); Academic Press, New York, 1958.

87. Cook, R. P., Distribution of Sterols in Organisms and in Tissues, in R. P. Cook, ed., "Cholesterol," p. 145–80, Academic Press, New York, 1958.

88. Bergmann, W., Evolutionary Aspects of the Sterols, in R. P. Cook, ed., "Cholesterol," p. 435–43, Academic Press, New York, 1958.

89. Horning, M. G., The Sterol Requirements of Insects and of Protozoa, in R. P. Cook, ed., "Cholesterol," p. 445–55, Academic Press, New York, 1958.

90. Cook, R. P., Some Relations of Cholesterol to Other Lipids, in R. P. Cook, ed., "Cholesterol," p. 465–79, Academic Press, New York, 1958.

91. Cook, R. P., The Chemistry and Biochemistry of the Sterols, *Proc. Nutrition Soc. (Engl. and Scot.)* **15,** 41 ff (1956).

92. Bergmann, W., The Plant Sterols, *Ann. Rev. Plant Physiol.* **4,** 383–426 (1953).

93. Bergmann, W., Sterols, *Progr. in Chem. Fats Lipids* **1,** 18–69 (1952).

b. Biosynthesis

94. Staple, E., and Whitehouse, M. W., Recent Aspects of Cholesterol Biosynthesis and Catabolism, *Ann. N. Y. Acad. Sci.* **72,** 803–12 (1959).

95. Henning, U., Die Biosynthese des Cholesterins, *Deut. med. Wochschr.* **84,** 760–4 (1959).

96. Popják, G., Biosynthesis of Cholesterol and Related Substances, *Ann. Rev. Biochem.* **27,** 533–60 (1958).

97. Cornforth, J. W., and Popják, G., Biosynthesis of Cholesterol, *Brit. Med. Bull.* **14,** 221–6 (1958).

98. Bloch, K., Biogenesis and Transformations of Squalene, *Proc. Intern. Congr. Biochem., 4th Congr., Vienna*, **1958,** Symposium IV, p. 50–7.

99. Lynen, F., Eggerer, H., Henning, U., and Kessel, I., Farnesyl-pyrophosphat und 3-Methyl-Δ^3-butenyl-1-pyrophosphat, die biologischen Vorstufen des Squalens, *Angew. Chem.* **70,** 738–42 (1958).

100. Rilling, H., Tchen, T. T., and Bloch, K., On the Mechanism of Squalene Biogenesis, *Proc. Natl. Acad. Sci.* **44**, 167–73 (1958).

101. Gould, R. G., Biosynthesis of Cholesterol, in R. P. Cook, ed., "Cholesterol," p. 210–35, Academic Press, New York, 1958.

102. Bloch, K., The Biological Synthesis of Cholesterol, *Vitamins and Hormones* **15**, 119–50 (1957).

103. Anon., Cholesterol Biosynthesis, *Nutrition Revs.* **15**, 282–3 (1957).

104. Anon., Inhibitors of Cholesterol Biosynthesis, *Nutrition Revs.* **15**, 309–11 (1957).

105. Anon., Squalene and Cholesterol Synthesis in the Human Skin, *Nutrition Revs.* **14**, 138–9 (1956).

106. Cornforth, J. W., Biosynthesis of Cholesterol, *Revs. Pure and Appl. Chem. (Australia)* **4**, 275–302 (1955).

107. Popják, G., Chemistry, Biochemistry, and Isotopic Tracer Technique, *Roy. Inst. Chem. Lectures, Monographs and Repts.* **No. 2**, 59 p. (1955).

108. Anon., Inhibition of Cholesterol Formation, *Nutrition Revs.* **13**, 310–11 (1955).

109. Bloch, K., Biological Synthesis of Cholesterol, *Harvey Lectures Ser.* **48**, 68–88 (1954).

c. Metabolism

110. Gould, R. G., and Cook, R. P., The Metabolism of Cholesterol and Other Sterols in the Animal Organism, in R. P. Cook, ed., "Cholesterol," p. 237–307, Academic Press, New York, 1958.

111. Hechter, O., Conversion of Cholesterol to Steroid Hormones, in R. P. Cook, ed., "Cholesterol," p. 309–47, Academic Press, New York, 1958.

112. Anon., Fatty Acids and Cholesterol Metabolism, *Nutrition Revs.* **16**, 81–2 (1958).

113. Le Roy, G. V., Role of Cholesterol in Steroidogenesis, *Trans. Assoc. Am. Physicians* **70**, 202–15 (1957).

114. Kritchevsky, D., Some Aspects of Cholesterol Metabolism, *J. Am. Med. Women's Assoc.* **12**, 423–9 (1957).

115. Paget, M., Quelques aspects de la biochemie du cholestérol, *Ann. biol. clin. (Paris)* **15**, 127–55 (1957).

116. Friedman, M., Byers, S. O., and St. George, S., Cholesterol Metabolism, *Ann. Rev. Biochem.* **25**, 613–40 (1956).

117. Anon., Vitamin A and Cholesterol Metabolism, *Nutrition Revs.* **14**, 245–6 (1956).

118. Anon., The Origin of Urinary Cholesterol, *Nutrition Revs.* **11**, 189–91 (1953).

119. Anon., Metabolism of Dietary Cholesterol by the Liver, *Nutrition Revs.* 10, 174–5 (1952).

d. Serum Cholesterol

120. Boyd, G. S., and Olivier, M. F., The Physiology of the Circulating Cholesterol and Lipoproteins, in R. P. Cook, ed., "Cholesterol," p. 181–208, Academic Press, New York, 1958.

121. Anon., Cholesterol in Diet and Serum, *Nutrition Revs.* **16**, 42–4 (1958).

122. Anon., Dietary Fat and Plasma Cholesterol, *Nutrition Revs.* **16**, 68–70 (1958).

123. Anon., Corn Oil and Plasma Cholesterol, *Nutrition Revs.* **16**, 83–4, (1958).

124. Sherber, D. A., Hypercholesterolemia, *Am. Practitioner* **8**, 776–83 (1957).

125. Favarger, P., Les mécanismes régulateurs du cholestérol sanguin, *Ann. biol. clin. (Paris)* **15**, 156–76 (1957).

126. Tayeau, F., État et rôle du cholestérol circulant, *Ann. biol. clin. (Paris)* **15**, 177–94 (1957).

127. Anon., Dietary Protein and Serum Cholesterol, *Nutrition Revs.* **15**, 227–9 (1957).

128. Anon., Reduction of Serum Cholesterol by Diet, *Nutrition Revs.* **15**, 352 (1957).

129. Anon., Unsaturated Fatty Acids and Serum Cholesterol Levels, *Nutrition Revs.* **14**, 327–8 (1956).

130. Ludat, M.-H., "Les stéroïdes plasmatiques. Étude théoretique et pratique," Foulon, Paris, 1956.

131. Anon., Variability of Serum Cholesterol and Lipoproteins in Man, *Nutrition Revs.* **13**, 72–4 (1955).

132. Tayeau, F., Quelques aspects physico-chimiques et physio-pathologiques du cholestérol sérique, *Exposés ann. biochim. méd.* **17**, 213–49 (1955).

133. Byers, S. O., Friedman, M., and Rosenman, R. H., Review: On the Regulation of Blood Cholesterol, *Metabolism* **1**, 479–503 (1952).

134. Anon., Effect of Plant Sterols on Plasma and Liver Cholesterol in the Chick, *Nutrition Revs.* **10**, 345–7 (1952).

e. Nutrition

135. Anon., Cholesterol Absorption in the Human, *Nutrition Revs.* **16**, 168–70 (1958).

136. Anon., Plant Sterols and Cholesterol Absorption, *Nutrition Revs.* **15**, 45–7 (1957).

137. Anon., Nutritional State and Cholesterogenesis, *Nutrition Revs.* **15**, 85–6 (1957).

138. Anon., Cholesterol Absorption in the Rabbit, *Nutrition Revs.* **15**, 95 (1957).

139. Anon., Dietary Factors Affecting Cholesterol Excretion, *Nutrition Revs.* **15**, 143–5 (1957).

140. Halden, W., "Cholesterin, Ernährung, Gesundheit," Urban und Schwarzenberg, Munich, 1957.

141. Favarger, P., Données récentes sur l'absorption intestinale des graisses et du cholestérol, *Ann. nutrition et aliment.* **10**, 211–36 (1956).

142. Anon., Influence of Fasting and of Diet on Cholesterol Synthesis, *Nutrition Revs.* **10**, 345–7 (1952).

f. Medicine

143. Adlersberg, D., and Sobotka, H., Pathological Manifestations of Abnormal Cholesterol Metabolism, in R. P. Cook, ed., "Cholesterol," p. 375–425, Academic Press, New York, 1958.

144. Page, I. H., Treatment of Disorders of Cholesterol Metabolism, in R. P. Cook, ed., "Cholesterol," p. 427–33, Academic Press, New York, 1958.

145. Hieger, I., Cholesterol Carcinogenesis, *Brit. Med. Bull.* **14**, 159–60 (1958).

146. Thannhauser, S. J., Miscellaneous Disorders of Metabolism VI. Lipidoses, in R. H. S. Thompson and E. J. King, eds., "Biochemical Disorders in Human Disease," p. 697–737, Academic Press, New York, 1957.

147. Lower, E. S., Cholesterol, *Drug and Cosmetic Ind.* **74**, 52–3; 127–32; 200–1; 294–301; 356–7; 432–4 (1954).

148. Anon., Cholesterol Synthesis from Acetate in Diabetes, *Nutrition Revs.* **11**, 158–9 (1953).

g. Atherosclerosis

149. Dock, W., Cardiovascular Diseases (Atherosclerosis), *Ann. Rev. Med.* **10**, 77–92 (1959).

150. Pincus, G., ed., "Hormones and Atherosclerosis, Proc. Conf., Brighton, Utah, 1958," Academic Press, New York, 1959.

151. Page, I. H., ed., "Chemistry of Lipides as Related to Atherosclerosis; a Symposium," C. C. Thomas, Springfield, Illinois, 1958.

152. Katz, L. N., Stamler, J., and Pick, R., "Nutrition and Atherosclerosis," Lea and Febiger, Philadelphia, 1958.

153. Olson, R. E., Atherosclerosis—A Primary Hepatic or Vascular Disorder? *Perspectives Biol. and Med.* **2**, 84–121 (1958).

154. Oliver, M. F., and Boyd, G. S., Hormonal Aspects of Coronary Artery Disease, *Vitamins and Hormones* **16**, 148–78 (1958).

155. Connor, W. E., Atherosclerosis: Current Status of Dietary and Hormonal Factors, *Am. Practitioner* **8**, 1920–6 (1957).

156. Keys, A., ed., "Arteriosclerosis; A Symposium Presented by the Minnesota Heart Assoc. and the Univ. of Minnesota, Sept. 7–9, 1955," Univ. of Minnesota Press, Minneapolis, 1956.

157. Symposium on Atherosclerosis, Natl. Res. Council, Publication 338, Washington, D. C., 1955.

158. Friedman, M., Rosenman, R. H., and Byers, S. O., Deranged Cholesterol Metabolism and its Possible Relationship to Human Atherosclerosis: a Review, *J. Gerontol.* **10**, 60–85 (1955).

159. Anon., Diet, Cholesterol and Atherosclerosis, *Nutrition Revs.* **13**, 138–40 (1955).

160. Favarger, P., Le rôle du cholésterol dans l'athéromatose, *Exposés ann. biochim. méd.* **15**, 93–129 (1953).

5. VITAMIN D GROUP

161. Lythgoe, B., Some Recent Advances in the Chemistry of the D Vitamins, *Proc. Chem. Soc.* **1959**, 141–9.

162. Inhoffen, H. H., and Irmscher, K., Fortschritte der Chemie der Vitamine D und ihrer Abkömmlinge, *Fortschr. Chem. org. Naturstoffe* **17**, 246–86 (1959).

163. Ames, S. R., Fat-soluble Vitamins, *Ann. Rev. Biochem.* **27**, 371–402 (1958).

164. Anon., Provitamin D in Animal Tissues, *Nutrition Revs.* **16**, 16–7 (1958).

165. Huber, H., Vitamin D und Kariesprophylaxe; Bericht über die I. wissenschaftliche Tagung am Zahnärztlichen Institut der Universität Bern, 8–9. März 1956; *Internationale Zeitschrift für Vitaminforschung*, **Beiheft nr. 7** (1958).

166. Raoul, Y., La cétone 250, nouveau type de vitamine antirachitique, *Intern. Z. Vitaminforsch.* **28**, 306–27 (1958).

167. Blaxter, K. L., The Fat-soluble Vitamins, *Ann. Rev. Biochem.* **26**, 275–306 (1957).

168. Anon., The Action of Vitamin D on Bone Accretion and Resorption, *Nutrition Revs.* **15**, 70–1 (1957).

169. Anon., Intakes of Vitamins A and D, *Nutrition Revs.* **15**, 74–5 (1957).

170. Anon., Vitamin D and Cortisone: Synergists and Antagonists? *Nutrition Revs.* **15**, 251–3 (1957).

171. Anon., Vitamin D and Citrate Oxidation, *Nutrition Revs.* **15**, 253–4, (1957).

172. Anon., Vitamin D in the Newborn, *Nutrition Revs.* **15**, 262–4 (1957).

173. Swoboda, W., "Die genuine Vitamin D-resistente Rachitis," Maudrich, Vienna, 1956. (Wiener Beiträge zur Kinderheilkunde, Bd. 6).

174. Hövels, O., Der Einfluss der Vitamine auf die Verkalkung, *Colloq. Ges. physiol. Chem.* **7**, 114–31 (1956).

175. Kodicek, E., Fat-soluble Vitamins, *Ann. Rev. Biochem.* **25**, 497–536 (1956).

176. Dam, H., The Biochemistry of Fat-soluble Vitamins, *Progr. in Chem. Fats, Lipids* **3**, 172–8 (1955).

177. Sebrell, W. H., Jr., and Harris, R. S., eds., Vitamin D Group, in "The Vitamins," Vol. II, p. 131–266, Academic Press, New York, 1954.

178. Inhoffen, H. H., and Brückner, K., Probleme und neuere Ergebnisse in der Vitamin D-Chemie, *Fortrchr. Chem. org. Naturstoffe* **11**, 83–123 (1954).

179. Schepp, J., "Vitamin D; seine Strukturformen, Wirkungen und Anwendung," M. and H. Schaper, Hannover, 1953.

180. Nicolaysen, R., and Eeg-Larsen, N., Biochemistry and Physiology of Vitamin D, *Vitamins and Hormones* **11**, 29–60 (1953).

181. György, P., ed., "Vitamin Methods," Academic Press, New York, 1950.

6. SAPONINS

182. Maheas, J. de, Sapogénines stéroliques, *Rev. pathol. gén. comparée* **57**, 537–43 (1957).

183. Sokol'skaya, A. M., [Steroidal Saponins], *Vestnik Akad. Nauk Kazakh. S. S. R.* **11** (6) 69–84 (1955).

184. Bouché, R., Les saponines, Aperçu historique et généralités, *J. pharm. Belg.* **9**, 311–17 (1954).

185. Heine, E. W., Saponine. Bericht über einige Eigenschaften, die chemische Struktur im Rahmen verwandter Stoffe und die Saponinhämolyse, *Pharmazie* **8**, 467–77 (1953).

7. ALKALOIDS

186. Voigt, K.-D., and Kallistratos, G., Über stickstoffhaltige Steroide, *Endokrinologie* **35**, 56–64 (1958).

187. Tschesche, R., C_{21} Steroide des Pflanzenreiches, *Proc. Intern. Congr. Biochem., 4th Congr., Vienna*, **1958**, Symposium IV, p. 21–7.

188. Morgan, K. J., and Barltrop, J. A., Veratrum Alkaloids, *Quart. Revs. (London)* **12**, 34–60 (1958).

189. Schreiber, K., Neuere Untersuchungen auf dem Gebiete der Solanum-Alkaloide, *Abhandl. deut. Akad. Wiss. Berlin* **1957**, 143–57.

190. Petrotschenko, E. I., Die Glykoalkaloide der Nachtschattengewächse, *Abhandl. deut. Akad. Wiss. Berlin* **1957**, 158–65.

191. Wintersteiner, O., The Veratrum Alkamines, in S. Graff, ed., "Essays in Biochemistry," p. 308–21, Wiley, New York, 1956.

192. Schreiber, K., Die Glykoalkaloide der Solanaceen, *Chem. Tech. (Berlin)* **6,** 648–58 (1954).

193. Wintersteiner, O., The Chemistry of the Veratrum Alkaloids, *Record Chem. Progr. (Kresge-Hooker Sci. Lib.)* **14,** 19–34 (1953).

194. Prelog, V., and Jeger, O., The Chemistry of Solanum and Veratrum Alkaloids, in R. H. F. Manske and H. L. Holmes, eds., "The Alkaloids," Vol. III, p. 248–312, Academic Press, New York, 1953.

195. McKenna, J., Steroidal Alkaloids, *Quart. Revs. (London)* **7,** 231–54 (1953).

8. CARDIAC GLYCOSIDES
a. Chemistry

196. Tamm, C., Neuere Ergebnisse auf dem Gebiete der glykosidischen Herzgifte, *Fortschr. Chem. org. Naturstoffe* **13,** 138–231 (1956) and **14,** 72–140 (1957).

197. Stoll, A., and Renz, J., Herzwirksame Glykoside in Digitalis-Arten, *Verhandl. naturforsch. Ges. Basel* **67,** 392–446 (1956).

198. Bisset, N. G., The Steroid Glycosides of the Apocynaceae, *Indonesian J. Nat. Sci.* **111,** 76–117 (1955).

199. Reichstein, T., Chemie der herzaktiven Glykoside, *Angew Chem.* **63,** 412–21 (1951).

200. Heusser, H., Konstitution, Konfiguration und Synthese digitaloider Aglykone und Glykoside, *Fortschr. Chem. org. Naturstoffe* **7,** 87–166 (1950).

201. Stoll, A., Über die herzwirksamen Glykoside der Digitalisgruppe, *Pharmazie* **5,** 328ff (1950).

202. Renz, J., Sobre los glucosidos cardiotonicos, *Farmacognosia (Madrid)* **10** (17), 107–73 (1950).

b. Pharmacology

203. Balotin, N. M., Digitalis: Its Use and Abuse; Literature Review, *J. Lancet* **79,** 8–13 (1959).

204. Alhopuro, U. M., Cardiac Digitalis Glycosides, *Farm. Aikakauslehti* **68,** 16–32 (1959).

205. Hajdu, S., and Leonard, E., The Cellular Basis of Cardiac Glycoside Action, *Pharmacol. Revs.* **11,** 173–209 (1959).

206. Hofmann, H., Die Pharmakologie herzwirksamer Glykoside, *Z. ärztl. Fortbild.* **52,** 720–2 (1958).

207. Krantz, J. C., Jr., The Cardiac Glycosides in Medical Practice, *Postgrad. Med.* **24,** 224–30 (1958).

208. Grettve, J., and Johansson, B., Digitalis Allergy: Review of the Literature and Report of a Case, *Cardiologia* **32**, 374–82 (1958).

209. Moran, N. C., Pharmacological Actions of Cardiac Glycosides, *Mod. Hosp.* **89** (No. 2), 102–10 (1957).

210. Popov, S. E., O mekhanizme deistviia naperstianki na metabolizm nedostatochnoi serdechnoi myshtsy, obzor, [Mechanism of Action of Digitalis on a Deficient Cardiac Muscle; Review,] *Terap. Arkh.* **29**, 3–14 (1957).

211. Dimond, E. G., ed., "Digitalis," C. C. Thomas, Springfield, Illinois, 1957.

212. Hopkins, S. J., Cardiac Drugs; Their Nature and Use, *Chemist and Druggist* **164**, 553-6 (1955).

213. Wilbrandt, W., Zum Wirkungsmechanismus der Herzglykoside, *Schweiz. med. Wochschr.* **85**, 315–20 (1955).

214. Proctor, C. D., A Hypothesis for a Mechanism of Cardiac Glycoside Action, *Ann. N. Y. Acad. Sci.* **62**, 377–402 (1955).

215. Lown, B., and Levine, S. A., "Current Concepts in Digitalis Therapy," Little, Brown and Co., Boston, 1954.

216. Chen, K. K., and Henderson, F. G., Pharmacology of Sixty-four Cardiac Glycosides and Aglycones, *J. Pharmacol. Exptl. Therap.* **111**, 365–83 (1954).

217. Granata, G., "I glucosidi cardioattivi nella pratica pediatrica," Istituto di Ricerche V. Baldacci Edit., Pisa, 1953. (Omnia therapeutica, Suppl. 6).

218. Rossi, G. V., The Cardiac Glycosides; a Review, *Am. J. Pharm.* **124**, 77–93 (1952).

219. Chen, K. K., Henderson, F. G., and Anderson, R. C., Comparison of Forty-two Cardiac Glycosides and Aglycones, *J. Pharmacol. Exptl. Therap.* **103**, 420–30 (1951).

220. Ashelford, P. J., The Pharmacological Assessment of Cardiac Glycosides, *Australasian J. Pharm.* **52**, 793–4 (1951).

221. Kern, B., "Die orale Strophanthin-Behandlung; ärztliche Studie über ihre Erneuerung und ihren Einfluss auf die Kardiologie," F. Enke, Stuttgart, 1951.

9. BILE ACIDS

222. Bergström, S., Bile Acids: Formation and Metabolism, *Proc. Intern. Congr. Biochem.*, *4th Congr.*, *Vienna*, **1958**, Symposium IV, p. 160–73.

223. Lambiotte, M., and Fallot, P., Métabolisme des acides biliaires, *Comm. energie atomique (France)* **Rappt. No. 787**, 541–56 (1958).

224. Haslewood, G. A. D., Recent Developments in our Knowledge of Bile Salts, *Physiol. Revs.* **35**, 178–96 (1955).

225. Bergström, S., Bile Acids and Steroids XX: Formation and Metabolism of Bile Acids, *Record Chem. Progr.* (*Kresge-Hooker Sci. Lib.*) **16,** 63–83 (1955).

10. HORMONES
a. General Biochemistry

226. Bersin, P. T., "Biochemie der Hormone," Akad. Verlagsges., Leipzig, 1959.

227. Hanč, O., "Hormone, Einführung in ihre Chemie und Biologie," Fischer, Jena, 1959.

228. Samuels, L. T., Biosynthesis of Steroid Hormones, *Reproduction and Infertility, 3rd Symp.*, *Fort Collins, Colo.*, **1957,** 19–28 (1958).

229. Dorfman, R. I., Biochemistry of the Steroid Hormones, *Ann. Rev. Biochem.* **26,** 523–60 (1957).

230. Pincus, G., The Hormones, their Present Significance, their Future, in D. E. Green, ed., "Currents in Biochemical Research," p. 176–97, Interscience, New York, 1956.

231. Engel, L. L., Some Thoughts on the Biochemistry of the Steroid Hormones, in S. Graff, ed., "Essays in Biochemistry," p. 85–93, Wiley, New York, 1956.

232. Corona Toledo, L., "Bioquímica clínica de las hormonas-esteroides," Zig-Zag, Santiago de Chile, 1956.

233. Callow, R. K., Biochemistry of the Gonadal Hormones, *Brit. Med. Bull.* **11,** 126–30 (1955).

234. Roberts, S., and Szego, C. M., Biochemistry of the Steroid Hormones, *Ann. Rev. Biochem.* **24,** 543–96 (1955).

235. Gallagher, T. F., Biochemical Problems of the Steroid Hormones, in F. R. N. Gurd, ed., "Chemical Specificity in Biological Interactions," p. 50–64, Academic Press, New York, 1954.

236. Lieberman, S., and Teich, S., Recent Trends in the Biochemistry of the Steroid Hormones, *Pharmacol. Revs.* **5,** 285–380 (1953).

237. Gordon, E. S., ed., "Symposium on Steroid Hormones," Univ. of Wisconsin Press, Madison, 1950.

b. Metabolism

238. Lieberman, S., Erlanger, B. F., Beiser, S. M., and Agate, F. J., Jr., Steroid-Protein Conjugates: Their Chemical, Immunochemical, and Endocrinological Properties, *Recent Progr. in Hormone Research* **15,** 165–96 (1959).

239. Orzechowski, G., Stoffwechsel der Steroid-Hormone, *Medizinische* **42,** 1649–52 (1958).

240. Savard, K., Études récentes sur la stéroïdogenèse dans les gonades humaines, *Exposés ann. biochim. méd.* **19,** 219–29 (1957).

241. Ciba Foundation, "Hormones in Blood," Little, Brown and Co., Boston, 1957. (Ciba Foundation Colloquia on Endocrinology, Vol. XI).

242. Sandberg, A. A., Slaunwhite, W. R., Jr., and Antoniades, H. N., The Binding of Steroids and Steroid Conjugates to Human Plasma Proteins, *Recent Progr. in Hormone Research* **13**, 209–60 (1957).

243. Borth, R., Steroids in Human Blood, *Vitamins and Hormones* **15**, 259–90 (1957).

244. Levvy, G. A., Glucuronide Metabolism, with Special Reference to Steroid Hormones, *Vitamins and Hormones* **14**, 267–303 (1956).

245. Dorfman, R. I., Metabolism of Androgens, Estrogens, and Corticoids, *Am. J. Med.* **21**, 679–87 (1956).

246. Rosenkilde, H., and Schroeder, W., Stoffwechsel und Bestimmung der neutralen Steroide, *Z. Vitamin-Hormon-u. Fermentforsch.* **8**, 132–204; 250–381 (1956).

247. Iachia, B., Il metabolismo degli ormoni steroidi, *Farmaco (Pavia)*, *Ed. pract.* **11**, 522–33 (1956).

248. Samuels, L. T., Metabolism of the Steroid Hormones, *Progr. in Chem. Fats, Lipids* **3**, 395–447 (1955).

249. Dorfman, R. I., Steroid Hormone Metabolism, in G. Pincus and K. V. Thimann, eds., "The Hormones," Vol. III, p. 589–664, Academic Press, New York, 1955.

250. Pincus, G., "Aspects du métabolisme des stéroïdes hormonaux," Masson et Cie, Paris, 1955 (Actualités biochimiques, no. 19).

251. Pearlman, W. H., Oestrogen and Progesterone Metabolism in Human Pregnancy: Recent Studies, *Acta Endocrinol.* **17**, 321–8 (1954).

252. Gajdos, A., Le rôle du foie dans le métabolisme des hormones stéroïdes, *Exposés ann. biochim. méd.* **15**, 131–56 (1953).

253. Zini, F., [Glucuronides, Steroid Hormones, and β-Glucuronidase] *Riv. ostet. e ginecol.* **8**, 718–23 (1953).

254. Dorfman, R. I., and Ungar, F., "Metabolism of Steroid Hormones," Burgess Publishing Co., Minneapolis, 1953.

255. Samuels, L. T., and West, C. D., The Intermediary Metabolism of the Non-benzenoid Steroid Hormones, *Vitamins and Hormones* **10**, 251–95 (1952).

256. Ciba Foundation, "Steroid Metabolism and Estimation," Blakiston (McGraw-Hill), New York, 1952 (Ciba Foundation Colloquia on Endocrinology, Vol. II).

257. Serchi, G., [Metabolism of Steroid Hormones. Relationship between Steroid Hormones, Vitamins, and Enzymes], *Rend. seminar. fac. sci. univ. Cagliari* **21**, 156–86 (1951).

258. Heusghem, C., Métabolisme et analyse des hormones stéroïdes, *Actualités biochim.* **14**, 1–71 (1950).

259. Pincus, G., Chemistry and Metabolism of the Steroid Hormones, *Ann. Rev. Biochem.* **19**, 111–24 (1950).

c. Enzymes

260. Dirscherl, W., Einwirkung von Steroidhormonen auf Enzyme und Enzymsysteme, *Proc. Inter. Congr. Biochem.*, *4th Congr.*, *Vienna*, **1958**, Symposium IV, p. 123–39.

261. Mueller, G. C., A Discussion of the Mechanism of Action of Steroid Hormones, *Cancer Research* **17**, 490–506 (1957).

262. Tomkins, G. M., Enzymatic Mechanisms of Hormone Metabolism I. Oxidation-Reduction of the Steroid Nucleus, *Recent Progr. in Hormone Research* **12**, 125–33 (1956).

263. Isselbacher, K. J., Enzymatic Mechanisms of Hormone Metabolism II. Mechanism of Hormonal Glucuronide Formation, *Recent Progr. in Hormone Research* **12**, 134–46 (1956).

264. Dirscherl, W., Über die Einwirkung von Steroidhormonen auf Gewebestoffwechsel und Fermente, *Ergeb. Physiol. biol. Chem. u. exp. Pharmakol.* **48**, 112–229 (1955).

265. Dorfman, R. I., Steroids and Tissue Oxidation, *Vitamins and Hormones* **10**, 331–370 (1952).

266. Conference on the Influence of Hormones on Enzymes, June 5–6, 1951, *Ann. N. Y. Acad. Sci.* **54**, 531–728 (1951).

d. General Endocrinology

267. Hall, P. F., "The Functions of the Endocrine Glands," Saunders, Philadelphia, 1959.

268. Hertz, R., Some Biological and Clinical Effects of Steroids, *Proc. Intern. Congr. Biochem.*, *4th Congr.*, *Vienna*, **1958**, Symposium IV, p. 268–75.

269. Dodds, C., "Biochemical Contributions to Endocrinology; Experiments in Hormonal Research," Stanford Univ. Press, Stanford, Calif. 1957. (Stanford Studies in the Medical Sciences, 8).

270. Hertz, R., Physiologic Effects of Androgens and Estrogens in Man, *Am. J. Med.* **21**, 671–8 (1956).

271. Csapo, A., The Mechanism of Effect of the Ovarian Steroids, *Recent Progr. in Hormone Research* **12**, 405–27 (1956).

272. Hechter, O. M., Concerning Possible Mechanisms of Hormone Action, *Vitamins and Hormones* **13**, 293–346 (1955).

273. Gesellschaft für physiol. Chemie, 5. Colloquium, "Hormone und ihre Wirkungsweise," Springer Verlag, Berlin, 1955.

274. Junkmann, K., Die extragenitalen Wirkungen der Sexualhormone, *Med. Klin.* (*Munich*) **50**, 1666–71 (1955).

275. Orr, W. H., "Hormones, Health and Happiness: Glands and Personality," Macmillan, New York, 1954.

276. Craig, R. L., ed., "Hormones in Health and Disease. Symposium Presented at Twenty-fifth Graduate Fortnight of the New York Academy of Medicine," Macmillan, New York, 1954.

277. Deutsche Gesellschaft für Endokrinologie, "Stoffwechselwirkungen der Steroidhormone," Springer Verlag, Berlin, 1954.

278. Cameron, A. T., "Recent Advances in Endocrinology," 7th ed., Blakiston (McGraw-Hill), New York, 1954.

279. Folley, S. J., The Use of Hormones in Nutrition: Some Practical Possibilities, in F. Verzár, ed., "Present Problems in Nutrition Research; Symposium," p. 214–29, Verlag Birkhäuser, Stuttgart, 1953.

280. Serran, M., "Les hormones," Hachette, Paris, 1952.

281. Vallejo, S. R., [Hormones Derived from 13-Methylcyclopentano-phenanthrene], *Farm. Chilena* 25, 3–16 (1951).

282. Burrows, H., "Biological Actions of Sex Hormones," 2nd rev. ed., Cambridge Univ. Press, New York, 1950.

e. Specific Effects

283. Blecher, M., and White, A., Effects of Steroids on the Metabolism of Lymphoid Tissue, *Recent Progr. in Hormone Research* 15, 391–418 (1959).

284. Gassner, F. X., Reifenstein, E. C., Jr., Alego, J. W., and Mattox, W. E., Effects of Hormones on Growth, Fattening, and Meat Production Potential of Livestock, *Recent Progr. in Hormone Research* 14, 183–210 (1958).

285. Albeaux-Fernet, M., and others, Action des oestrogènes, des androgènes, des gluco-corticoïdes, de l'hormone thyroïdienne et de l'hormone de croissance sur le métabolisme phospho-calcique, *Année endocr.* 10, 216–30 (1958).

286. Leathem, J. H., Hormones and Protein Nutrition, *Recent Progr. in Hormone Research* 14, 141–76 (1958).

287. Symposium on Endocrines and Nutrition, New York, National Vitamin Foundation, 1957. (Nutrition Symposium Series, no. 15).

288. Hoagland, H., ed., "Hormones, Brain Function, and Behavior," Academic Press, New York, 1957.

289. Olson, R. E., Role of Hormones in Protein Metabolism, *J. Am. Med. Assoc.* 164, 1758–65 (1957).

290. Roche, M., Nutrition et hormones sexuelles, *Ann. nutrition et aliment.* 11, A99–120 (1957).

291. Anon., The Effect of Steroids on Human Leukocyte Metabolism, *Nutrition Revs.* 15, 31 (1957).

292. Gordan, G. S., Influence of Steroids on Cerebral Metabolism in Man, *Recent Progr. in Hormone Research* 12, 153–70 (1956).

293. Langworthy, O. R., Neuropathology, Endocrinology, and Biochemistry, *Am. J. Psychiat.* **112,** 514–7 (1956).

294. Bullough, W. S., Hormones and Mitotic Activity, *Vitamins and Hormones* **13,** 261–92 (1955).

295. Ellinger, F., Endocrine Influences on Radiosensitivity; a Review, *Radiol. Clin.* **23,** 182–9 (1954).

296. Albeaux-Fernet, M., and others, L'action des hormones sur le néphron, *Année endocr.* **6,** 144–69 (1954).

297. Albeaux-Fernet, M., and others, Fatigue et endocrinologie, *Année endocr.* **6,** 18–29 (1954).

298. Ciba Foundation, "Hormonal Factors in Carbohydrate Metabolism," Little, Brown and Co., Boston, 1953. (Ciba Foundation Colloquia on Endocrinology, Vol. VI).

299. Ciba Foundation, "Anterior Pituitary Secretion and Hormonal Influences in Water Metabolism," Blakiston (McGraw-Hill), New York, 1953. Ciba Foundation Colloquia on Endocrinology, Vol. IV).

300. Ciba Foundation, "Hormones, Psychology and Behavior" and "Steroid Hormone Administration," Blakiston (McGraw-Hill), New York, 1952. (Ciba Foundation Colloquia on Endocrinology, Vol. III).

301. Van de Velde, J., and de Smet, J., Rôle des hormones dans le métabolisme des lipides, *Exposés ann. biochim. méd.* **13,** 227–54 (1951).

302. Dallemagne, M.-J., Squelette et hormones sexuelles, *Exposés ann. biochim. méd.* **13,** 17–47 (1951).

f. Reproduction

303. Riley, G. M., "Gynecologic Endocrinology," Harper, New York, 1959.

304. Vande Wiele, R., and Jailer, J. W., Placental Steroids, *Ann. N. Y. Acad. Sci.* **75,** 931–41 (1959).

305. Albeaux-Fernet, M., and others, Variations physiologiques au cours du cycle menstruel, *Année endocr.* **10,** 165–9 (1958).

306. Lyons, W. R., Li, C. H., and Johnson, R. E., The Hormonal Control of Mammary Growth and Lactation, *Recent Progr. in Hormone Research* **14,** 219–47 (1958).

307. Nalbandov, A. V., "Reproductive Physiology. Comparative Reproductive Physiology of Domestic Animals, Laboratory Animals and Man," W. H. Freeman and Co., San Francisco, 1958.

308. Velardo, J. T., ed., "Endocrinology of Reproduction," Oxford Univ. Press, New York, 1958.

309. Sato, M., [Sex Hormones.] *Yakkyoku* **8,** 777–9, 890–2 (1957).

310. Albeaux-Fernet, M., and others, Le blocage hormonal de la lactation, *Année endocr.* **9,** 123–7 (1957).

311. Albeaux-Fernet, M., and others. Aperçus récents sur la physiologie du testicule, *Année endocr.* **9,** 159–64 (1957).

312. Giro, C., Il ruolo degli ormoni nella biologia sessuale feminile, *Endocrinol. e sci. costituz.* **23,** 257–71 (1956).

313. Lax, H., Rückblick und Ausblick in der gynäkologischen Endokrinologie, *Zentr. Gynäkol.* **78,** 7–27 (1956).

314. Pincus, G., The Physiology of Ovarian and Testis Hormones, in G. Pincus and K. V. Thimann, eds., "The Hormones," Vol. III, p. 665–84, Academic Press, New York, 1955.

315. De Merre, L. J., "The Female Sex Hormones," Vantage Press, New York, 1954.

316. Société Nationale pour l'Étude de la Stérilité et de la Fécondité, "La fonction luteale, biologie, exploration fonctionelle et pathologie," Masson et Cie, Paris, 1954.

317. Albeaux-Fernet, M., and others, Endocrinologie de la gestation, *Année endocr.* **6,** 93–119 (1954).

318. Société de Gynécologie de d'Obstétrique de Paris, "Les stéroïdes urinaires. Étude biologique et clinique au cours de la gestation normale et pathologique," Publication des Colloques sur la Fonction Lutéale, Masson et Cie, Paris, 1954.

319. Szego, C. M., and Roberts, S., Steroid Action and Interaction in Uterine Metabolism, *Recent Progr. in Hormone Research* **8,** 419–60 (1953).

320. Roberts, S., and Szego, C. M., Steroid Interaction in the Metabolism of Reproductive Target Organs, *Physiol. Revs.* **33,** 593–629 (1953).

321. Anon., Sex Hormones; a Review, *Am. J. Pharm.* **124,** 125–33 (1952).

322. Chwalla, R., "Urologische Endokrinologie; Endokrinologie der Harn- und Geschlechtsorgane des Mannes und der Sexualität," Springer Verlag, Vienna, 1951.

323. Gilbert-Dreyfus and Debrise, G., "Hormones et sexualité," René Juillard, Paris, 1951.

324. Courrier, R., Interactions between Estrogens and Progesterone, *Vitamins and Hormones* **8,** 179–214 (1950).

325. Albeaux-Fernet, M., and others, Les facteurs de la menstruation, *Année endocr.* **2,** 67–71 (1950).

326. Albeaux-Fernet, M., and others, Le diagnostic biologique et chimique de la grossesse, *Année endocr.* **2,** 80–4 (1950).

327. Pincus, G., The Physiology of Ovarian Hormones, in G. Pincus and K. V. Thimann, eds., "The Hormones," Vol. II, p. 1–31, Academic Press, New York, 1950.

g. Medicine

328. Landau, R. L., Endocrinology, *Ann. Rev. Med.* **10**, 159–82 (1959).

329. Hardy, J. D., Endocrinology (Surgery of the Endocrines). *Ann. Rev. Med.* **10**, 183–206 (1959).

330. Asper, S. P., Jr., and Wilson, E. H., Jr., Endocrinology, *Ann. Rev. Med.* **9**, 209–56 (1958).

331. Paschkis, K. E., Rakoff, A. E., and Cantarow, A., "Clinical Endocrinology," Hoeber-Harper, New York, 1958.

332. Gallagher, T. F., Experimental Studies of Adrenal Hyperfunction in Man, *Proc. Intern. Congr. Biochem.*, *4th Congr.*, *Vienna*, **1958**, Symposium IV, p. 143–52.

333. Morris, J. M., and Scully, R. E., "Endocrine Pathology of the Ovary," Mosby, St. Louis, 1958.

334. Albeaux-Fernet, M., and others, Quelques acquisitions récentes sur les ménorragies et les métrorragies, *Année endocr.* **10**, 173–4 (1958).

335. Jailer, J. W., and Christy, N. P., Endocrinology, *Ann. Rev. Med.* **8**, 193–238 (1957).

336. Jailer, J. W., and Longson, D., Adrenal Diseases, in R. H. S. Thompson and E. J. King, eds., "Biochemical Disorders in Human Disease," p. 242–88, Academic Press, New York, 1957.

337. Mason, A. S., "Introduction to Clinical Endocrinology," C. C. Thomas, Springfield, Illinois, 1957.

338. Bishop, P. M. F., and Sommerville, I. F., Disorders of the Reproductive Organs, in R. H. S. Thompson and E. J. King, eds., "Biochemical Disorders in Human Disease," p. 738–83, Academic Press, New York, 1957.

339. Buchholz, R., Neue Erkenntnisse auf dem Gebiete der Sexualhormonforschung und ihre Bedeutung für die Praxis, *Geburtsh. und Frauenh.* **17**, 581–95 (1957).

340. Albeaux-Fernet, M., and others. Pathogénie de la tension prémenstruelle, *Année endocr.* **9**, 131–5 (1957).

341. Albeaux-Fernet, M., and others, Traitements actuels de la stérilité masculine d'origine endocrinienne, *Année endocr.* **9**, 168–71 (1957).

342. Vivanco, F., Valor diagnóstico de las dosificaciones hormonales en endocrinología, *Rev. ibér. endocr.* **4**, 575–650 (1957).

343. Soffer, L. J., "Diseases of the Endocrine Glands," 2nd rev. ed., Lea and Febiger, Philadelphia, 1956.

344. Dodds, C., Garrod, O., and Simpson, S. A., Endocrinology: the Hormones, *Ann. Rev. Med.* **7**, 41–88 (1956).

345. Albeaux-Fernet, M., and others, Les aménorrhées fonctionnelles, *Année endocr.* **7**, 184–91 (1955).

346. Albeaux-Fernet, M., and others, De l'aide apportée par le laboratoire au diagnostic étiologique de la puberté précoce, *Année endocr.* **7,** 192–7 (1955).

347. Antognetti, L., Adezati, L., Pende, G., and Scopinaro, D., "Sindromi cliniche da alterato metabolismo ormonico steroideo," N. 16, Collana di monografie dell'Archivo "E. Maragliano" di Patologia e Clinica, Genoa (1955).

348. Jones, G. E. S., "Management of Endocrine Disorders of Menstruation and Fertility," C. C. Thomas, Springfield, Ill., 1954.

349. American Medical Association Council on Pharmacy and Chemistry, "Glandular Physiology and Therapy," 5th rev. ed., J. B. Lippincott Co., Philadelphia, 1954.

350. Albeaux-Fernet, M., and others, Endocrinologie et médecine du travail, *Année endocr.* **6,** 170–81 (1954).

351. Albeaux-Fernet, M., and others, Le traitement hormonal de la stérilité féminine, *Année endocr.* **6,** 120–6 (1954).

352. Le Marquand, H. S., and Tozer, F. H. W., "Endocrine Disorders in Childhood and Adolescence," 2nd. ed., English Univ. Press, London, 1954.

353. Hurxthal, L. M., and Musulin, N., "Clinical Endocrinology," J. B. Lippincott Co., Philadelphia, 1953.

354. Ratschow, M., "Grundlagen der Therapie mit Sexualhormonen in der inneren Medizin," F. Enke, Stuttgart, 1952.

355. Albeaux-Fernet, M., and others, Les traitements hormonaux en dermatologie, *Année endocr.* **4,** 190–9 (1952).

356. Albeaux-Fernet, M., and others, Gynécomastie, *Année endocr.* **3,** 77–97 (1951).

357. Albeaux-Fernet, M., and others, Les aménorrhées fonctionnelles, *Année endocr.* **3,** 98–112 (1951).

358. Albeaux-Fernet, M., and others, Le traitement hormonal des métrorragies fonctionnelles, *Année endocr.* **3,** 113–20 (1951).

359. Albeaux-Fernet, M., and others, La Δ^5-pregnénolone et la testostérone dans le traitement du rhumatisme, *Année endocr.* **3,** 121–4 (1951).

360. Giudici, E., L'utilizzazione terapeutica degli ormoni sessuali in ostetrica, *Ann. ostet. e ginecol.* **73,** 323–86 (1951).

361. Kneer, M., "Die Sexualhormone: Klinische Bedeutung und therapeutische Anwendung in der Frauenheilkunde und Geburtshilfe," F. Enke, Stuttgart, 1951.

362. Albeaux-Fernet, M., and others, Le diagnostic étiologique des aménorrhées, *Année endocr.* **2,** 76–9 (1950).

h. Oncology

363. Ciba Foundation, "Hormone Production in Endocrine Tumours,"

Little, Brown and Co., Boston, 1958. (Ciba Foundation Colloquia on Endocrinology, Vol. XII).

364. Bielschowsky, F., and Horning, E. S., Aspects of Endocrine Carcinogenesis, *Brit. Med. Bull.* **14,** 106–15 (1958).

365. Huggins, C., Mainzer, K., and Briziarelli, G., Molecular Structure of Steroids and Phenanthrene Derivatives Related to the Growth of Transplanted Mammary Tumors, *Recent Progr. in Hormone Research* **14,** 77–87 (1958).

366. Van Rymenant, M., and Tagnon, H., Le rôle des hormones comme agents modificateurs des conditions hormonales des cancéreaux; hormonothérapie du cancer généralisé du sein, *Acta Chir. Belg.* **57** (Suppl. 1), 79–129 (1958).

367. Noble, R. L., Hormonal Regulation of Tumor Growth, *Pharmacol. Revs.* **9,** 367–426 (1957).

368. Hertz, R., An Appraisal of the Concepts of Endocrine Influence on the Etiology, Pathogenesis, and Control of Abnormal and Neoplastic Growth, *Cancer Research* **17,** 423–31 (1957).

369. Kirschbaum, A., The Role of Hormones in Cancer: Laboratory Animals, *Cancer Research* **17,** 432–53 (1957).

370. Huggins, C., Control of Cancers of Man by Endocrinologic Methods, *Cancer Research* **17,** 467–72 (1957).

371. Hechter, O., Reflections about Hormone Action and Implications for the Cancer Problem, *Cancer Research* **17,** 512–19 (1957).

372. Lacassagne, A., Glandular Cancers of Hormonal Origin, *Canad. Cancer Conf.* **2,** 267–86 (1957).

373. Snellen, W. M., and Everse, J. W., Hormone Therapy of Mammary Carcinoma in Women, *Hormones, Oss* **10,** 1–12 (1957).

374. Perrault, M., Le traitement hormonal du cancer du sein chez la femme, *Progr. méd., Par.* **85,** 355–6 (1957).

375. Beck, J. C., Hormonal Therapy of Carcinoma of the Breast, *Can. Serv. Med. J.,* **13,** 607–13 (1957).

376. Lipschütz, A., "Steroid Homeostasis, Hypophysis, and Tumorigenesis," Heffer, Cambridge, England, 1957.

377. Dannenberg, H., Stoffwechsel und endogene Krebsentstehung, in H. Martius and H. Hartl, eds., "Krebsforschung und Krebsbekämpfung," p. 36–49, Urban & Schwarzenberg, Munich, 1957.

378. Dannenberg, H., Relacion entre los esteroides y substancias carcinogenicas, *Fol. Clin. Internac.* **6,** No. 1 (1956).

379. Schubert, K. R., "Steroide und Krebs. Probleme und neuere Ergebnisse," Steinkopff, Dresden, 1956 (Beiträge zur Krebsforschung, Bd. 5).

380. Symposium on Hormones and Cancer Therapy, *Am. J. Med.* **21,** 657–738 (1956).

381. Albeaux-Fernet, M., and others, Hormonothérapie dans les cancers du sein et de la prostate, *Année endocr.* **8**, 155–69 (1956).

382. Botelho, L. da S., Hormonas sexuais e cancro, *Clin. contemp.* **8**, 119–38 (1954).

383. Ciba Foundation, "Steroid Hormones and Tumor Growth" and "Steroid Hormones and Enzymes," Blakiston (McGraw-Hill), New York, 1952. (Ciba Foundation Colloquia on Endocrinology, Vol. I).

384. Lipschütz, A., "Steroid Hormones and Tumors," Williams and Wilkins, Baltimore, 1950.

i. Gerontology

385. Sobel, H., and Marmorston, J., Hormonal Influences upon Connective Tissue Changes of Aging, *Recent Progr. in Hormone Research* **14**, 457–74 (1958).

386. Asboe-Hansen, G., Hormonal Effects on Connective Tissue, *Physiol. Revs.* **38**, 446–62 (1958).

387. Albeaux-Fernet, M., and others, Gériatrie et glandes surrénales, *Année endocr.* **7**, 56–63 (1955).

388. Engle, E. T., and Pincus, G., eds., "Hormones and Aging Process," Proc. Conf., Harriman, N. Y., 1955, Academic Press, New York, 1956.

389. Pincus, G., Dorfman, R. I., Romanoff, L. P., Rubin, B. L., Bloch, E., Carlo, J., and Freeman, H., Steroid Metabolism in Aging Men and Women, *Recent Progr. in Hormone Research* **11**, 307–41 (1955).

390. Albeaux-Fernet, M., and others, Andropause, *Année endocr.* **6**, 133–5 (1954).

391. Albeaux-Fernet, M., and others, Les dosages des stéroïdes en fonction de l'âge. Déductions physio-pathologiques, *Année endocr.* **5**, 144–51 (1953).

392. Kirk, J. E., Steroid Hormones and Aging; a Review, *J. Gerontol.* **6**, 253–62 (1951).

j. Pharmacology

393. Stoughton, R. B., Steroid Therapy in Skin Disorders, *J. Am. Med. Assoc.* **170**, 1311–15 (1959).

394. Hecht-Lucari, G., Steroidi ed esteri della serie sessuale nuovi e quasi nuovi, *Recenti progr. med., Roma* **24**, 583–607 (1958).

395. Bernstein, S., The Chemistry and Biological Activities of 16-Hydroxylated Steroids, *Recent Progr. in Hormone Research* **14**, 1–27 (1958).

396. Drill, V. A., and Riegel, B., Structural and Hormonal Activity of Some New Steroids, *Recent Progr. in Hormone Research* **14**, 29–76 (1958).

397. Junkmann, K., and Horst, W., "The Chemistry and Pharmacology of Steroid Hormone Esters," Squibb Institute for Medical Research, New Brunswick, N. J., 1958. (*Monographs on Therapy, v. 3, Supplement*).

398. Junkmann, K., Long-Acting Steroids in Reproduction, *Recent Progr. in Hormone Research* **13**, 389–416 (1957).

399. Kern, R. A., The Use and Abuse of Steroid Therapy, Notably in Allergic Disorders, *Am. J. Med. Sci.* **233**, 430–47 (1957).

400. Glyn, J. H., and Newton, D. R., Steroid Therapy, *Ann. Phys. Med., Lond.* **4**, 121–36 (1957).

401. Sannié, C., and Panouse, J. J., Récents progrès dans la chimie et l'action physiologique des stéroïdes, *Exposés ann. biochim. méd.* **19**, 193–218 (1957).

402. Hartley, F., Steroids in Pharmacy and Medicine, *J. Pharm. and Pharmacol.* **9**, 705–29 (1957).

403. American Medical Association. Council on Pharmacy and Chemistry, "Conference on Comparison of the Biological Properties of Steroids and Hormones, October 1954," Chicago, 1956.

404. Hecht-Lucari, G., [Pharmacological Basis of Combined Estrogen and Androgen Therapy in Gynecology], *Gynaecologia* **140**, 169–87 (1955).

405. Zacco, M., and Dalfino, G., [Clinical Use of Estrogens and of Progesterone (Corpus luteum Hormone)], *Clin. terap.* **6**, 596–630 (1954).

406. d'Almeida, A. F., Farmacologia das hormonas ováricas, *Med. contemp., Lisb.* **72**, 57–99 (1954).

407. Everse, J. W. R., Over gelijktijdige toediening van oestrogeen en androgeen hormoon [On simultaneously administered estrogenic and androgenic hormones], *Hormoon* **16**, 49–62 (1951).

408. Pharmaceutical Society of Great Britain, "Hormones: A Survey of their Properties and Uses," Pharmaceutical Press, London, 1951.

409. White, A., ed., "Symposium on Steroids in Experimental and Clinical Practice," McGraw-Hill, New York, 1951.

k. Analysis

410. Schneider, J. J., and Lewbart, M. L., Fractionation and Isolation of Steroid Conjugates, *Recent Progr. in Hormone Research* **15**, 201–25 (1959).

411. Loraine, J. A., "The Clinical Application of Hormone Assay," E. & S. Livingstone, Ltd., Edinburgh & London, 1958.

412. Lott, H., Clinical Significance of Quantitative Chemical Analysis of Hormones, *J. Louisiana State Med. Soc.* **110**, 429–35 (1958).

413. Langecker, H., Die Bedeutung der chemischen Bestimmungsmethoden von Steroidhormonen für die Klinik, *Berliner Medizin* **9**, 375–9 (1958).

414. Jayle, M.-F., Methode de fractionnement et d'hydrolyse des sulfates et glucuronosides de stéroïdes, *Proc. Intern. Congr. Biochem.*, *4th Congr. Vienna*, **1958**, Symposium IV, p. 44–9.

415. Huis in't Veld, L. G., The Use of Chromatographic Methods in Clinical Steroid Analysis, *Scand. J. Clin. & Lab. Invest.* **10**, Suppl. 31, 113–21 (1957).

416. Kellie, A. E., The Determination of 17-Oxo Steroids (17-Keto Steroids) and 17-Oxogenic Steroids (17-Ketogenic Steroids); a Review, *Analyst* **82**, 722–34 (1957).

417. Henry, R., Acquisitions récentes relatives aux dosages et à l'identification des 17 céto-stéroïdes et des corticoïdes, *Rec. trav. chim.* **74**, 442–66 (1955).

418. Zimmermann, W., "Chemische Bestimmungsmethoden von Steroidhormonen in Körperflüssigkeiten," Springer, Berlin, 1955.

419. Emmens, C. W., Biological Assay of the Gonadal and Gonadotrophic Hormones, *Brit. Med. Bull.* **11**, 135–40 (1955).

420. Engel, L. L., and Baggett, B., Estimation of Alcoholic Steroids, *Recent Progr. in Hormone Research* **9**, 251–65 (1954).

421. Venning, E. H., Dyrenfurth, I., and Kazmin, V. E., Hydrolysis and Extraction of Corticoids and 17-Ketosteroids from Body Fluids, *Recent Progr. in Hormone Research* **8**, 27–50 (1953).

422. Loraine, J. A., Recent Developments in the Clinical Application of Hormone Assay, *J. Obstet. Gynaecol. Brit. Empire*, **59**, 535–57 (1952).

423. Albeaux-Fernet, M., and others, Le dosage des stéroïdes urinaires, *Année endocr.* **3**, 144–9 (1951).

424. Emmens, C. W., ed., "Hormone Assay," Academic Press, New York, 1950.

11. PROGESTERONE

425. MacGregor, T. N., Progesterone and Ethisterone, *Practitioner* **180**, 83–7 (1958).

426. Greenblatt, R. B., and Clark, S. L., The Use of Newer Progestational Preparations in Clinical Practice, *Med. Clin. N. Am.* **41**, 587–603 (1957).

427. Davis, M. E., and Plotz, E. J., Progesterone, the Pregnancy Hormone, *Fertility and Sterility* **8**, 603–18 (1957).

428. Zander, J., Die gestagen wirksamen Hormone in Organismus, *Geburtsh. und Frauenh.* **17**, 876–95 (1957).

429. Davis, M. E., and Plotz, E. J., The Metabolism of Progesterone and its Clinical Use in Pregnancy, *Recent Progr. in Hormone Research* **13**, 347–79 (1957).

430. Rock, J., Garcia, C. R., and Pincus, G., Synthetic Progestins in the Normal Human Menstrual Cycle, *Recent Progr. in Hormone Research*, **13**, 323–39 (1957).

431. Rakoff, A. E., ed., "New Steroid Compounds with Progestational Activity," *Ann. N. Y. Acad. Sci.* **71**, 479–806 (1956).

432. Kaiser, R., Oestrogene und Progesteronstoffwechsel, *Klin. Wochschr.* **33**, 15–23 (1955).

433. Kaufmann, C., Progesteron, sein Schicksal im Organismus und seine Anwendung in der Therapie, *Klin. Wochschr.* **33**, 345–7 (1955).

434. Colomer, L. A., [Extragenital Actions of Progesterone], *Med. españ.* **37**, 17–29 (1954).

435. Pearlman, W. H., Recent Experiences in the Detection, Estimation, and Isolation of Progesterone and Related C_{21} Steroids, *Recent Progr. in Hormone Research* **9**, 27–39 (1954).

436. Albeaux-Fernet, M., and others, La progestérone en thérapeutique. Bases et indications de son emploi, *Année endocr.* **4**, 185–90 (1952).

437. do Amaral, C., Progesterona; sua origem e propriedades químio-fisiológicas, *Anais brasil. ginecol.* **32**, 55–67 (1951).

12. CORTICOSTEROIDS
a. Biochemistry

438. Rosenkilde, H., "The Biochemistry of the Adreno-Cortical Hormones," Pergamon Press, New York, in press.

439. Wettstein, A., Biochemie der Corticoide, *Proc. Intern. Congr. Biochem., 4th Congr., Vienna,* **1958**, Symposium IV, p. 233–58.

440. Saint, E. G., The Corticosteroids, *Australian J. Dermatol.* **4**, 71–6 (1957).

441. Gross, F., Der heutige Stand der Forschung über die Nebennierenrindenhormone. *Die Ärztl. Fortbildung* **7**, 153–9 (1957).

442. Wettstein, A., and Anner, G., Advances in the Field of Adrenal Cortical Hormones, *Experientia* **10**, 397–416 (1954).

443. Reichstein, T., Die wichtigsten Hormone der Nebennierenrinde, *Acta Endocrinol.* **17**, 375–84 (1954).

444. Kendall, E. C., Hormones of the Adrenal Cortex in Health and Disease. *Proc. Am. Phil. Soc.* **97**, 8–11 (1953).

445. Ballabio, C. B., Cavallero, C., and Sala, G., "Cortisone," Amborsiana, Milan, 1951.

446. Bénard, H., and Horn, A., [The corticoadrenal hormones, particularly the 11-oxy-corticosteroids], *Actualités pharmacol.* **3**, 199–219 (1951).

447. Reichstein, T., La chimie des hormones corticosurrénales, *Chim. & ind. (Paris)* **66**, 323–9; 488–94 (1951).

448. Kendall, E. C., Cortisone, *Ann. Internal Med.* **33**, 787–96 (1950).

b. Biosynthesis

449. Pincus, G., Recent Developments in the Study of Adrenal Cortical Steroid Biogenesis, *Proc. Intern. Congr. Biochem.*, *4th Congr.*, *Vienna*, **1958**, Symposium IV, p. 61–73.

450. Staudinger, Hj., Über die Wirking der Ascorbinsäure auf die Hydroxylierung von Steroiden in der Nebennierenrinde, *Proc. Intern. Congr. Biochem.*, *4th Congr.*, *Vienna*, **1958**, Symposium IV, p. 74–81.

451. Pincus, G., The Biosynthesis of Adrenal Cortical Steroids, *Bull. N. Y. Acad Med.* **33**, 587–98 (1957).

452. Hayano, M., Saba, N., Dorfman, R. I., and Hechter, O., Some Aspects of the Biogenesis of Adrenal Steroid Hormones, *Recent Progr. in Hormone Research* **12**, 79–123 (1956).

453. Pincus, G., The Biosynthesis of Adrenal Steroids, *Ann. N. Y. Acad. Sci.* **61**, 283–90 (1955).

454. Hechter, O. M., and Pincus, G., Genesis of the Adrenocortical Secretion, *Physiol. Revs.* **34**, 459–96 (1954).

455. Ciba Foundation, "Synthesis and Metabolism of Adrenocortical Steroids," Little, Brown and Co., Boston, 1953. (Ciba Foundation Colloquia on Endocrinology, Vol. VII).

456. Haines, W. J., Aspects of Steroid Hormone Chemistry and Physiology. Studies on the Biosynthesis of Adrenal Cortex Hormones. *Recent Progr. in Hormone Research* **7**, 255–99 (1952).

457. Hechter, O., Zaffaroni, A., Jacobsen, R. P., Levy, H., Jeanloz, R. W., Schenker, V., and Pincus, G., The Nature and the Biogenesis of the Adrenal Secretory Product, *Recent Progr. in Hormone Research* **6**, 215–41 (1951).

c. Metabolism

458. Peterson, R. E., The Miscible Pool and Turnover Rate of Adrenocortical Steroids in Man, *Recent Progr. in Hormone Research* **15**, 231–61 (1959).

459. Orzechowski, G., [Metabolism of Corticoid Hormones], *Med. Monatsschr.* **12**, 215–17 (1958).

460. Anon., Hydrocortisone Content of Human Adrenal Vein Blood, *Nutrition Revs.* **15**, 274–5 (1957).

461. Albeaux-Fernet, M., and others, Le métabolisme intermédiaire des hormones corticales. Les formes d'élimination urinaires, *Année endocr.* **7**, 30–9 (1955).

462. Dorfman, R. I., Special Aspects of Adrenocortical Steroid Metabolism, *Ann. N. Y. Acad. Sci.* **61**, 291–6 (1955).

463. Anon., The Fate of Hydrocortisone in Man, *Nutrition Revs.* **13**, 164–5 (1955).

464. Anon., Metabolism of Adrenal Steroids in Man, *Nutrition Revs.* **13**, 263–5 (1955).

465. Anon., Metabolism of Cortical Hormones, *Nutrition Revs.* **10**, 341–3 (1952).

d. Aldosterone

466. Farrell, G., The Physiological Factors Which Influence the Secretion of Aldosterone, *Recent Progr. in Hormone Research* **15**, 275–97 (1959).

467. Bartter, F. C., Mills, I. H., Biglieri, E. G., and Delea, C., Studies on the Control and Physiologic Action of Aldosterone, *Recent Progr. in Hormone Research* **15**, 311–35 (1959).

468. Wolff, H. P., and Koczorek, K. R., Aldosterone and Electrolyte Metabolism in Liver Diseases, *Gastroenterologia* **90**, 216–30 (1958).

469. Muller, A. F., and O'Connor, C. M., eds. "International Symposium on Aldosterone," Little, Brown and Co., Boston, 1958.

470. Rominger, E., Aldosteron, *Arch. Kinderh.* **158**, 105–9 (1958).

471. Luetscher, J. A., and Lieberman, A. H., Aldosterone, *A.M.A. Arch. Internal Med.* **102**, 314–30 (1958).

472. August, J. T., Nelson, D. H., and Thorn, G. W., Aldosterone, *New Eng. J. Med.* **259**, 917–23; 967–71 (1958).

473. Farrell, G., Regulation of Aldosterone Secretion, *Physiol. Revs.* **38**, 709–28 (1958).

474. Giroud, C. J., and McCall, M. F., Aldosterone in Experimental and Clinical Medicine, *Pediat. Clin. N. America* **1958**, 397–416.

475. Albeaux-Fernet, M., and others, La regulation physiologique de la sécrétion d'aldostérone et le problème des oedèmes, *Année endocr.* **10**, 10–34 (1958).

476. Albeaux-Fernet, M., and others, L'hypercorticisme à forme mineralocorticoïde: l'hyperaldostéronisme primaire, *Année endocr.* **10**, 35–6 (1958).

477. Anon., Aldosterone and Steroid Glycosuria in the Cat, *Nutrition Revs.* **16**, 177–8 (1958).

478. Kuczewska, K., and Tatón, J., [Aldosterone in the Pathogenesis of Various Clinical Syndromes], *Polskie Arch. Med. Wewnętrznej* **28**, 95–106 (1958).

479. Küchel, O., [The Relation of Aldosterone to the Circulatory System with Reference to Cardiac Failure], *Časopis lékařů českych* **97**, 1358–63 (1958).

480. Wettstein, A., L'aldostérone, *Exposés ann. biochim. méd.* **19**, 171–91 (1957).

481. Albeaux-Fernet, M., and others, L'aldostérone: étude biologique et clinique, *Année endocr.* **9**, 5–41 (1957).

482. Genest, J., Clinical States Associated with Abnormal Aldosterone Excretion, *Can. Med. Assoc. J.* **77**, 780–5 (1957).

483. Jacob, J., and Rissi, E., L'aldostérone, *Thérapie* **11**, 1219–34 (1956).

484. Mach, R.-S., Aldosteron in der Klinik, *Wien. klin. Wochschr.* **68**, 277–9 (1956).

485. Mach, R.-S., and Mach, E., L'aldostérone, *Exposés ann. biochim. méd.* **18**, 63–86 (1956).

486. Luetscher, J. A., Jr., Aldosterone, *Advances in Internal Med.* **8**, 155–203 (1956).

487. Garrod, O., Simpson, S. A., and Tait, J. F., The Significance of the Assay of Aldosterone in Human Urine and Blood, *Proc. Roy. Soc. Med.* **49**, 885–8 (1956).

488. Luetscher, J. A., Jr., Studies of Aldosterone in Relation to Water and Electrolyte Balance in Man, *Recent Progr. in Hormone Research* **12**, 175–84 (1956).

489. Gross, F., Nebennierenrinde und Wasser-Salzstoffwechsel unter besonderer Berücksichtigung von Aldosteron, *Klin Wochschr.* **34**, 929–41 (1956).

490. Wettstein, A., Aldosteron und andere Nebennierenrinden-Hormone, *Verhandl. schweiz. naturforsch. Ges.* **136**, 22–41 (1956).

491. Simmer, H., Aldosteron, *Deut. med. Wochschr.* **80**, 1314–15 (1955).

492. Gaunt, R., Renzi, A. A., and Chart, J. J., Aldosterone; a Review, *J. Clin. Endocrinol. and Metabolism* **15**, 621–46 (1955).

493. Simpson, S. A., and Tait, J. F., Recent Progress in Methods of Isolation, Chemistry, and Physiology of Aldosterone, *Recent Progr. in Hormone Research* **11**, 183–210 (1955).

494. Genest, I., The Present Status of Aldosterone in Clinical Medicine, *Can. Med. Assoc. J.* **73**, 876–83 (1955).

495. Bannerjee, D. K., Aldosterone, *Soc. Biol. Chemists, India* **1955**, 234–6.

496. Villiaumey, J., Connaissances actuelles sur l'aldostérone, *Semaine hôp.* **31**, 3873–8 (1955).

497. Anon., The Structure and Physiologic Properties of Aldosterone, *Nutrition Revs.* **12**, 280–2 (1954).

498. Engelund, A., Electrocortin, A New Adrenal Cortical Hormone, *Arch. Pharm. Chem.* **61**, 133–5 (1954).

e. Physiology

499. Mason, J. W., Psychological Influences on the Pituitary-Adrenal Cortical System, *Recent Progr. in Hormone Research* **15**, 345–78 (1959).

500. Saffran, M., and Saffran, J., Adenohypophysis and Adrenal Cortex, *Ann. Rev. Physiol.* **21,** 403–44 (1959).

501. Sayers, G., Redgate, E. S., and Royce, P. C., Hypothalamus, Adenohypophysis and Adrenal Cortex, *Ann. Rev. Physiol.* **20,** 243–74 (1958).

502. Anon., The Adrenal Cortex in Carbohydrate Metabolism, *Nutrition Revs.* **16,** 185–6 (1958).

503. Anon., Cortisone Effects on Bone Mineral Metabolism, *Nutrition Revs.* **16,** 247–8 (1958).

504. Albeaux-Fernet, M., and others, Le rythme nycthéméral des corticoïdes urinaires, *Année endocr.* **10,** 5–9 (1958).

505. Jones, I. C., "The Adrenal Cortex," Cambridge Univ. Press, London, 1957.

506. Albeaux-Fernet, M., and others, Etude comparative des principaux stéroïdes corticaux, *Année endocr.* **9,** 87–90 (1957).

507. Albeaux-Fernet, M., and others, Étude clinique et biologique du stress chez l'homme, *Année endocr.* **9,** 71–86 (1957).

508. Anon., Effects of Prolonged Cortisone Therapy on Growth, *Nutrition Revs.* **15,** 94–5 (1957).

509. Anon., Cortisone and Food Consumption, *Nutrition Revs.* **15,** 115–16 (1957).

510. Anon., Cortisone and Protein Metabolism, *Nutrition Revs.* **15,** 23–5 (1957).

511. Donovan, B. T., and Harris, G. W., Pituitary and Adrenal Glands, *Ann. Rev. Physiol.*, **19,** 439–66 (1957).

512. Long, C. N. H., Pituitary-adrenal Relationships, *Ann. Rev. Physiol.* **18,** 409–32 (1956).

513. Anon., Effect of Cortisone on Protein Metabolism, *Nutrition Revs.* **14,** 279–81 (1956).

514. Selye, H., "The Stress of Life," McGraw-Hill, New York, 1956.

515. Selye, H., and Heuser, G., "Annual Report on Stress," Acta, Inc., Montreal, 1st-4th, 1951–54; 5th Report, M. D. Publications, New York, 1956.

516. Albeaux-Fernet, M., and others, Les corticostéroïdes et le métabolisme hydro-minéral, *Année endocr.* **8,** 33–59 (1956).

517. Albeaux-Fernet, M., and others, Les corticostéroïdes urinaires dans l'exploration de la fonction cortico-surrénale, *Année endocr.* **8,** 69–95 (1956).

518. Albeaux-Fernet, M., and others, La sécrétion du cortex surrénal, *Année endocr.* **7,** 5–29 (1955).

519. Nelson, D. H., The Significance of Plasma Corticosteroids as a Measure of Adrenal Cortical Function, *Naval Medical Research Institute. Lecture and Review Series* **1,** 235–44 (1955).

520. Anon., Cortisone and the Metabolic Response to Injury, *Nutrition Revs.* **13**, 251–4 (1955).

521. Noble, R. L., Physiology of the Adrenal Cortex, in G. Pincus and K. V. Thimann, eds., "The Hormones," Vol. II, p. 65–180, 1950, and Vol. III, p. 685–819, 1955.

522. Ciba Foundation, "The Human Adrenal Cortex," Little, Brown and Co., Boston, 1955. (Ciba Foundation Colloquia on Endocrinology, Vol. VIII).

523. Hoagland, H., Studies of Brain Metabolism and Electrical Activity in Relation to Adrenocortical Physiology, *Recent Progr. in Hormone Research* **10**, 29–63 (1954).

524. Albeaux-Fernet, M., and others, L'exploration fonctionnelle du cortex surrénal par le dosage des 17-hydroxycorticostéroïdes urinaires, *Année endocr.* **6**, 30–8 (1954).

525. European Symposium on Cortisone and the Suprarenal Cortex, Milan, 1953, Redi, Milan, 1954. (Biblioteca de Reumatismo, v. 1).

526. Anon., Cortisone and Protein Synthesis, *Nutrition Revs.* **11**, 184–6 (1953).

527. Albeaux-Fernet, M., and others, A. C. T. H., cortisone et psychiatrie, *Année endocr.* **5**, 50–7 (1953).

528. Albeaux-Fernet, M., and others, Cortisone, A.C.T.H. et fonction thyroïdienne, *Année endocr.* **5**, 75–6 (1953).

529. Ingle, D. J., and Baker, B. L., "Physiological and Therapeutic Effects of Corticotrophin (ACTH) and Cortisone," C. C. Thomas, Springfield, Illinois, 1953.

530. Albeaux-Fernet, M., and others, Les procédés actuels d'exploration de la fonction cortico-surrénale, *Anné endocr.* **4**, 33–56 (1952).

531. Soffer, L. J., ACTH and Cortisone; Physiologic and Clinical Considerations, *Med. Clin. N. Am.* **36**, 791–805 (1952).

532. Verzár, F., The Influence of Corticoids on Enzymes of Carbohydrate Metabolism, *Vitamins and Hormones* **10**, 297–330 (1952).

533. Albeaux-Fernet, M., and others, Action physiologique de l'A.C.T.H. et de la cortisone, *Année endocr.* **3**, 5–9 (1951).

534. Mach, R.-S., and Mach, E., Effets metaboliques de la cortisone et de l'"A.C.T.H.", *Exposés ann. biochim. méd.* **13**, 1–16 (1951).

535. Ralli, E. P., ed., "Adrenal Cortex; Transaction of the Third Conference," Josiah Macy, Jr. Foundation, New York, 1951.

536. Selye, H., "The Physiology and Pathology of Exposure to Stress. A Treatise based on the Concepts of the General Adaptation Syndrome and the Diseases of Adaptation," Acta Inc., Montreal, 1950.

537. Sayers, G., The Adrenal Cortex and Homeostasis, *Physiol Revs.* **30**, 241–320 (1950).

f. Pathology

538. Albeaux-Fernet, M., and others, Les hypocorticismes chroniques non Addisoniens, *Année endocr.* **10**, 67–77 (1958).

539. Albeaux-Fernet, M., and others, Dyscorticisme et fatigue chronique, *Année endocr.* **10**, 78–85 (1958).

540. Albeaux-Fernet, M., and others, Les fonctions cortico-surrénales dans l'acromégalie, *Année endocr.* **10**, 156–8 (1958).

541. West, H. F., Corticosteroid Metabolism and Rheumatoid Arthritis, *Ann. Rheumatic Diseases* **16**, 173–82 (1957).

542. Gray, C. H., Études cliniques des corticoïdes urinaires, *Exposés ann. biochim. méd.* **18**, 47–61 (1956).

543. Jailer, J. W., Advances in Physiology of Clinical Disorders of the Adrenal Cortex, *Advances in Internal Med.* **7**, 125–55 (1955).

544. Laroche, C., and Leprat, J., Les hypercorticismes, *Actual. biol.* **1**, 313–80 (1954).

545. Albeaux-Fernet, M., and others, Aspects récemment décrits de la maladie d'Addison, *Année endocr.* **6**, 5–14 (1954).

546. Albeaux-Fernet, M., and others, L'hypercorticisme chez l'adulte, *Année endocr.* **5**, 11–40 (1953).

547. Anon., Ascorbic Acid and Desoxycorticosterone in Rheumatic Disease, *Nutrition Revs.* **8**, 276–8 (1950).

548. Anon., "DOCA" and Ascorbic Acid in Arthritis, *Nutrition Revs.* **8**, 319 (1950).

g. Pharmacology

549. Tamm, J., The Biochemical Basis for Treatment with Adrenocortical Hormones, *Hormones* **12**, No. 2, 1–11 (1959).

550. Thorn, G. W., Nelson, D. H., and Renold, A. E., Current Status of the Treatment of Adrenal Disorders, *J. Am. Med. Assoc.* **168**, 2130–7 (1958).

551. Spence, A. W., Cortisone and Hydrocortisone, *Practitioner* **180**, 22–30 (1958).

552. Casolo, G., Indicazioni, effetti, collaterali e controindicazioni della terapia cortisonica, *Osped. maggiore* **46**, 445–56 (1958).

553. Oberdisse, K., Die Anwendung des Cortisons und verwandter Verbindungen bei nicht-endokrinen Erkrankungen, *Deut. med. Wochschr.* **83**, 1538–44 (1958).

554. Korting, G. W., Der gegenwärtige Erfahrungsstand der allgemeinen und lokalen Corticoid-Therapie von Dermatosen, *Medizinische* **24**, 969–76 (1958).

555. Staemmler, H. J., Gynäkologische und geburtsshilfliche Indikationen zur Anwendung von Nebennierenrindenhormonen und ACTH, *Geburtsh. und Frauenh.* **18**, 1201–15 (1958).

556. Kless, H., Nebennierenrindenhormontherapie in der Praxis; Möglichkeiten und Grenzen, *Wien. med. Wochschr.* **107,** 475–81 (1957).

557. Jorden, P. J., Recent Trends in the Clinical Use of Adrenocortical Steroids, *Quart. Bull. Northwestern Univ. Med. School* **31,** 124–31 (1957).

558. Strean, L. P., "Cortisone in Dentistry," Dental Items of Interest Publ. Co., Brooklyn, N. Y., 1957 (Modern Dentistry Series).

559. Douglas, B. L., and Kresberg, H., Cortisone in Dentistry, *Oral Surg. Oral Med. Oral Pathol.* **9,** 978–84 (1956).

560. Cyriax, J. H., "Hydrocortisone in Orthopaedic Medicine," Cassell, London, 1956.

561. Borasi, M., Farmacologia degli ormoni surrenocorticali, *Farmaco (Pavia), Ed. sci.* **11,** 953–76 (1956).

562. Fiegel, G., and Kelling, H. W., Zur klinischen Brauchbarkeit von ACTH und Cortison; Gesamtübersicht, *Münch. med. Wochschr.* **98,** 1218–22; 1255–8 (1956).

563. Hirsch, P., Adrenocortical Steroids, Their Derivatives, and Corticotropin, *A.M.A. Arch. Dermatol.* **73,** 342–54 (1956).

564. Floris, V., and Zappi, F., Applicazioni cliniche dell' ACTH e cortisone in neurologia, *Riv. neurol.* **26,** 295–333 (1956).

565. Thorn, G. W., Goldfien, A., and Nelson, D. H., The Treatment of Adrenal Dysfunction, *Med. Clin. N. Am.* **40,** 1261–79 (1956).

566. Jeffries, W. M., The Present Status of Adrenocorticotropin (ACTH), Cortisone, and Related Steroids in Clinical Medicine, *New Engl. J. Med.* **253,** 441–6 (1955).

567. de Gennes, L., "Comment traiter par la cortisone et l'A.C.T.H.," Flammarion, Paris, 1955.

568. Lukens, F. D. W., ed., "Medical Uses of Cortisone," Blakiston (McGraw-Hill), New York, 1954.

569. Copeman, W. S. C., ed., "Cortisone and A.C.T.H. in Clinical Practice," Butterworth & Co., London, 1953.

570. Thorn, G. W., Jenkins, D., Laidlaw, J. C., Goetz, F. C., Dingman, J. F., Arons, W. L., Streeten, D. H. P., and McCraken, B. H., Pharmacologic Aspects of Adrenocortical Steroids and Adrenocorticotropic Hormone, *New Engl. J. Med.* **248,** 232–45; 323–37; 369–78; 414–23; 588–601; 632–46; (1953).

571. Ragan, C., Corticotropin, Cortisone and Related Steroids in Clinical Medicine, *Bull. N. Y. Acad. Med.* **29,** 355–76 (1953).

572. Albeaux-Fernet, M., and others, La cortisone et l'A.C.T.H. en gynécologie et en obstétrique, *Année endocr.* **5,** 68–74 (1953).

573. Greiner, T., The Current Uses of Cortisone and ACTH, *Am. J. Med. Sci.* **223,** 553–68 (1952).

574. Albeaux-Fernet, M., and others, A.C.T.H. et cortisone dans le traitement de la maladie de Bouillaud, *Année endocr.* **4,** 86–7 (1952).

575. Anon., Cortisone and ACTH in Nontropical Sprue, *Nutrition Revs.* **10,** 169–172 (1952).

576. Derbes, V. de P. J., "Untoward Reactions of Cortisone and ACTH," C. C. Thomas, Springfield, Illinois, 1951.

577. Albeaux-Fernet, M., and others, Emploi thérapeutique de l'A.C.T.H. et de la cortisone, *Année endocr.* **3,** 14–44 (1951).

578. Albeaux-Fernet, M., and others, Emploi thérapeutique d'une hormone surrénale: la cortisone et d'une hormone hypophysaire: la corticotrophine, *Année endocr.* **2,** 18–24 (1950).

579. Hench, P. S., and Staff of Mayo Clinic, Symposium on Cortisone and ACTH in Clinical Medicine, *Proc. Staff Meetings, Mayo Clinic* **25,** 473–502 (1950).

h. Analogs

580. Fried, J., and Borman, A., Synthetic Derivatives of Cortical Hormones, *Vitamins and Hormones* **16,** 304–74 (1958).

581. Bolund, E. W., 16α-Methyl-corticosteroids. A New Series of Antiinflammatory Compounds; Clinical Appraisal of their Antirheumatic Potencies, *Calif. Med.,* **88,** 417–22 (1958).

582. Soffer, L. J., ed., Biological and Clinical Investigations of Newer Hydrocortisone Analogs, *Metabolism* **7,** 383–574 (1958).

583. Forsham, P. H., ed., Symposium on Adrenal Corticoid Therapy, *Metabolism, Clin. and Exp.* **7,** 3–89 (1958).

584. Siegenthaler, W., Siegenthaler, G., and Isler, U., Grundlagen und Indikationen für die Behandlung innerer Krankheiten mit Cortisonen unter spezieller Berücksichtigung von Prednisolon, *Medizinische* **1958,** 2019–30; 2090–8.

585. Huang, W.-Y., [Modified Corticosteroidal Hormones], *K'o Hsüeh T'ung Pao* **1958,** 297–304.

586. Boland, E. W., Prednisone und Prenisolone in Rheumatoid Arthritis; an Evaluation of their Therapeutic Efficiency, *Med. Clin. N. Am.* **41,** 553–64 (1957).

587. Barceló, P., Santamaría, A., and Sanssolá, L., Tratamiento de diversas enfermedades reumáticas mediante la Δ¹-dehidrocortisona (prednisona, metacortandracina), *Rev. españ. reumat. y enfermedad. osteoarticulares* **7,** 140–54 (1957).

588. Squibb Institute for Medical Research, New Brunswick, N. J., "Florinef and its Clinical Applications; Original Reports by Clinical and Laboratory Investigators," New Brunswick, 1957, (Monographs on Therapy, v. 2, no. 2).

589. Albeaux-Fernet, M., and others, Nouveaux stéroïdes d'activité cortisonique, *Année endocr.* **8**, 60–68 (1956).
590. Schering Corporation, "Meti-steroid Bibliography," Bloomfield, New Jersey, 1956.
591. "International Conference on the Clinical and Metabolic Effects of Meticorten and Meticortelone, Proceedings, 1st Conf.," Schering Corporation, Bloomfield, New Jersey, 1955.
592. Niinobe, S., [New Synthetic Adrenocortical Hormones with Enhanced Activity], *Japan, J. Pharm. & Chem.* **27**, 498–509 (1955).
593. Logemann, W., and Giraldi, P., [The Corticoid Hormones and Synthetic "Models" of Them], *Raccolta pubbl. chim. biol. e med.* **1**, 391ff. (1953).

i. Gastroenterology

594. Kaplan, M. H., ACTH and Cortisone in Gastroenterology, *Am. J. Gastroenterol.* **27**, 163–79 (1957).
595. McHardy, G., McHardy, R., Craighead, C. C., Browne, D. C., Bobear, J. B., Ward, S., and Williams, G. T., The Use of the Adrenocorticosteroids in Gastroenterology, *Gastroenterology* **32**, 816–28 (1957).
596. Zetzel, L., The Use of ACTH and Adrenocorticosteroids in Diseases of the Digestive System, *New Engl. J. Med.* **257**, 1170–80 (1957).

j. Infections

597. Perianes Carro, J., El ACTH y los corticosteroides en el tratamiento de las infecciones, *Rev. clín espan.* **72**, 113–19 (1959).
598. Romansky, M. J., Steroid Therapy in Systemic Infections, *J. Am. Med. Assoc.* **170**, 1179–83 (1959).
599. De Caprio, P., Indicazioni e limiti della terapia cortisonica nelle malattie infettive dell' infanzia, *Pediatria* **66**, 266–78 (1958).
600. Hewes, T., The Use of Adrenocorticotrophins (ACTH) and Adrenal Steroids in the Treatment of Infections, *Med. Bull. U. S. Army Europe* **14**, 235–9 (1957).
601. Spink, W. W., ACTH and Adrenocorticosteroids as Therapeutic Adjuncts in Infectious Diseases, *New Engl. J. Med.* **257**, 979–83; 1031–5 (1957).
602. Anon., Cortisone and Resistance to Infection, *Nutrition Revs.* **15**, 157–8 (1957).
603. Cheymol, P., "Corticothérapie et infections microbiennes non tuberculeuses," Maloine, Paris, 1957.
604. Magrassi, F., Aspetti teoretici e pratici dell'applicazione di cor-

tisonici nelle malattie infettive, *Gior. clin. med. (Bologna)* **37**, 897–919 (1956).

605. Albeaux-Fernet, M., and others, L'emploi thérapeutique des hormones anti-inflammatoires en pathologie infectieuse, *Année endocr.* **8**, 185–203 (1956).

606. Shwartzman, G., ed., "The Effect of ACTH and Cortisone upon Infection and Resistance; Symposium held at New York Academy of Medicine, March 27 and 28, 1952," Columbia Univ. Press, New York, 1953.

607. Albeaux-Fernet, M., and others, A.C.T.H., cortisone et tuberculose, *Année endocr.* **4**, 88–90 (1952).

k. Liver Disease

608. Demeulenaere, L., and Vermeulen, A., Aspects physiopathologiques des relations hépatocorticosurrénaliennes et thérapeutique des affections hépatiques par les stéroïdes corticosurrénaliens et leurs dérivés, *Acta Gastroenter. Belg.* **21**, 503–47 (1958).

609. Havens, W. P., Jr., The Use of Cortisone and ACTH in Liver Disease, *Med. Clin. N. Am.* **41**, 1639–45 (1957).

610. Albeaux-Fernet, M., and others, La cortisone dans le traitement de la cirrhose du foie, *Année endocr.* **5**, 45–9 (1953).

l. Oncology

611. Anglesio, E., and Pelocchino, A. M., Cortisone e tumori, *Minerva med.* **49**, 3854–62 (1958).

612. Gallagher, T. F., On Alterations in Adrenal Function, Especially with Adrenocortical Carcinoma, *Cancer Research* **17**, 520–9 (1957).

613. Reid, E., Growth Hormone and Adrenocortical Hormones in Relation to Experimental Tumors: a Review, *Cancer Research* **14**, 249–66 (1954).

m. Ophthalmology

614. Ros, A., "La cortisona en oftalmología," Mexico City, 1957.

615. Wright, W. A., Steroid Therapy in Diseases of the Eye, Ear, Nose and Throat, *J. Am. Osteopath. Assoc.* **56**, 519–23 (1957).

616. Gordon, D. M., "The Clinical Use of Corticotropin, Cortisone, and Hydrocortisone in Eye Diseases," C. C. Thomas, Springfield, Illinois, 1954.

617. Calamandrei, G., "Ormone corticotropo e cortisone in oftalmolgia," Edizioni Aggiornamenti di terapia oftalmologia, Pisa, 1953.

n. Rheumatology

618. Stillman, J. S., Current Status of Steroid Therapy in Rheumatic Disorders, *New Engl. J. Med.* **259**, 820–6 (1958).

619. Scheiffarth, F., and Zicha, L., Der gegenwärtige Stand der Corti-coidtherapie allergischer und rheumatischer Erkrankungen, *Medizinische* **1958,** 1652–8.

620. Glyn, J. H. H., "Cortisone Therapy, Mainly Applied to the Rheumatic Diseases," Philosophical Library, New York, 1957.

621. Visintine, R. E., The Clinical Use of Adrenocortical Steroids in Collagen Diseases, *Rev. Allergy* **11,** 469–80 (1957).

622. Fellinger, K., Die Nebennierenrindenhormone in der Rheumatherapie, *Z. Rheumaforsch* **16,** 90–104 (1957).

623. Dobbins, W. O., The Clinical Use of Adrenocortical Steroids in Collagen Diseases, *J. Med. Assoc. State Alabama* **26,** 295–306 (1957).

624. Polley, H. F., Present Therapeutic Status of Cortisone and its Derivatives, with Special Reference to Rheumatic Diseases, *Brit. Med. J.* **1956,** 1253–9.

625. Freyberg, R. H., The Use of Hormones in Rheumatic Diseases, *J. Chronic Diseases* **2,** 559–82 (1955).

626. Hench, P. S., "Cortisone, hydrocortisone, et corticotropine (ACTH) dans la polyarthrite chronique évolutive," Geigy, Basle, 1955. (Documenta rheumatologica. Ed. française, no. 5).

627. Coste, F., "Cortisone et corticostimuline (ACTH) en rhumatologie," Masson et Cie, Paris, 1953.

628. Albeaux-Fernet, M., and others, L'hydrocortisone et le traitement local des rhumatismes, *Année endocr.* **5,** 58–67 (1953).

629. Albeaux-Fernet, M., and others, A.C.T.H. et cortisone en rhumatologie, *Année endocr.* **4,** 79–85 (1952).

o. Surgery

630. Lichtwitz, A., and Parlier, R., Corticosurrénale et chirurgie. I. Notions chimiques et physiologiques élémentaires sur la corticosurrénale, *Concours méd.* **80,** 401–3 (1958).

631. Porter, H. R., "ACTH and Corticoids in the Surgical Patient," U. S. Veterans Administration Center, Des Moines, 1957. (Surgical Staff Meetings, v. 10, no. 2).

632. Albeaux-Fernet, M., and others, De la possibilité d'une insuffisance surrénale créée par le traitement à la cortisone; son danger dans les suites postopératoires, *Année endocr.* **6,** 51–3 (1954).

633. Albeaux-Fernet, M., and others, A.C.T.H., cortisone et chirurgie de l' organisme, *Année endocr.* **4,** 91–2 (1952).

p. Analysis

634. Moore, J. A., and Heftmann, E., Chemistry of the Adrenocortical

Hormones, in H. W. Deane, ed., "Handbuch der experimentellen Pharmakologie," Chapter III, Springer Verlag, Berlin, in press.

635. Neher, R., Determination of Individual Adrenocortical Steroids, *Advances in Clin. Chem.* **1**, 127–92 (1958).

636. Neher, R., Modern Methods of Isolation and Determination of Individual Corticosteroids, *Proc. Intern. Congr. Biochem.*, *4th Congr.*, *Vienna*, **1958**, Symposium IV, p. 28–43.

637. Bongiovanni, A. M., Free and Conjugated 17-Hydroxycorticosteroids in Plasma, in D. Seligson, ed., "Standard Methods of Clinical Chemistry," Vol. II, p. 61–8, Academic Press, New York, 1958.

638. Albeaux-Fernet, M., and others, Techniques récents pour le dosage des corticoïdes dans les urines—techniques et applications cliniques, *Année endocr.* **9**, 42–70 (1957).

639. Silber, R. H., and Porter, C. C., Determination of 17,21-Dihydroxy-20-ketosteroids in Urine and Plasma, *Methods of Biochem. Anal.*, **4**, 139–69 (1957).

640. Gold, J. J., Blood Corticoids: Their Measurement and Significance —a Review, *J. Clin. Endocrinol. and Metabolism* **17**, 296–316 (1957).

641. Diczfalusy, E., Birke, G., and Plantin, L.-O., Corticosteroidbestimmungen und ihre klinische Bedeutung, *Klin. Wochschr.* **34**, 225–31 (1956).

642. Borth, R., Problems Related to the Chemical Assay of Corticosteroids in Human Body Fluids, *Acta Endocrinol.* **22**, 125–35, (1956).

643. Gemzell, C. A., Methods of Estimating Corticosteroids in Plasma, *Acta Endocrinol.* **18**, 342–50 (1955).

644. Plantin, L.-O., Infrared Spectrographic Analysis of Corticosteroids, *Acta Endocrinol.* **18**, 351–5 (1955).

645. Mason, H. L., Hydrolysis of Conjugates and Extraction of Urinary Corticosteroids, *Recent Progr. in Hormone Research* **9**, 267–78 (1954).

646. Haines, W. J., and Karnemaat, J. N., Chromatographic Separation of the Steroids of the Adrenal Gland, *Methods of Biochem. Anal.* **1**, 171–204 (1954).

647. Zaffaroni, A., Micromethods for the Analysis of Adrenocortical Steroids, *Recent Progr. in Hormone Research* **8**, 51–83 (1953).

648. Eckstein, P., and Zuckerman, S., eds., "The Determination of Adrenocortical Steroids and their Metabolites," Dennis Dobson, Ltd., London 1953 (Memoirs of the Society for Endocrinology, no. 2).

649. Dorfman, R. I., The Bioassay of Adrenocortical Hormones, *Recent Progr. in Hormone Research* **8**, 87–116 (1953).

650. Ciba Foundation, "Bioassay of Anterior Pituitary and Adrenocortical Hormones," Little, Brown and Co., Boston, 1953. (Ciba Foundation Colloquia on Endocrinology, Vol. V).

13. ANDROGENS
a. General

651. Dorfman, R. I., Metabolism of Androgens, *Proc. Intern. Congr. Biochem., 4th Congr., Vienna,* **1958,** Symposium IV, p. 175–95.

652. Kochakian, C. D., Metabolism of Androgens by Tissue Enzymes, *Proc. Intern. Congr. Biochem., 4th Congr., Vienna,* **1958,** Symposium IV, p. 196–207.

653. Lieberman, S., and Vande Wiele, R., Dehydroisoandrosterone, its Origin and Importance as a Precursor of Urinary 17-ketosteroids, *Proc. Intern. Congr. Biochem., 4th Congr., Vienna,* **1958,** Symposium IV, p. 153–9.

654. Dorfman, R. I., and Shipley, R. A., "Androgens. Biochemistry, Physiology and Clinical Significance," Wiley, New York, 1956.

655. Junkmann, K., [Androgens. Chemistry, Biochemistry and Identification] *Symp. deut. Ges. Endokrinol. 1953,* 187–201 (1955).

656. Mason, H. L., and Engstrom, W. W., The 17-Ketosteroids: Their Origin, Determination and Significance, *Physiol. Revs.* **30,** 321–74 (1950).

657. Albeaux-Fernet, M., and others, Les 17-cétostéroïdes, *Année endocr.* **2,** 103–6 (1950).

b. Endocrinology

658. Albeaux-Fernet, M., and others, Étude critique de la valeur du dosage des 17-cétostéroïdes dans les affections testiculaires, *Année endocr.* **9,** 172–80 (1957).

659. Albeaux-Fernet, M., and others, Étude critique des données de la chromatographie des 17-cétostéroïdes neutres urinaires dans l'exploration de la fonction androgénique ches l'homme, *Année endocr.* **9,** 181–9 (1957).

660. Montuori, E., Acción metabólica extrasexual de los andrógenos, *Rev. argent. endocr.* **3,** 224–58 (1957).

661. Mann, T., Male Sex Hormone and Its Role in Reproduction, *Recent Progr. in Hormone Research* **12,** 353–68 (1956).

662. Leach, R. B., Maddock, W. O., Tokuyama, I., Paulsen, C. A., and Nelson, W. O., Clinical Studies of Testicular Hormone Production, *Recent Progr. in Hormone Research* **12,** 377–403 (1956).

663. Albeaux-Fernet, M., and others, État actuel du problème de l'hirsutisme, *Année endocr.* **8,** 10–32 (1956).

664. Foglia, V. G., Nociones de química y fisiología de los andrógenos, *Rev. asoc. méd. arg.* **68,** 547–52 (1954).

665. Anon., Urinary Excretion of 17-Ketosteroids in Scurvy, *Nutrition Revs.* **10,** 253–5 (1952).

c. **Pharmacology**

666. Crooke, A. C., The Androgens, *Practitioner* **180,** 13–21 (1958).
667. Hamblen, E. C., Androgenic Therapy of Woman, *Southern Med. J.* **50,** 743–52 (1957).
668. Natoli, A., Il deidroisoandrosterone in clinica, *Progr. med.* **13** (suppl.), 577–640 (1957).
669. Schechter, D. C., Androgen Therapy in Gynecology; a Review, *Obstet. Gynecol. Survey* **11,** 389–405 (1956).
670. Conference on the Clinical Use of Anabolic Agents, Chicago, 1956, Proceedings, G. D. Searle and Co., Chicago, 1956.
671. Gordan, G. S., Practical Therapeutics. Evaluation and Use of Anabolic Steroids, *GP, J. Am. Acad. Gen. Pract.* **10,** 87–102 (1954).
672. Albeaux-Fernet, M., and others, Indications thérapeutiques des androgènes dans le sexe féminin, *Année endocr.* **4,** 169–84 (1952).
673. Albeaux-Fernet, M., and others, Méthylandrostènediol, *Année endocr.* **5,** 122–30 (1953).
674. Henderson, E., and Weinberg, M., Methylandrostenediol: (An Endocrine Review), *J. Clin. Endocrinol.* **11,** 641–52 (1951).
675. Turner, H. H., "The Clinical Use of Testosterone," C. C. Thomas, Springfield, Illinois, 1950.
676. Linsk, J. A., Testosterone Therapy in Children; Review of Literature, *Arch. Pediat.* **67,** 371–382 (1950).
677. Sanchez Ibañez, F. M., Androgenoterapia en ginecologia, *Rev. port. obst ginec. e cir.* **3,** 125–71 (1950).

d. **Analysis**

678. Chaney, A. L., 17-Ketosteroids in Urine, in D. Seligson, ed., "Standard Methods of Clinical Chemistry," Vol. II, p. 79–85, Academic Press, New York, 1958.
679. Huis in't Veld, L. G., Les 17-cétostéroïdes neutres dans l'urine. Leur signification pour le diagnostic clinique, *Exposés ann. biochim. méd.* **18,** 17–46 (1956).
680. Munson, P. L., and Kenny, A. D., Colorimetric Analytical Methods for Neutral 17-Ketosteroids of Urine, *Recent Progr. in Hormone Research* **9,** 135–61 (1954).
681. Robinson, A. M., The Uses and Limitations of Adsorption Chromatography for the Separation of Urinary Ketosteroids, *Recent Progr. in Hormone Research* **9,** 163–76 (1954).
682. Savard, K., Some Theoretical and Some Practical Aspects of Partition Chromatography of Ketosteroids, *Recent Progr. in Hormone Research* **9,** 185–208 (1954).

683. Engel, L. L., The Assay of Urinary Neutral 17-Ketosteroids, *Methods of Biochem. Anal.* **1,** 479–509 (1954).

684. Lieberman, S., Mond, B., and Smyles, E., Hydrolysis of Urinary Ketosteroid Conjugates, *Recent Progr. in Hormone Research* **9,** 113–30 (1954).

685. Albeaux-Fernet, M., and others, Données nouvelles sur la chromatographie des 17-cétostéroïdes, *Année endocr.* **6,** 39–45 (1954).

686. Albeaux-Fernet, M., and others, Fractionnement chromatographique des 17-cétostéroïdes, *Année endocr.* **4,** 57–60 (1952).

687. Albeaux-Fernet, M., and others, La chromatographie des 17-cétostéroïdes urinaires, *Année endocr.* **3,** 152–9 (1951).

14. ESTROGENS
a. General

688. Marrian, G. F., The Biochemistry of the Oestrogenic Hormone, *Proc. Intern. Congr. Biochem., 4th Congr., Vienna,* **1958,** Symposium IV, p. 208–22.

689. Leibson, L. G., Estrogeny; ikh obrazovanie, obmen, metody opredeleniia i soderzhanie v organizme [Estrogens; their formation, metabolism, methods of determination and content in the body], *Problemy Endokrinol. i Gormonoterap.* **3,** No. 2, 91–102 (1957).

690. Simões, J. J., Metabolismo dos estrógenos, *Arquiv. brasil. med. naval (Rio de Janeiro)* **18,** 5597–5610 (1957).

691. Engel, L. L., The Biosynthesis of Estrogens, *Cancer* **10,** 711–15 (1957).

692. Bradbury, R. B., and White, D. E., Estrogens and Related Substances in Plants, *Vitamins and Hormones* **12,** 207–31 (1954).

693. Zacco, M., "Gli ormoni estrogeni," Pensiero Sci., Rome, 1953.

694. Jayle, M.-F., Biogenèse et métabolisme intermédiaire de la folliculine, *Exposés ann. biochim. méd.* **14,** 189–214 (1952).

695. Salaber, J. A., Estado actual sobre algunos aspectos de los estrógenos, *Medicina (Buenos Aires)* **10,** 116–27 (1950).

b. Endocrinology

696. Villee, C. A., Some Current Speculations on the Action of Estrogens, *Perspectives Biol. Med.* **2,** 290–308 (1959).

697. Mueller, G. C., Herranen, A. M., and Jervell, K. F., Studies on the Mechanism of Action of Estrogens, *Recent Progr. in Hormone Research* **14,** 95–139 (1958).

698. Merrill, R. C., Estriol: A Review, *Physiol. Revs.* **38,** 463–80 (1958).

699. Mueller, G. C., Some Biochemical Studies on the Mechanism of Action of Estrogens, *Cancer* **10,** 716–20 (1957).

700. Anon., The Action of Estrogens on Calcium Metabolism, *Nutrition Revs.* **15**, 343–5 (1957).

701. Villee, C. A., Effects of Estrogens and Anti-Estrogens in Vitro, *Cancer Research* **17**, 507–11 (1957).

702. Larson, J. A., Collective Review; Estrogens and Endometrial Carcinoma, *Obstet Gynecol. Survey* **3**, 551–72 (1954).

703. Albeaux-Fernet, M., and others, Oestrogènes et cholestérol, *Année endocr.* **6**, 127–9 (1954).

704. Albeaux-Fernet, M., and others, Oestrogènes et rétention hydrique, *Année endocr.* **6**, 130–2 (1954).

705. Burrows, H., and Horning, E. S., "Oestrogens and Neoplasia," C. C. Thomas, Springfield, Illinois, 1952.

706. Everse, J. W. R., Oestrogeen hormoon en kerndeling [Estrogen Hormone and Mitosis], *Hormoon* **15**, 125–34 (1951).

707. Anon., Estrogen and Calcium Metabolism, *Nutrition Revs.* **9**, 100–1 (1951).

c. Pharmacology

708. Bishop, P. M. F., The Oestrogens, *Practitioner* **180**, 5–12 (1958).

709. Grundy, J., Artificial Estrogens, *Chem. Revs.* **57**, 281–416 (1957).

710. Calandra, D., Indicaciones y contraindicaciones de los estrógenos, *Prensa méd. argent.* **44**, 2233–41 (1957).

711. Dodds, C., Synthetic Oestrogens, *Brit. Med. Bull.* **11**, 131–4 (1955).

712. Martins, A., [Synthetic Estrogens], *Rev. port. farm.* **4**, 253–76 (1954).

713. Rodríguez-Soriano, J. A., Indicaciones y peligros de la terapéutica con estrógenos, *Rev. ibér. endocr.* **1**, 365–425 (1954).

714. Ulagay, R., [Estrogenic Hormones], *Folia Pharm.* (*Istanbul*) **2**, 142–7 (1953).

715. Gennari, F., Relazione fra struttura chimica ed attivita biologica degli ormoni estrogeni di sintesi, *Gazz. med. ital.* **112**, 22–5 (1953).

716. Höller, H., and Schneider, W., Properties and Applications of Estrogenic Compounds, *Subsidia med.* **4**, 217–27 (1952).

717. Danneberg, P., Chemische Konstitution und Wirksamkeit von Östrogenen, *Arzneimittel-Forsch.* **1**, 339–50 (1951).

718. Albeaux-Fernet, M., and others, Les oestrogènes de synthèse en thérapeutique générale, *Année endocr.* **2**, 87–95 (1950).

719. Albeaux-Fernet, M., and others, Le traitement de certains accidents gravidiques par les oestrogènes de synthèse, *Année endocr.* **2**, 96–101 (1950).

d. Analysis

720. Diczfalusy, E., Chemical Determination of Oestrogens in the Urine, *Acta Endocrinol.*, Suppl. **31**, 11–26 (1957).

721. Bauld, W. S., and Greenway, R. M., Chemical Determination of Estrogens in Human Urine, *Methods of Biochem. Anal.* **5,** 1–63 (1957).

722. Albeaux-Fernet, M., and others, Le dosage des oestrogènes urinaires, *Année endocr.* **9,** 152–7 (1957).

723. Eckstein, P., and Zuckerman, S., eds., "The Technique and Significance of Oestrogen Determinations," Dennis Dobson, Ltd., London, 1955. (Memoirs of the Society for Endocrinology, no. 3).

724. Katzman, P. A., Straw, R. F., Buehler, H. J., and Doisy, E. A., Hydrolysis of Conjugated Estrogens, *Recent Progr. in Hormone Research* **9,** 45–68 (1954).

725. Axelrod, L. R., The Chromatographic Fractionation and Identification of Compounds Related to the Estrogens, *Recent Progr. in Hormone Research* **9,** 69–94 (1954).

726. Bates, R. W., Spectrophotometric and Fluorometric Methods for the Determination of Estrogenic Steroids, *Recent Progr. in Hormone Research* **9,** 95–112 (1954).

727. Grant, G. A., and Bell, D., Studies on Estrogen Conjugates, *Recent Progr. in Hormone Research* **5,** 307–34 (1950).

15. UNCLASSIFIED LITERATURE ADDED IN PROOF

728. Pincus, G., and Vollmer, E., eds., "Biological Activities of Steroids in Relation to Cancer. Proceedings of a 1959 Symposium," Academic Press, New York, 1960

729. Djerassi, C., "Optical Rotatory Dispersion. Applications to Organic Chemistry," McGraw-Hill, New York, 1960.

730. Albeaux-Fernet, M., and others, Les récents progrès dans l'étude et la determination cliniques des corticoïdes urinaires, *Année endocr.* **11,** 5–13 (1959).

731. Albeaux-Fernet, M., and others, Travaux récents sur l'élimination urinaire des stéroïdes, *Année endocr.* **11,** 14–23 (1959).

732. Albeaux-Fernet, M., and others, L'hyperplasie surrénale congénitale, *Année endocr.* **11,** 24–54 (1959).

733. Albeaux-Fernet, M., and others, Acquisitions récentes sur l'aldostérone, *Année endocr.* **11,** 55–88 (1959).

734. Albeaux-Fernet, M., and others, Les fonctions cortico-surrénales au cours du myxoedème primaire, *Année endocr.* **11,** 89–93 (1959).

735. Albeaux-Fernet, M., and others, Le testicule féminisant, *Année endocr.* **11,** 127–32 (1959).

736. Albeaux-Fernet, M., and others, Le dosage des trois oestrogènes au cours de la grossesse, *Année endocr.* **11,** 133–5 (1959).

737. Albeaux-Fernet, M., and others, Masculinisation foetale imputable

à l'administration d'hormones lutéoïdes de synthèse pendant la grossesse, *Année endocr.* **11**, 136–42 (1959).

738. Albeaux-Fernet, M., and others, Vaginites et troubles hormonaux, *Année endocr.* **11**, 143–9 (1959).

739. Albeaux-Fernet, M., and others, Endocrinologie et psychiatrie, *Année endocr.* **11**, 151–70 (1959).

740. Ingle, D. J., Current Status of Adrenocortical Research, *Am. Scientist* **47**, 413–26 (1959).

741. Crabbé, P., Biogenesis of Tetracyclic Triterpenes, *Record Chem. Progr. (Kresge-Hooker Sci. Lib.)* **20**, 189–207 (1959).

742. Engel, L. L., Mechanism of Action of Estrogens, *Vitamins and Hormones* **17**, 205–22 (1959).

743. Pincus, G., Progestational Agents and the Control of Fertility, *Vitamins and Hormones* **17**, 307–24 (1959).

744. Beiglböck, W., Chemie und Pharmakologie der neuen Kortikosteroide, *Wien. med. Wochschr.* **109**, 585–94 (1959).

745. Baïchikov, A. G., Barmenkov, A. S., and Eroshin, V. K., [Biosynthesis of Steroids (Steroid Hormones) with the Aid of Microorganisms], *Med. Prom. S.S.S.R.* **13**, No. 6, 15–31 (1959).

746. Katzman, P. A., Doisy, E. A., Jr., Matschiner, J. T., and Doisy, E. A., Metabolism of Steroids, *Ann. Rev. Biochem.* **28**, 257–90 (1959).

747. Dodds, C., Hormones and Cancer, *Acta Unio Intern. contra Cancrum* **15**, 56–61 (1959).

748. Mühlbock, O., Hormones in the Genesis of Cancer, *Acta Unio Intern. contra Cancrum* **15**, 62–6 (1959).

749. Martz, G., [Hormonal Treatment of Prostatic Carcinoma], *Oncologia* **12**, 179–92 (1959).

750. Bachigalupo, D., [The Aspects and Results of Hormone Therapy in Oncology], *Voprosy Onkol.* **5**, No. 8, 171–7 (1959).

751. Lin, T.-M., and Chen, K. K., [Cholesterol and its Relation to Atherosclerosis], *Fortschr. Arzneimittelforsch.* **1**, 127–58 (1959).

752. Pelc, B., 19-Norsteroidy [19-Norsteroids], *Chem. listy* **53**, 1032–45 (1959).

753. Klyne, W., Chemical, Pharmacological, and Clinical Aspects of the 19-Norsteroids, *Proc. Roy. Soc. Med.* **52**, 509–11 (1959).

754. Venturi, V. M., [Selectivity of Action of Cardiotonic Drugs], *Arch. ital, sci. farmacol.* **9**, 87–114 (1959).

755. Drury, A., ed., The Influence of Hormones on Lipide Metabolism in Relation to Arteriosclerosis, *Ann. N. Y. Acad. Sci.* **72**, 787–1054 (1959).

756. Bunim, J. J., ed., A Decade of Anti-inflammatory Steroids from Cortisone to Dexamethasone, *Ann. N. Y. Acad. Sci.* **82**, 797–1014 (1959).

757. Aka, T., [Adrenocortical Hormones], *Yakkyoku no Ryôiki* **8**, No. 2, 9–15 (1959).

758. Kobayashi, T., and Ito, Y., [Cardiotonic Glycosides], *Sôgô Rinshô* **8**, 1589–98 (1959).

759. Hanč, O., [Synthetic Derivatives and Analogs of Cortical Hormones], *Chemie* **10**, 313–22 (1958).

760. Pitra, J. and Čekan, Z., [Cardiotonic Glycosides], *Chemie* **10**, 559–75 (1958).

761. Glaz, E., and Weisz, P., [Aldosterone. II], *Orvosi Hetilap* **98**, 1520–7 (1958).

762. Kaufmann, C., Über Sexualhormone der Frau. Rückblick und Ausblick, *Klin. Wochschr.* **36**, 1145–52 (1958).

763. Reiss, M., Psychoendocrinology, *Psychoendocrinology* **1958**, 1–40.

764. Rees, L., Premenstrual Tension Syndrome, *Psychoendocrinology* **1958**, 82–95.

765. Takemoto, T., and Kometani, K., [Cardiotonic Glycosides of Digitalis], *Yakugaku Kenkyu* **30**, 135–70 (1958).

766. Urashiro, J., [Bile and Cholesterol], *Sôgô Rinshô* **7**, 2255–63 (1958).

767. Tazaka, S., Tomono, T., and Mogami, T., [Internal Secretion and Cholesterol Metabolism], *Sôgô Rinshô* **7**, 2264–80 (1958).

768. Oji, K., and Matsuo, S., [Essential Fatty Acids and Cholesterol Metabolism], *Sôgô Rinshô* **7**, 2296–303 (1958).

769. Kobayashi, T., [The Progress of Digitalis Therapy], *Nippon Rinshô* **15**, 637–40 (1957).

770. Nakao, T., [Hormones and their Clinical Application], *Nippon Rinshô* **15**, 719–25 (1957).

771. Ibayashi, H., [Corticotropin and Adrenocortical Hormones], *Nippon Rinshô* **15**, 726–39 (1957).

772. Ochiai, K., [Androgens], *Nippon Rinshô* **15**, 747–52 (1957).

773. Jailer, J. W., and Vande Wiele, R., Role of the Adrenal Cortex in Gynecology, *Progr. in Gynecol.* **3**, 267–76 (1957).

774. West, C. D., and Rawson, R. W., Role of Hormones in the Growth and Control of Tumors Arising in the Female Reproductive System, *Progr. in Gynecol.* **3**, 277–97 (1957).

Subject Index

Page numbers in **boldface** refer to structural formulae. Numbers in *italics* correspond to reference numbers in the literature section (pp. 171–218).